PRELIMINARY
EDITION

Theory of Functions *of a* Real Variable

by EDWIN HEWITT

Holt, Rinehart and Winston, New York

Theory of Functions
of a
Real Variable

PRELIMINARY
EDITION

Theory of Functions *of a* Real Variable

by EDWIN HEWITT
Professor of Mathematics
The University of Washington

with the editorial assistance of KENNETH A. ROSS

Holt, Rinehart and Winston, New York

Library of Congress Catalog Card Number: 60-15648
23596-0110
Printed in the United States of America

INTRODUCTION

This book is a preliminary edition of a text which is planned for letterpress publication in about 1965. It has grown, as such books often do, from lectures given by the author over a number of years. As presented at the University of Washington, it covers a first-year graduate course in the theory of functions of a real variable. The book presupposes some knowledge of the elementary theory of functions of a real variable, contained for example in Chapters 1, 2, 3, 4, 8, 9, and 13 of Mathematical Analysis by Tom M. Apostol (Addison-Wesley Publishing Co., Reading, Mass., 1957). The necessary background material is presented briefly, by way of review, in sections 1.1 - 1.4 and 1.6 - 1.8. Experience has shown that this background material is usually mystifying to students who lack previous contact with the subject.

The point of view adopted is somewhat abstract. Thus, linear functionals and normed linear spaces are introduced and studied wherever possible. The construction of Lebesgue measure is connected with the general theory of Caratheodory outer measures. The proof of F. Riesz's representation theorem is given for continuous functions on the line (Chapter 4) but can be carried over *verbatim* for functions on any locally compact Hausdorff space. The book is designed as a sort of "What every young functional analyst should know." In the belief that every advanced course should contain about two hard proofs, the author has included proofs of the well-ordering theorem and of Vitali's covering theorem.

An earlier version of the book was prepared from the author's lectures by Mr. Peter M. Rinearson. The present version was prepared from the author's lectures by Dr. Kenneth A. Ross, whose truly tireless efforts have eliminated many mistakes, solecisms, and obscurities. The typescript was prepared by Miss Lynne Harper and Mrs. Sandra Smith, and symbols were inserted by Mr. Stuart L. Anderson. Mr. Anderson and Dr. Ross have compiled the index and proofread the typescript. For all of this devoted assistance the author is deeply grateful. Responsibility for remaining errors, of course, rests with him.

The author will be grateful for corrections and comments from users of the book.

Edwin Hewitt

Seattle

June 1960

TABLE OF CONTENTS

Theory of Functions *of a* Real Variable

Chapter 1.

PRELIMINARIES

1.0 References.

Aumann, G. "Reelle Funktionen." Berlin, Springer, 1954. (Die Grundlehren der mathematischen Wissenschaften in Einzeldarstellungen, Bd. 68).

Halmos, P. R. "Measure theory." New York, Van Nostrand, 1950.

Naĭmark, M. A. "Normed rings." Moscow, Gosudarstv. Izdatel'stvo Teh.-Teor. Lit., 1956.

Natanson, I. "Theory of functions of a real variable." Translated by L. F. Boron, edited by E. Hewitt. New York, F. Ungar Pub. Co., 1955.

Riesz, F. and Sz.-Nagy, B. "Leçons d'analyse fonctionnelle." Academie des Sciences de Hongrie, Budapest, 1952.

Saks, S. "Theory of the Integral." 1937. (Monografje matematyczne, Warszawa-Lwow, v. 7).

1.1 The theory of sets. We shall take the notion of set as being already known. Roughly speaking, a set (collection, assemblage, aggregate) is any identifiable collection of objects of any sort. We identify a set by stating what its members are. The theory of sets has been described axiomatically, in terms of the notion of "member of". To build the complete theory of sets from these axioms is a long, difficult process, and it is somewhat remote from classical analysis, which is the subject matter of the present text. Therefore we shall make no effort to be rigorous in dealing with the concept of sets, but will appeal throughout section 1.1 to intuition and elementary logic.

1.1.1 Notation. Elements of sets will be denoted by small letters: a, b, ..., z. Sets will be denoted by capital letters: A, B, ..., Z. Families of sets will be denoted by script letters: $\mathcal{A}$, $\mathcal{B}$, $\mathcal{C}$, ...

A set is defined by its elements. A set is often defined by some properties of its elements. We will write $\{x\colon P(x)\}$ (where $P(x)$ is some property of elements) to denote the set of elements with that property.

If the object x is in the set A, we will write $x \in A$; $x \notin A$ will mean that the object x is not in the set A.

We write 0 for the void set; it contains no elements at all. Thus $0 = \{x\colon x$ is a unicorn in the Seattle Zoo$\} = \{x\colon x$ is a real number and $x^2 < 0\}$.

1.1.2 The algebra of sets.

1.1.21 Definitions. If $x \in A$ always implies that $x \in B$, then we write $A \subset B$ or $B \supset A$. In this case, A is said to be a subset of B. If $A \subset B$ and $B \subset A$, then we write $A = B$. Thus two sets are equal if and only if they have exactly the same elements. If $A \subset B$ and $A \neq B$, then we often write $A \subsetneq B$ and say that A is a proper subset of B.

1.1.22 <u>Definition</u>. Let A and B be any sets. Then we define $A \cup B = \{x: x \varepsilon A \text{ or } x \varepsilon B\}$. This set is called the union of A and B. Let $\{A_\iota\}_{\iota \varepsilon I}$ be any family of sets. Then we define $\bigcup_{\iota \varepsilon I} A_\iota = \{x: x \varepsilon A_\iota \text{ for some } \iota \varepsilon I\}$.

1.1.221 <u>Theorem</u>. Let A, B, and C be sets. Then the following relations hold:

i) $A \cup B = B \cup A$;

ii) $A \cup A = A$;

iii) $0 \cup A = A$;

iv) $A \cup (B \cup C) = (A \cup B) \cup C$;

v) $A \subset A \cup B$;

vi) $A \subset B$ if and only if $A \cup B = B$.

1.1.23 <u>Definition</u>. Let A and B be any sets. Then we define $A \cap B = \{x: x \varepsilon A \text{ and } x \varepsilon B\}$. This set is called the intersection of A and B. Let $\{A_\iota\}_{\iota \varepsilon I}$ be a family of sets. Then we define $\bigcap_{\iota \varepsilon I} A_\iota = \{x: x \varepsilon A_\iota \text{ for all } \iota \varepsilon I\}$.

1.1.231 <u>Theorem</u>. Let A, B, and C be sets. Then the following relations hold:

i) $A \cap B = B \cap A$;

ii) $A \cap A = A$;

iii) $0 \cap A = 0$;

iv) $A \cap (B \cap C) = (A \cap B) \cap C$;

v) $A \cap B \subset B$;

vi) $A \subset B$ if and only if $A \cap B = A$.

1.1.24 Theorem. Let A, B, and C be sets. Then

i) $A \cap (B \cup C) = (A \cap B) \cup (A \cap C)$;

ii) $A \cup (B \cap C) = (A \cup B) \cap (A \cup C)$.

Proof. These and similar identities may be verified schematically; the verification of i) follows:

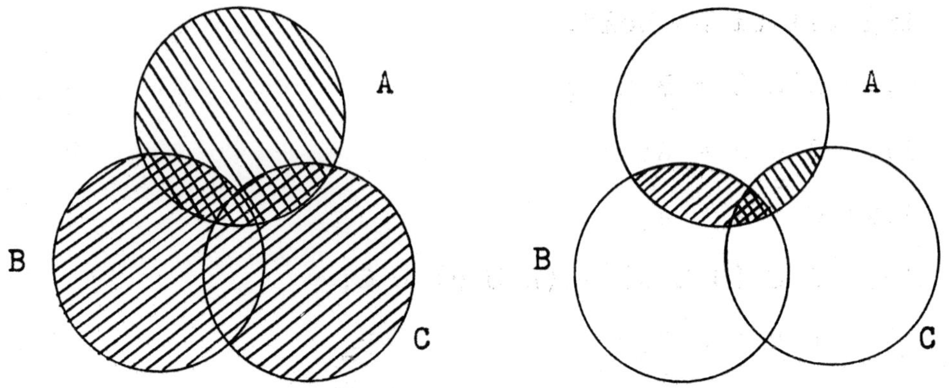

$A \cap (B \cup C)$ $(A \cap B) \cup (A \cap C)$

A similar schematic procedure could be applied to ii). However, we may use i) and the previous laws as follows:

$(A \cup B) \cap (A \cup C) = ((A \cup B) \cap A) \cup ((A \cup B) \cap C) =$

$(A \cap A) \cup (B \cap A) \cup (A \cap C) \cup (B \cap C) = A \cup (B \cap C) \cup$

$(B \cap A) \cup (A \cap C) = A \cup (B \cap C)$;

the last equality follows since $B \cap A \subset A$ and $A \cap C \subset A$.

1.1.25 Definition. For $A \subset E$, let $A' = \{x:\ x \in E$ and $x \notin A\}$; A' is called the complement of the set A (with respect to E).

1.1.251 Theorem. (De Morgan's laws) Suppose that all sets under consideration are subsets of some fixed set E; all complements are to be taken with respect to E. Then

i) $(A \cup B)' = A' \cap B'$;

ii) $(A \cap B)' = A' \cup B'$;

iii) $(\bigcup_{\iota \in I} A_\iota)' = \bigcap_{\iota \in I} A_\iota'$;

iv) $(\bigcap_{\iota \in I} A_\iota)' = \bigcup_{\iota \in I} A_\iota'$.

1.1.26 Definition. Let A and B be any sets. Then we define $A \triangle B = (A \cap B') \cup (A' \cap B)$. This set is called the symmetric difference of A and B. Schematically, we have

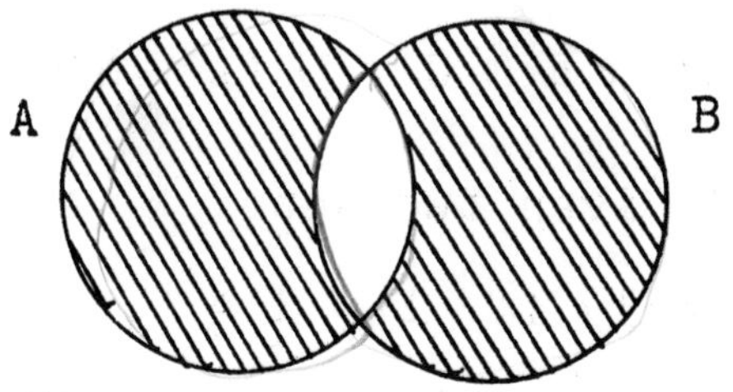

$A \triangle B$

1.1.3 Notation. Throughout this text the following notation will be adhered to: N will denote the set of all integers; R will denote the set of all real numbers; K will denote the set of all complex numbers.

We denote the set $\{x: x \in R \text{ and } a < x < b\}$ as $]a, b[$. Such sets are called open intervals. Similarly, we write $[a, b]$ for the set $\{x: x \in R \text{ and } a \leq x \leq b\}$. Such sets are called closed intervals. The symbols $[a, b[$ and $]a, b]$ are defined analogously; these sets are called half-open intervals. We also write $]-\infty, a]$ for $\{x: x \in R \text{ and } x \leq a\}$, the symbols $]-\infty, a[$,

$[a, +\infty[$, $]a, +\infty[$, and $]-\infty, \infty[$ being defined analogously. For convenience, we agree that the void set is not an open (or a closed) interval.

1.1.4 <u>Exercises</u>.

1.1.41 <u>Exercise</u>. Simplify as much as possible:

i) $(A \cup (B \cap (C \cup W')))'$;

ii) $((X' \cup Y)' \cap (X \cup Y'))'$.

1.1.42 <u>Exercise</u>. Simplify

$(A \cap B \cap C) \cup (A' \cap B \cap C) \cup (A \cap B' \cap C) \cup (A \cap B \cap C')$
$\cup (A \cap B' \cap C') \cup (A' \cap B \cap C') \cup (A' \cap B' \cap C)$.

1.1.43 <u>Exercise</u>. (Poretsky) Given two sets X and Y, prove that $X = 0$ if and only if $Y = X \triangle Y$.

1.1.44 <u>Exercise</u>. Describe in words the sets $\bigcup_{n=1}^{\infty} (\bigcap_{k=n}^{\infty} A_k)$ and $\bigcap_{n=1}^{\infty} (\bigcup_{k=n}^{\infty} A_k)$ where $\{A_1, A_2, \ldots, A_k, \ldots\}$ is any sequence of sets.

1.1.45 <u>Exercise</u>. In how many integers n, $1000 \leq n \leq 9999$, do at least two 3's appear in the ordinary decimal expansion? In how many integers n, $1000 \leq n \leq 9999$, do at least one 3 and at least one 4 appear?

1.1.46 <u>Exercise</u>. Prove

i) $A \triangle (B \triangle C) = (A \triangle B) \triangle C$;

ii) $A \cap (B \triangle C) = (A \cap B) \triangle (A \cap C)$;

iii) $A \triangle A = 0$;

iv) $0 \triangle A = A$.

1.2 <u>Relations and functions</u>. We here take up the concepts of relation and function, familiar in several forms from elementary analysis. As in the case of sets, we content ourselves with an informal, non-rigorous discussion of the subject.

1.2.1 <u>Definition</u>. Let P and Q be any sets. We define the Cartesian product $P \times Q$ of P and Q to be the set of all ordered pairs (p, q), where $p \in P$ and $q \in Q$.

Note that $(p, q) \neq (q, p)$ if $p \neq q$.

1.2.11 <u>Definition</u>. Let P and Q be any sets. A relation f is any subset of $P \times Q$. The relation f may be void; it is then said to be the void relation.

1.2.12 <u>Definitions</u>. Let P and Q be sets and $f \subset P \times Q$ be a relation. The domain of f consists of all $p \in P$ such that $(p, q) \in f$ for some $q \in Q$. That is, it is the set $\{p: \ p \in P \text{ and } (p, q) \in f \text{ for some } q \in Q\}$. The range of f is the set $\{q: \ q \in Q \text{ and } (p, q) \in f$ for some $p \in P\}$.

We define f^{-1} to be the relation (a subset of $Q \times P$) such that $(q, p) \in f^{-1}$ if and only if $(p, q) \in f$.

1.2.13 <u>Example</u>. Let $P = Q$. The identity relation (or function) on P is the subset of $P \times P$ consisting of all pairs (p, p) where $p \in P$. That is, it is the diagonal of $P \times P$.

1.2.14 Definition. Let $f \subset P \times Q$ and $g \subset R \times S$ be any two relations. We define $g \circ f$ (called the composition, product, or iterate of f and g) to be the subset of $P \times S$ such that $(p, s) \in g \circ f$ if and only if there is an element $x \in Q \cap R$ where $(p, x) \in f$ and $(x, s) \in g$.

The relation $g \circ f$ can easily be void; in fact, $g \circ f$ is non-void if and only if the range of f and the domain of g have elements in common.

1.2.15 Definition. If f and g are relations and $f \subset g$, then we say that g is an extension of f.

Note that we have $f = g$ if and only if f and g have equal domains and equal values at every point of their common domain.

1.2.16 Definitions. A relation f is single-valued if $(p, q) \in f$ and $(p, q') \in f$ imply $q = q'$. If f and f^{-1} are single-valued, f is said to be a one-to-one relation. The definitions of many-to-one, one-to-many, and many-to-many relations are analogous.

The relations most commonly met with in the theories of measure, integration, and linear spaces are single-valued. Hence we make the following definition.

1.2.17 Definition. A function (mapping, transformation, operator, application, correspondence) is a single-valued relation.

1.2.18 Examples. The sine function, $\{(x, \sin x):\ x \in R\} \subset$

$R \times R$, is a many-to-one function. The arcsine, $\{(\sin x, x): x \in R\} \subset R \times R$, is a one-to-many relation. The relation $\{(x, y): x, y \in R, x^2 + y^2 = 1\}$ is a many-to-many relation.

1.2.19 <u>Definition</u>. A sequence is any function whose domain is $\{1, 2, \ldots, n, \ldots\}$, $\{0, 1, 2, \ldots, n, \ldots\}$ or $\{\ldots, -n, \ldots, -2, -1, 0, 1, 2, \ldots, n, \ldots\}$.

1.2.2 <u>The algebra of relations</u>.

1.2.21 <u>Remark</u>. A set consisting of exactly one element x is often written as $\{x\}$. One should observe that x and $\{x\}$ are not the same object.

Suppose that $f \subset P \times Q$ is a relation. Let $X \subset P$ be the domain of f and $Y \subset Q$ be the range of f. Clearly $f \subset X \times Y$. Throughout the remainder of 1.2, we shall consider f as a subset of $X \times Y$, where the domain of f is X and the range of f is Y.

1.2.22 <u>Definition</u>. For $A \subset X$, let $f(A) = \{y: y \in Y$ and $(x, y) \in f$ for some $x \in A\}$. In particular, $f(\{a\})$ is defined as a set if $a \in X$. If f is a function, so that $f(\{a\})$ consists of exactly one element for each $a \in X$, then we write $f(a)$ for the unique element in $f(\{a\})$. That is, $f(a)$ is an element of Y, not a subset of Y.

Note that $f^{-1}(B)$ for $B \subset Y$ is already defined since f^{-1} is a relation.

1.2.23 Theorem. Let $\{A_\iota\}_{\iota\varepsilon I}$ be a family of subsets of X and $\{B_\iota\}_{\iota\varepsilon I}$ be a family of subsets of Y. For $A \subset X$, let A' be the complement of A with respect to X; similarly for $B \subset Y$, let B' be the complement of B with respect to Y. For any relation f, we have

i) $f(\bigcup_{\iota\varepsilon I} A_\iota) = \bigcup_{\iota\varepsilon I} f(A_\iota)$;

ii) $f(\bigcap_{\iota\varepsilon I} A_\iota) \subset \bigcap_{\iota\varepsilon I} f(A_\iota)$;

iii) $f^{-1}(f(A)) \supset A$;

iv) $f(A') \supset f(A)'$.

The following results are valid for functions, but may fail for arbitrary relations:

v) $f^{-1}(\bigcap_{\iota\varepsilon I} B_\iota) = \bigcap_{\iota\varepsilon I} f^{-1}(B_\iota)$;

vi) $f^{-1}(B') = (f^{-1}(B))'$;

vii) $f(f^{-1}(B)) = B$;

viii) $f(f^{-1}(B) \cap A) = B \cap f(A)$.

The reader should verify the relations in the above theorem, and prove by examples that the inclusions listed may be proper.

1.2.24 Note. From theorem 1.2.23, it follows that the domain and range of a one-to-one function cannot be distinguished from each other by any purely set-theoretic properties. If X and Y are sets for which there is a one-to-one function f with domain X and range Y, then for any subset A of X we have $f(A') = f(A)'$. For any family

$\{A_\iota\}_{\iota \in I}$ of subsets of X, we have $f(\bigcup_{\iota \in I} A_\iota) = \bigcup_{\iota \in I} f(A_\iota)$ and $f(\bigcap_{\iota \in I} A_\iota) = \bigcap_{\iota \in I} f(A_\iota)$. Similar statements hold for subsets of Y and f^{-1}. Thus, all Boolean operations ($\cup$, $\cap$, Δ, $'$) are preserved under f and f^{-1}.

1.2.3 Exercises.

1.2.31 Exercise. Verify that $(f \circ g) \circ h = f \circ (g \circ h)$ for all relations f, g, h.

1.2.32 Exercise. Show that the equality $f(f^{-1}(B) \cap A) = B \cap f(A)$ fails for every relation that is not a function.

1.3 General Cartesian products.

1.3.1 Definition. Let $\{A_\iota\}_{\iota \in I}$ be any family of sets. The Cartesian product of this family of sets, written $\underset{\iota \in I}{P} A_\iota$, is the set of all functions f with domain I and range contained in $\bigcup_{\iota \in I} A_\iota$, and such that $f(\iota) \in A_\iota$ for all $\iota \in I$. If $I = \{1, 2, \ldots, n\}$ and each A_ι is a fixed set A ($\iota = 1, \ldots, n$), we write $\underset{\iota \in I}{P} A_\iota = A^n$. Similarly, if $I = \{1, 2, 3, \ldots\}$ and each A_ι is a fixed set A ($\iota = 1, 2, \ldots$), we write $\underset{\iota \in I}{P} A_\iota = A^\infty$.

1.3.2 Examples. For every positive integer n, ordinary n-dimensional real Euclidean space is the Cartesian product $R^n = \{(x_1, \ldots, x_n) : x_i \in R \text{ for } i = 1, \ldots, n\}$. Similarly, complex n-dimensional Euclidean space (sometimes called unitary space) is the Cartesian product

$K^n = \{(z_1, \ldots, z_n)\colon\ z_j \in K \text{ for } j = 1, \ldots, n\}$. Also we have $K^\infty = \{(z_1, \ldots, z_n, \ldots)\colon\ z_j \in K \text{ for } j = 1, 2, 3, \ldots\}$. An important family of subspaces of K^∞ are the ℓ_p $(p > 0)$ spaces:

$\ell_p = \{z\colon\ z \in K^\infty \text{ and } \sum_{n=1}^{\infty} |z_n|^p < \infty\}$. The space ℓ_2 is of particular interest since it is a Hilbert space.

Let $A = \{0, 1\}$. Let A^∞ be the Cartesian product of a sequence of spaces each equal to A; A^∞ consists of all functions defined on $\{1, 2, 3, \ldots\}$ with values in $A = \{0,1\}$; i.e., all sequences $a = \{a_1, \ldots, a_n, \ldots\}$ where each a_k is 0 or 1. In some ways this set resembles Cantor's ternary set $C = [0,1] \cap (]\frac{1}{3}, \frac{2}{3}[\cup]\frac{1}{9}, \frac{2}{9}[\cup]\frac{7}{9}, \frac{8}{9}[\cup \ldots)'$. The map f defined by $f(a) = f(\{a_1, \ldots, a_n, \ldots\}) = 2(\sum_{n=1}^{\infty} \frac{a_n}{3^n})$ is a one-to-one map of A^∞ onto C. Anticipating future developments, we remark also that A^∞ can be made a metric space by introducing the metric ρ, where $\rho(a,b) = \frac{1}{n}$ if $a_1 = b_1, \ldots, a_{n-1} = b_{n-1}$, and $a_n \neq b_n$; and $\rho(a,b) = 0$ if $a = b$. Under this metric, f is continuous and so is f^{-1}. The set A^∞ is an Abelian group with the operation $+$ defined as follows: $\{a_1, \ldots, a_n, \ldots\} + \{b_1, \ldots, b_n, \ldots\} = \{(a_1 + b_1) \bmod 2,\ (a_2 + b_2) \bmod 2, \ldots, (a_n + b_n) \bmod 2, \ldots\}$.

1.3.3 <u>The axiom of choice</u>. Consider the following question. If I is a non-void index class and A_ι is non-void for all $\iota \varepsilon I$, must $\underset{\iota \varepsilon I}{P} A_\iota$ be non-void? Unfortunately this question has not been answered on the basis of the axioms of set theory usually assumed. However, K. Gödel has proved that if the other axioms of set theory are consistent, then adding the above statement (in the affirmative) as an axiom will not destroy the consistency of the system. (The consistency of the other axioms has never been shown.) As a result, many mathematicians assume the following axiom.

1.3.31 <u>Axiom of choice</u>. If I is a non-void index class and A_ι is non-void for all $\iota \varepsilon I$, then $\underset{\iota \varepsilon I}{P} A_\iota$ is non-void.

There are many assertions logically equivalent to the axiom of choice, and we shall meet some of them further on.

The following are generalizations of the distributive laws (see 1.1.24).

1.3.4 <u>Theorem</u>. Let $\{I_\lambda\}_{\lambda \varepsilon \Lambda}$ be a family of index classes. For every $\lambda \varepsilon \Lambda$ and every $\iota_\lambda \varepsilon I_\lambda$, let there be given a set A_{ι_λ}. Then we have

i) $\bigcap_{\lambda \varepsilon \Lambda} \left(\bigcup_{\iota_\lambda \varepsilon I_\lambda} A_{\iota_\lambda} \right) = \bigcup_{\phi \varepsilon \underset{\lambda \varepsilon \Lambda}{P} I_\lambda} \left(\bigcap_{\lambda \varepsilon \Lambda} A_{\phi(\lambda)_\lambda} \right);$

ii) $\bigcup_{\lambda \varepsilon \Lambda} (\bigcap_{\iota_\lambda \varepsilon I_\lambda} A_{\iota_\lambda \lambda}) = \bigcap_{\phi \varepsilon P_{\lambda \varepsilon \Lambda} I_\lambda} (\bigcup_{\lambda \varepsilon \Lambda} A_{\phi(\lambda)_\lambda})$.

The proof is left to the reader. It is actually quite simple.

1.4 Cardinal numbers. Let A and B be sets for which there is a one-to-one correspondence f with domain A and range B. As noted in 1.2.24, the sets A and B cannot be told apart by any purely set-theoretic properties, although of course they may be totally different entities. This observation leads us to the following definition.

1.4.1 Definition. With every set A, we associate a symbol, called the cardinal number of A, such that two sets A and B have the same symbol attached to them if and only if they can be put into a one-to-one correspondence. We will write $A \sim B$ to mean that such a one-to-one correspondence exists. If $A \sim B$, we say that A and B are equivalent (or have the same cardinality, or have the same power). We write $\bar{\bar{A}}$ for the cardinal number of A.

1.4.11 Examples. We denote $\bar{\bar{0}} = 0$, $\overline{\overline{\{a\}}} = 1$, and $\overline{\overline{\{a_1, \ldots, a_n\}}} = n$ if $i \neq j$ implies $a_i \neq a_j$. Certain other sets are so commonly encountered that we name their cardinal numbers by special symbols. Thus $\overline{\overline{\{1, 2, \ldots, n, \ldots\}}}$ is written as $\aleph_0$ (read "aleph nought") and $\bar{\bar{R}}$ is written as c (for continuum).

1.4.2 *Definition*. Let A and B be disjoint sets, that is, $A \cap B = 0$. Then we define $\bar{\bar{A}} + \bar{\bar{B}} = \overline{\overline{A \cup B}}$. For any two sets A and B we define $\bar{\bar{A}} \cdot \bar{\bar{B}} = \overline{\overline{A \times B}}$ and $(\bar{\bar{A}})^{\bar{\bar{B}}} = \{f:$ f is a function with domain B and range contained in $A\}$.

1.4.3 *Definitions*. (Dedekind) A set is infinite if it can be placed in one-to-one correspondence with a proper subset of itself. (Tarski)* A set A is finite if every family $\mathfrak{F}$ of subsets of A contains a minimal element (i.e., there exists a $B \varepsilon \mathfrak{F}$ such that no member of $\mathfrak{F}$ is a proper subset of B).

1.4.31 *Remark*. One may show that a set is infinite (Dedekind) if and only if it is non-finite (Tarski). One may also show that these definitions are consistent with our intuition, i.e., a set A is finite if and only if there is an $n \varepsilon \{0, 1, 2, \ldots\}$ such that $\bar{\bar{A}} = n$.

1.4.4 *Definition*. A set that is finite or has cardinality $\aleph_0$ is said to be countable.

1.4.41 *Examples*. The positive integers, the set of all rational numbers, and the set of all algebraic numbers are examples of countable, infinite sets. For example, the mapping $f(n) = n + 1$ shows that $\{1, 2, 3, \ldots\}$ is infinite using Dedekind's definition, and the family of subsets

---

* Fundamenta Mathematicae, vol. 6 (1924), pp. 45-95.

$\{\{1, 2, 3, \ldots\}, \{2, 3, 4, \ldots\}, \ldots, \{n, n+1, n+2, \ldots\}, \ldots\}$ shows that $\{1, 2, 3, \ldots\}$ is non-finite in Tarski's sense.

1.4.5 Theorem. If m is any cardinal and n is finite, then $m^n = \underbrace{m \cdot m \cdot \ldots \cdot m}_{n}$.

1.4.51 Theorem. If n is finite, then $n + \aleph_0 = \aleph_0$.

Proof. Suppose $A = \{a_1, \ldots, a_n\}$ and $B = \{b_1, \ldots, b_n, \ldots\}$ are disjoint sets with cardinalities n and $\aleph_0$, respectively. Let f be defined as follows: $f(k) = a_k$, $1 \leq k \leq n$; $f(n+k) = b_k$, $1 \leq k$. Then f is a one-to-one mapping of $\{1, 2, \ldots, n, \ldots\}$ onto $A \cup B$.

1.4.52 Theorem. $\aleph_0 + \aleph_0 = \aleph_0$.

Proof. Let $A = \{a_1, \ldots, a_n, \ldots\}$ and $B = \{b_1, \ldots, b_n, \ldots\}$ be disjoint sets with cardinality $\aleph_0$. Let f be defined as follows: $f(k) = a_{\frac{k+1}{2}}$, k odd; $f(k) = b_{\frac{k}{2}}$, k even. Then f maps $\{1, 2, \ldots, n, \ldots\}$ in a one-to one way onto $A \cup B$.

1.4.53 Theorem. $\aleph_0^{\,2} = \aleph_0 \cdot \aleph_0 = \aleph_0$.

Proof. Let $A = \{1, 2, \ldots, n, \ldots\}$; then by definition $\bar{A} = \aleph_0$. The set $A \times A$ consists of all ordered pairs (m,n) where $m,n \in A$. The members of $A \times A$ can be listed as follows:

$$\begin{array}{cccccccc}
(1,1) & (1,2) & (1,3) & (1,4) & \dots & (1,n) & \dots \\
(2,1) & (2,2) & (2,3) & (2,4) & \dots & (2,n) & \dots \\
(3,1) & (3,2) & (3,3) & (3,4) & \dots & (3,n) & \dots \\
(4,1) & (4,2) & (4,3) & (4,4) & \dots & (4,n) & \dots \\
\vdots & \vdots & \vdots & \vdots & & \vdots &
\end{array}$$

The sequence $\{(1,1), (1,2), (2,1), (1,3), (2,2), (3,1), (1,4), \dots\}$ gives a one-to-one correspondence ϕ between $A \times A$ and $A = \{1, 2, \dots, n, \dots\}$.

1.4.54 Theorem. For every positive integer n, $\aleph_0{}^n = \aleph_0$.

1.4.6 Definition. Let $\bar{\bar{A}}$ and $\bar{\bar{B}}$ be any cardinal numbers. Then we define $\bar{\bar{A}} \leq \bar{\bar{B}}$ if A is in one-to-one correspondence with a subset of B. We will write $\bar{\bar{A}} < \bar{\bar{B}}$ to mean that $\bar{\bar{A}} \leq \bar{\bar{B}}$ and $\bar{\bar{A}} \neq \bar{\bar{B}}$.

We state, without proof, some theorems concerning this ordering.

1.4.61 Theorem. Every infinite set contains a countably infinite subset; that is, $\aleph_0 \leq m$ for all infinite cardinals m.

Thus $\aleph_0$ is the smallest infinite cardinal.

1.4.62 Theorem. (Schröder-Bernstein) If $A \sim A_1 \subset B$ and $B \sim B_1 \subset A$, then $A \sim B$.

Restated, this theorem says that if $\bar{\bar{A}} \leq \bar{\bar{B}}$ and $\bar{\bar{B}} \leq \bar{\bar{A}}$, then $\bar{\bar{A}} = \bar{\bar{B}}$.

1.4.63 Theorem. Any two cardinal numbers are comparable. More precisely, given any two sets A and B, exactly one of the following relations holds:

i) $\bar{\bar{A}} < \bar{\bar{B}}$;

ii) $\bar{\bar{A}} = \bar{\bar{B}}$;

iii) $\bar{\bar{B}} < \bar{\bar{A}}$.

1.4.64 <u>Theorem</u>. Let $\mathcal{C}$ be any non-void set of cardinal numbers. Then $\mathcal{C}$ contains a cardinal number m such that $m < n$ for all $n \in \mathcal{C}$, $n \neq m$.

1.4.7 <u>Theorem</u>. $\overline{\overline{]0,1[}} = c$ and $\overline{\overline{[0,1]}} = c$.

<u>Proof</u>. Let $\phi(x) = \frac{1}{\pi}$ Arc tan $(x + \frac{\pi}{2})$ for $x \in R$. Then ϕ maps R onto $]0,1[$ in a one-to-one manner. The second equality follows from the inequalities,

$c = \overline{\overline{]0,1[}} \leq \overline{\overline{[0,1]}} \leq \bar{\bar{R}} = c$.

1.4.71 <u>Theorem</u>. $c > \aleph_0$.

<u>Proof</u>. Clearly $c \geq \aleph_0$. Suppose that $c = \aleph_0$; i.e., suppose that $[0,1] = \{x_1, \ldots, x_n, \ldots\}$. Let A_1 be one of the closed intervals $[0,\frac{1}{3}]$, $[\frac{2}{3},1]$ such that $x_1 \notin A_1$. Having defined $A_{n-1} = [a_{n-1}, b_{n-1}]$, let A_n be one of the closed intervals $[a_{n-1}, a_{n-1} + \frac{1}{3}(b_{n-1} - a_{n-1})]$, $[b_{n-1} - \frac{1}{3}(b_{n-1} - a_{n-1}), b_{n-1}]$ such that $x_n \notin A_n$. That this can always be done is clear. Then $\{A_i\}_{i=1}^{\infty}$ is a decreasing (with respect to $\supset$) sequence of non-void closed sets. Hence $\bigcap_{i=1}^{\infty} A_i \neq 0$ (see Ex. 1.8.61). An element in $\bigcap_{i=1}^{\infty} A_i$ cannot be any x_k. This contradicts

the alleged equality $[0,1] = \{x_1, \ldots, x_n, \ldots\}$. Thus $c > \aleph_0$.

1.4.72 Theorem. $2^{\aleph_0} = c$.

Proof. Let $A = \{\phi\colon \phi$ is a sequence such that $\phi(j) = 0$ or 1 for all $j = 1, 2, \ldots\}$. It is clear that $\bar{\bar{A}} = 2^{\aleph_0}$ and $\overline{\overline{[0,1]}} = c$. The function f such that $f(\phi) = \sum_{n=1}^{\infty} \frac{\phi(n)}{3^n}$ is a one-to-one map of A into $[0,1]$. Thus $2^{\aleph_0} \leq c$. For each $t \in [0,1]$, let $t = \sum_{n=1}^{\infty} \frac{a_n}{2^n}$ be a representation of t where each a_n is 0 or 1. Every $t \in [0,1]$ not of the form $\frac{a}{2^b}$ (a and b positive integers) has exactly one representation of this type. Every number $\frac{a}{2^b} \in [0,1]$ has just two such representations. For such t's, choose either representation. The function f such that $f(t) = \phi \in A$ where $\phi(j) = a_j$ for $j = 1, 2, \ldots$ is a one-to-one map of $[0,1]$ into A. Thus $c \leq 2^{\aleph_0}$. Hence $2^{\aleph_0} = c$.

1.4.8 Definition. The symbol A^B will represent the set $\{f\colon f$ is a function with domain B and range contained in $A\}$. The symbol 2^D will represent the set $\{f\colon f$ is a function with domain D and range contained in $\{0,1\}\}$.

1.4.81 Note. It is evident that $\overline{\overline{A^B}} = \bar{\bar{A}}^{\bar{\bar{B}}}$. It is also easy to verify that $2^{\bar{\bar{D}}} = \overline{\overline{\{\text{all subsets of } D\}}}$.

1.4.82 Theorem. For every cardinal number m, we have $m < 2^m$.

We omit the proof.

1.4.83 Remark. The result of 1.4.82 leads us to the following paradox. Suppose that $\{A_\iota\}_{\iota \varepsilon I}$ is a family of sets such that for every cardinal number m, there is an A_ι with cardinality m. Let $B = \bigcup_{\iota \varepsilon I} A_\iota$. Clearly $\bar{\bar{B}} \geq \bar{\bar{A}}_\iota$ for all $\iota \varepsilon I$. In short, $\bar{\bar{B}}$ is the largest cardinal. From 1.4.82, we have $2^{\bar{\bar{B}}} > \bar{\bar{B}}$. This contradiction appears to arise from the fact that the family $\{A_\iota\}_{\iota \varepsilon I}$ above is "too big". Hence the axioms of set theory are chosen so that the "set" B described above is actually outlawed: no such set B is admitted.

1.4.84 Theorem. $m \cdot n = m + n = \max(m,n)$ if m and n are cardinal numbers such that $\max(m,n) \geq \aleph_0$, $m \neq 0$, and $n \neq 0$.

We omit the proof.

1.4.9 Exercises.

1.4.91 Exercise. Write down as explicitly as possible the correspondence $\phi(m,n)$ used in the proof of 1.4.53.

1.4.92 Exercise. Prove that if A is any uncountable set of positive real numbers, then there is a positive real number τ such that the set $\{x: x \varepsilon A \text{ and } x > \tau\}$ is infinite (actually uncountable).

1.4.93 Exercise. Let ϕ be a monotone increasing real-valued function defined on R. (ϕ is monotone increasing if $x_1 < x_2$ implies $\phi(x_1) \leq \phi(x_2)$.) Prove that ϕ has only a countable set of discontinuities. Construct an example to show that ϕ may be discontinuous at every rational point.

1.4.94 Exercise. Prove that $c^c = 2^c$.

1.4.95 Final Exercise # 1. Let f be a real-valued function defined on R such that for all $x \in R$, there is a $\delta(x) > 0$ such that $f(y) \geq f(x)$ whenever $|y-x| < \delta(x)$. Prove that the set $f(R)$ is countable. Construct an example of such a function f for each of the following conditions:

i) f assumes an infinite number of values;

ii) f is unbounded in $[0,1]$;

iii) f is monotone in no open interval containing 1.

1.5 Partially ordered sets.

1.5.1 Definition. Let S be a set. A partial ordering on S is a subset P of $S \times S$ such that for all $x, y, z \in S$,

i) $(x, y) \in P$ and $(y, x) \in P$ imply $x = y$ (antisymmetry);

ii) $(x,x) \in P$ (reflexivity);

iii) $(x,y) \in P$ and $(y,z) \in P$ imply $(x,z) \in P$ (transitivity).

We will write $x \leq y$ to mean $(x,y) \in P$, $x \geq y$ to mean $y \leq x$, $x < y$ to mean $x \leq y$ and $x \neq y$, and $x > y$ to mean $y < x$. Conditions (i), (ii), and (iii) now read

i) $x \leq y$ and $y \leq x$ imply $x = y$;

ii) $x \leq x$;

iii) $x \leq y$ and $y \leq z$ imply $x \leq z$.

1.5.11 Example. Let S be any set and $P = \{(x,x): x \in S\}$.

1.5.12 Example. Let A be a subset of the real numbers R and $\leq$ be its natural ordering.

1.5.13 Example. Let $A \subset R$ and let $S = \underset{\lambda \in \Lambda}{P} A_{(\lambda)}$ be all functions f with domain Λ and range contained in A. Define $f \leq g$ if $f(\lambda) \leq g(\lambda)$ for all $\lambda \in \Lambda$.

1.5.14 Example. Let $A \subset R$, and $S = A \times A$. Let $\leq$ be defined as follows: $(x,y) \leq (x',y')$ if $x < x'$ or $x = x'$ and $y \leq y'$. This ordering is called a lexicographic ordering.

1.5.15 Example. With finite partially ordered sets one may show the ordering graphically; a will be less than b if a is connected to b by a straight line and a is placed lower than b. For example,

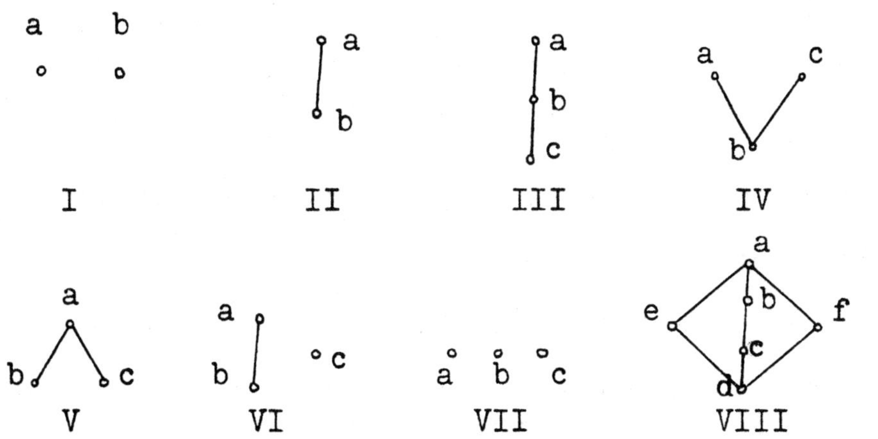

I and II are the only possible partial orderings of a set with two elements. III, IV, V, VI, and VII are all the possible partial orderings of a three-element set.

1.5.2 <u>Definition</u>. Let S be a partially ordered set. S is said to be directed if for all $x, y \varepsilon S$, there exists a $w \varepsilon S$ such that $w \geq x$ and $w \geq y$.

1.5.21 <u>Example</u>. Let X be any set and $\mathcal{S}$ be the set of all subsets of X. Partially order $\mathcal{S}$ by: $A \leq B$ means $A \subset B$ for $A \subset X$, $B \subset X$. Clearly $\mathcal{S}$ is directed, for if $A, B \varepsilon \mathcal{S}$ then $A \cup B \varepsilon \mathcal{S}$, $A \leq A \cup B$, and $B \leq A \cup B$.

1.5.3 <u>Definition</u>. Let X be a partially ordered set. If for every $x, y \varepsilon X$, either $x < y$, $x = y$, or $x > y$, X is said to be completely ordered.

1.5.31 <u>Example</u>. Any $A \subset R$ with the ordering inherited from R is completely ordered.

1.5.32 <u>Example</u>. $R \times R$ with the lexicographic ordering is completely ordered (see Example 1.5.14).

1.5.33 <u>Definition</u>. Let X be a partially ordered set. An element

$a \varepsilon X$ is the greatest element of X if $a \geq x$ for all $x \varepsilon X$. $a \varepsilon X$ is maximal in X if $b \varepsilon X$ and $b \geq a$ imply $b = a$. Least and minimal elements are defined similarly.

It is important to distinguish between greatest and maximal elements of a partially ordered set. For example, the ordering

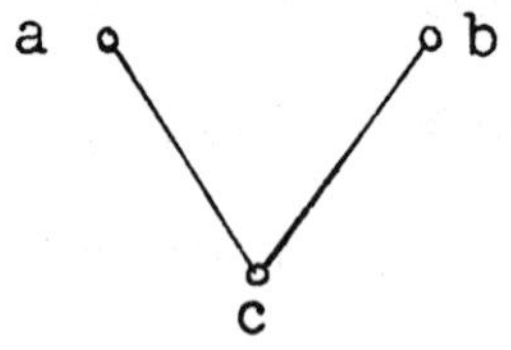

has no greatest element, but a and b are maximal elements. Obviously a partially ordered set can contain no more than one greatest element. The greatest element of a partially ordered set is obviously maximal.

1.5.34 <u>Definition</u>. Let X and Y be partially ordered sets. Suppose there is a one-to-one mapping ϕ of X onto Y such that $\phi(x) \leq \phi(y)$ if and only if $x \leq y$. Then X and Y are said to be ordinally similar.

1.5.35 <u>Exercise</u>. Prove that every non-void finite completely ordered set is ordinally similar to $\{1, 2, \ldots, n\}$ (for some positive integer n) with its natural ordering.

1.5.36 <u>Exercise</u>. Prove that every countable completely ordered set is ordinally similar to a subset of the rational numbers with their ordering as a subset of R.

1.5.37 <u>Final Exercise # 2</u>. Let X be any non-void countable completely ordered set such that:

i) for all $a, b \in X$ there is a $c \in X$ such that $a < c < b$;

ii) X has no greatest element and no least element.

Prove that X is ordinally similar to the set of all rational numbers.

1.5.4 Definition. A non-void set X is said to be well-ordered if X is completely ordered and every non-void subset A of X contains a least element.

1.5.41 Example. $[0,1]$ is not well-ordered; for example, $]0,1]$ contains no least element.

1.5.42 Example. The set $\{1, 2, \ldots, n\}$ is well-ordered. Hence by 1.5.35 any finite completely ordered set is well-ordered.

1.5.43 Example. $\{1, 2, \ldots, n, \ldots\}$ is well-ordered, under its natural ordering. This is an intuitively obvious fact about the set of all positive integers. It is a simple consequence of Peano's axioms for the positive integers. Other infinite well-ordered sets can easily be built up. Thus

$$\{1, 2, 3, \ldots, n, \ldots, \omega\}$$

where $\{1, 2, 3, \ldots, n, \ldots\}$ has its usual ordering and $\omega > n$ for all positive integers n, is obviously well-ordered and is ordinally dissimilar from $\{1, 2, 3, \ldots, n, \ldots\}$. In like manner, we can construct well-ordered sets $\{1, 2, 3, \ldots, n, \ldots, \omega, \omega+1, \omega+2, \omega+3, \ldots, \omega+m\}$, $\{1, 2, \ldots, n, \ldots, \omega, \omega+1, \omega+2, \ldots, \omega+n, \ldots\}$, $\{1, 2, \ldots, n, \ldots, \omega, \omega+1, \ldots, \omega+n, \ldots, \omega\cdot 2\}$, $\{1, 2, \ldots, n, \ldots, \omega, \omega+1, \ldots, \omega+n, \ldots, \omega\cdot 2, \omega\cdot 2+1, \ldots, \omega\cdot 2+n, \ldots\}$, $\{1, 2, \ldots, n, \ldots, \omega, \omega+1, \ldots, \omega+n, \ldots, \omega\cdot 2, \omega\cdot 2+1, \ldots, \omega\cdot 3\}$, $\{1, 2, \ldots, n, \ldots, \omega, \ldots, \omega\cdot 2, \ldots, \omega\cdot 3, \ldots, \omega\cdot 4, \ldots, \omega\cdot n, \ldots\}, \ldots$.

These sets are all ordinally dissimilar, and are obviously all countably infinite. These examples by no means exhaust all possible well-orderings of a countably infinite set.

1.5.44 Remark. Every non-void subset of a well-ordered set is well-ordered.

1.5.45 Remark. Suppose that b is a member of a well-ordered set X and that b is not the greatest element of X. Then b has an immediate successor, i.e., there is a $\tilde{b} \varepsilon X$ such that $\tilde{b} > b$ and whenever $\tilde{b} \geq x \geq b$ then $x = b$ or $x = \tilde{b}$. Proof: Since b is not the greatest element of X, there is an $x \varepsilon X$ such that $x \leq b$ fails. Thus $x > b$. Now $B = \{y: y \varepsilon X, y > b\}$ is a non-void subset of X and hence contains a least element $\tilde{b}$. Clearly $\tilde{b} > b$. $\tilde{b} \geq x \geq b$ implies $x = b$ or $x = \tilde{b}$, for if some x exists such that $\tilde{b} > x > b$ then $\tilde{b}$ is not the least element of B.

A well-ordered set may have elements that have no immediate predecessors. For example, if $X = \{1, 2, \ldots, n, \ldots, \omega\}$, then ω has no immediate predecessor.

1.5.5 Theorem. (Zermelo*) Suppose that the axiom of choice (1.3.31) holds for the family of all non-void subsets of the non-void set X. That is, suppose that there is a "choice" function ϕ with domain the family of all non-void subsets of X and range X such that $\phi(A)$ is a point of A for all $A, 0 \neq A \subset X$. Then X can be well-ordered.

Proof. For $0 \neq A \subset X$, let $A^* = A \cap \{\phi(A)\}'$. A family $\mathcal{C}$ of subsets of X is called a chain (this terminology will be used only in the present proof) if

i) $X \in \mathcal{C}$;

ii) $A \in \mathcal{C}$ implies $A^* \in \mathcal{C}$;

iii) $\{A_\lambda\}_{\lambda \in \Lambda} \subset \mathcal{C}$ implies $\bigcap_{\lambda \in \Lambda} A_\lambda \in \mathcal{C}$.

The family of all subsets of X is a chain. Let $\mathcal{D}$ be the family of subsets of X such that $A \in \mathcal{D}$ if and only if A is in all chains. Clearly $X \in \mathcal{D}$, so that $\mathcal{D}$ is non-void.

$A \in \mathcal{D}$ implies $A^* \in \mathcal{C}$ for all chains $\mathcal{C}$. Thus $A^* \in \mathcal{D}$. Suppose that $\{A_\lambda\}_{\lambda \in \Lambda} \subset \mathcal{D}$. Then $A_\lambda \in \mathcal{C}$ for all chains $\mathcal{C}$ and all $\lambda \in \Lambda$. Then $\bigcap_{\lambda \in \Lambda} A_\lambda \in \mathcal{C}$ for all chains $\mathcal{C}$. It follows that $\bigcap_{\lambda \in \Lambda} A_\lambda \in \mathcal{D}$. We have just shown that $\mathcal{D}$ is a chain; clearly $\mathcal{D}$ is contained in every chain.

* See Mathematische Annalen 65 (1908), page 107.

Let $\mathcal{D}_0$ be the family of sets $A \varepsilon \mathcal{D}$ having the property that for all $B \varepsilon \mathcal{D}$, either $B \supsetneq A$, $B = A$, or $B \subsetneq A$. We will ultimately show that $\mathcal{D}_0$ is a chain and hence that $\mathcal{D}_0 = \mathcal{D}$.

We note first that $X \varepsilon \mathcal{D}_0$.

For $A \varepsilon \mathcal{D}_0$, let $\mathcal{D}_1(A)$ be the set of all $B \varepsilon \mathcal{D}$ such that $B \supsetneq A$, $B = A$, or $B \subset A^*$. We will show that $\mathcal{D}_1(A)$ is a chain. Clearly $X \varepsilon \mathcal{D}_1(A)$. Suppose $B \varepsilon \mathcal{D}_1(A)$. If $B \supsetneq A$, then $B^* \varepsilon \mathcal{D}$ and therefore $B^* \supsetneq A$, $B^* = A$, or $B^* \subsetneq A$. $B^* \subsetneq A$ is impossible since then we would have $B^* \subsetneq A \subsetneq B$. This cannot happen, since $B^* = B \cap \{\phi(B)\}'$ and $\phi(B)$ is a single point. Thus either $B^* \supsetneq A$ or $B^* = A$, and hence $B^* \varepsilon \mathcal{D}_1(A)$. If $B = A$, then $B^* = A^*$, and thus $B^* \subset A^*$ so that $B^* \varepsilon \mathcal{D}_1(A)$ in this case also. Finally, if $B \subset A^*$, then $B^* \subsetneq B \subset A^*$, so that $B^* \varepsilon \mathcal{D}_1(A)$. We have just shown that $\mathcal{D}_1(A)$ satisfies condition ii) for a chain.

Let $\{B_\lambda\}_{\lambda \varepsilon \Lambda} \subset \mathcal{D}_1(A)$. If for all $\lambda \varepsilon \Lambda$, $B_\lambda \supset A$, then clearly $\bigcap_{\lambda \varepsilon \Lambda} B_\lambda \supset A$. Otherwise for some λ_0, $B_{\lambda_0} \subset A^*$, and we have $\bigcap_{\lambda \varepsilon \Lambda} B_\lambda \subset B_{\lambda_0} \subset A^*$. In either case, $\bigcap_{\lambda \varepsilon \Lambda} B_\lambda \varepsilon \mathcal{D}_1(A)$. Thus $\mathcal{D}_1(A)$ satisfies condition iii) for a chain and hence is a chain.

Since $\mathcal{D}$ is the smallest chain, we see that $\mathcal{D}_1(A) = \mathcal{D}$. That is, for all $B \varepsilon \mathcal{D}$, either $B \supsetneq A$, $B = A$, or $B \subset A^*$. We use this to show that for all

$B \in \mathcal{D}$, we have $B \supsetneq A^*$, $B = A^*$, or $B \subsetneq A^*$. If $B \supsetneq A$, then $B \supsetneq A \supsetneq A^*$; if $B = A$, then $B \supsetneq A^*$; if $B \subset A^*$, then $B = A^*$ or $B \subsetneq A^*$. Thus we see that if $A \in \mathcal{D}_0$, then $A^* \in \mathcal{D}_0$ (property ii) for a chain).

To see that $\mathcal{D}_0$ also satisfies property iii) for a chain, suppose $\{A_\lambda\}_{\lambda \in \Lambda} \subset \mathcal{D}_0$. Consider $B \in \mathcal{D}$. If for some λ_0, $B \supset A_{\lambda_0}$, then $B \supset A_{\lambda_0} \supset \bigcap_{\lambda \in \Lambda} A_\lambda$. Otherwise $B \subset A_\lambda$ for all $\lambda \in \Lambda$. Then $B \subset \bigcap_{\lambda \in \Lambda} A_\lambda$. Thus we see that $\mathcal{D}_0$ is a chain and hence $\mathcal{D}_0 = \mathcal{D}$. We thus have the following result.

1.5.51 <u>Lemma</u>. For every $A, B \in \mathcal{D}$, we have $B \supsetneq A, B = A$, or $B \subsetneq A$.

Let $P \subset X$, $P \neq 0$. Let $P_0 = \cap\{B\colon\ B \in \mathcal{D}$ and $B \supset P\}$. $P_0 \in \mathcal{D}$ by condition iii). We also have $\phi(P_0) \in P$. For, assume that $\phi(P_0) \notin P$; then $P \subset P_0 \cap \{\phi(P_0)\}' = P_0^* \subsetneq P_0$ and $P_0^* \in \mathcal{D}$. This is a contradiction, since P_0 is the smallest member of $\mathcal{D}$ containing P.

Let $P_1 \in \mathcal{D}$ and $P_1 \supsetneq P_0 \supset P$. Then we have $\phi(P_1) \notin P$. For assume that $\phi(P_1) \in P$. We see by 1.5.51 that either $P_1^* \supset P_0$ or $P_1^* \subsetneq P_0$. The inclusion $P_1^* \supset P_0$ fails since $\phi(P_1) \in P \subset P_0$ and $\phi(P_1) \notin P_1^*$; the proper inclusion $P_1^* \subsetneq P_0$ fails since then $P_1^* \subsetneq P_0 \subsetneq P_1$, contradicting the relation $P_1^* = P_1 \cap \{\phi(P_1)\}'$. It follows that $\phi(P_1) \notin P$.

Thus for every $0 \neq P \subset X$, there is exactly one set $P_0 \varepsilon \mathcal{D}$ such that $P_0 \supset P$ and $\phi(P_0) \varepsilon P$. In particular, for every $a \varepsilon X$, there is exactly one set, which we call $R(a)$, such that $R(a) \varepsilon \mathcal{D}$, $R(a) \supset \{a\}$, and $\phi(R(a)) \varepsilon \{a\}$. Equivalently, there is exactly one set $R(a) \varepsilon \mathcal{D}$ such that $a \varepsilon R(a)$ and $\phi(R(a)) = a$. If $a \neq b$, then $R(a) \neq R(b)$, since $R(a) = R(b)$ implies that $a = \phi(R(a)) = \phi(R(b)) = b$.

If $R(a) \supsetneq R(b)$, we write $a < b$ and if $R(a) \subsetneq R(b)$, we write $a > b$. By 1.5.51, we have exactly one of the relations $a < b$, $a = b$, or $a > b$ for all $a,b \varepsilon X$. With this ordering, X is thus completely ordered. It remains to show that X is well-ordered.

Suppose that $0 \neq P \subset X$. Let P_0 be the unique subset of X such that $P_0 \supset P$, $\phi(P_0) \varepsilon P$, and $P_0 \varepsilon \mathcal{D}$. Note that we have shown above that P_0 exists and is defined as $\cap\{B: B \varepsilon \mathcal{D}, B \supset P\}$. Since $R(\phi(P_0))$ is by definition the unique element $Q \varepsilon \mathcal{D}$ such that $\phi(Q) = \phi(P_0)$, it follows that $R(\phi(P_0)) = P_0$.

For every $p \varepsilon P$, $R(p) = \cap\{B: B \varepsilon \mathcal{D}, p \varepsilon B\} \subset \cap\{B: B \varepsilon \mathcal{D}, P \subset B\} = P_0 = R(\phi(P_0))$. That is, $R(p) \subset R(\phi(P_0))$ for every $p \varepsilon P$. By our definition of "$<$", this implies that $\phi(P_0) \leq p$ for all $p \varepsilon P$. Since $\phi(P_0) \varepsilon P$, we see that $\phi(P_0)$ is actually the least element of P. Thus X is well-ordered and the proof is complete.

1.5.6 Theorem. (Principle of complete or transfinite induction). Let Ψ be a property meaningful for elements of a well-ordered set W. Suppose that Ψ holds for every $x \in W$ provided that it holds for all y such that $y < x$. Then Ψ holds for all elements of W.

Proof. Assume that Ψ fails for some element of W. Then there is a unique $a \in W$ such that a is the least element for which Ψ fails. Then Ψ must hold for all $y \in W$ where $y < a$. By the inductive hypothesis, Ψ also holds for a; a contradiction since Ψ fails for a.

1.5.7 Theorem. (Zorn-Tukey-Kuratowski-Maximum). Let X be a set partially ordered by a relation $\preccurlyeq$. Suppose that every non-void completely ordered subset of X admits an upper bound in X. Then X contains a maximal element.

Proof. Well-order X under a relation $\leq$. We will define a subset C of X by transfinite induction. Let C contain the first element of X under $\leq$. Suppose that $x \in X$ and that for all $y < x$ it has been determined whether or not $y \in C$. Let $C_x = \{y: y < x$ and $y \in C\}$. If $x \succ y$ for all $y \in C_x$, then we put x into C. If, however, $x \not\succ y$ for some $y \in C_x$, then we omit x from C. By 1.5.6, C is a well-defined subset of X. C is completely ordered under $\preccurlyeq$, for suppose $x, x^* \in C$, $x \neq x^*$. Either $x < x^*$, in which case $x \prec x^*$, or $x^* < x$, in which case $x^* \prec x$. By the hypothesis on $\preccurlyeq$, there exists an upper bound b to C. That is, $b \succcurlyeq x$ for all $x \in C$. Then $x < b$ and $x \in C$ implies $x \prec b$ and therefore $b \in C$ by the definition of C. If $y > b$ and $y \in C$, then $y \succ b$ contradicting $b \succ y$. Thus we see that $y \in C$ implies that $y \leq b$.

The element b is maximal in X under $\preccurlyeq$. For assume that there is a $y \in X$ such that $y \succ b$. Then $y \notin C$. However, $y \succ b \succcurlyeq x$ for all $x < y$ where $x \in C$ and so $y \in C$. This is a contradiction and hence b is maximal in X.

1.5.71 Remarks. The hypothesis in 1.5.7 that completely ordered subsets admit upper bounds is essential. For example, consider the interval $[0,1[$ with its ordering as a subset of R. This completely ordered set obviously contains no maximal element, and no subset A of $[0,1[$ with supremum 1 admits an upper bound in $[0,1[$. Compact subsets of R satisfy the hypotheses of 1.5.7, and of course do admit maximal (i.e., greatest) elements.

In many applications of 1.5.7, the set X is a family $\mathcal{S}$ of subsets of some fixed set B, and the partial ordering is set-inclusion. The usual technique is to show that the union of any completely ordered subfamily of $\mathcal{S}$ again belongs to $\mathcal{S}$. (See exercises 1.5.82 and 1.5.86.)

1.5.8 Exercises.

1.5.81 Final Exercise # 3. Let W be a well-ordered set. For an arbitrary $a \varepsilon W$, the set $I(a) = \{x: x \varepsilon W, x < a\}$ is called an initial segment of W. For two well-ordered sets W and W^*, write $W \lesssim W^*$ if W is ordinally similar to W^* or to an initial segment of W^*.

i) Prove that W is ordinally similar to W^* if and only if $W \lesssim W^*$ and $W^* \lesssim W$.

ii) Identifying two well-ordered sets if they are ordinally similar, prove that any set of well-ordered sets is well-ordered under the relation $\lesssim$.

iii) Let m be any cardinal number, finite or infinite. Prove that there is a least well-ordered set, in the sense of the relation $\lesssim$ defined above for well-ordered sets, having cardinal number m.

iv) Prove that any set of cardinal numbers contains a least cardinal number (in the usual ordering for cardinal numbers).

1.5.82 <u>Exercise</u>. A set I of real numbers is said to be linearly independent (over the rational numbers Q) if $\sum_{i=1}^{n} r_i x_i = 0$ $(r_1, \ldots, r_n \varepsilon Q; x_1, \ldots, x_n \varepsilon I)$ implies that $r_1 = r_2 = \ldots = r_n = 0$. Prove that there is a set H of real numbers (called a Hamel basis for R over Q or simply a basis for R over Q) such that H is linearly independent and no proper superset of H in R is linearly independent.

1.5.83 <u>Exercise</u>. Let H be a Hamel basis for R over Q. Let

x be any real number. Prove that there exist $h_1, \ldots, h_m \in H$ and $r_1, \ldots, r_m \in Q$ such that $x = \sum_{i=1}^{m} r_i h_i$. Prove that every $x \in R$ has only one representation of this kind.

1.5.84 Exercise. Find the cardinal number of an arbitrary Hamel basis for R over Q.

1.5.85 Exercise. Let W and W^* be disjoint well-ordered sets. Order $W \cup W^*$ by letting $w < w^*$ for all $w \in W$ and $w^* \in W^*$, and maintaining the "internal" ordering of W and W^*. Prove that $W \cup W^*$ is well-ordered.

Order $W \times W^*$ lexicographically. That is, $(w,w^*) < (\bar{w},\bar{w}^*)$ if $w < \bar{w}$ or $w = \bar{w}$ and $w^* < \bar{w}^*$. Prove that $W \times W^*$ is well-ordered.

1.5.86 Exercise. Let G be a group and let H be a commutative subgroup of G. Prove that H is contained in a maximal commutative subgroup J of G; that is, J is commutative but no subgroup J^* such that $J^* \supsetneq J$ is commutative.

1.6 Structure of R.

1.6.1 Algebraic structure of R. There exists a mapping σ of $R \times R$ into R, for which we write $\sigma(x,y) = x + y$, such that:

A1 $x + (y + z) = (x + y) + z$ for all $x,y,z \in R$;

A2 there is an element $0 \in R$ such that $0 + x = x$ for all $x \in R$;

A3 for each $x \in R$, there is an element $(-x) \in R$ such that $(-x) + x = 0$;

A4 $x + y = y + x$ for all $x, y \in R$.

Axioms A1-A3 describe a group. Axioms A1-A4 describe a commutative or Abelian group (after the Norwegian mathematician N. H. Abel (1802 - 1829)). Further, there is a mapping π of $R \times R$ into R, for which we write $\pi(x,y) = x \cdot y = xy$, such that:

M1 $x(yz) = (xy)z$ for all $x, y, z \in R$;

M2 $x(y + z) = xy + xz$ for all $x, y, z \in R$;

M3 $xy - yx$ for all $x, y \in R$;

M4 there is an element $1 \in R$, $1 \neq 0$, such that $1 \cdot x = x$ for all $x \in R$;

M5 for all $x \in R$, $x \neq 0$, there is an element $\frac{1}{x} \in R$ such that $\frac{1}{x} \cdot x = 1$.

Axioms A1-A4 and M1-M3 together define a commutative ring. M4 postulates the existence of a unit. M5 asserts that the non-zero elements of R form a group under multiplication. Any set with operations σ and π satisfying A1-A4 and M1-M5 is called a field. We take it as known that R is a field.

1.6.2 *The ordering of R.* The field R has additional structure, namely its ordering. We describe the ordering of R by describing the set of positive elements. There is a set $P \subset R$, called the set of positive elements of the field, such that

P1 $x, y \in P$ implies $x + y \in P$ and $x \cdot y \in P$;

P2 given any $x \varepsilon R$, exactly one of the following is true: $x \varepsilon P$, $-x \varepsilon P$, $x = 0$.

We now write $x < y$ whenever $y - x \varepsilon P$. From postulates P1-P2, the following laws can be easily proved:

i) $x < y$ and $x' < y'$ imply $x + x' < y + y'$;

ii) $x < y$ and $z > 0$ imply $xz < yz$;

iii) $0 < x < y$ imply $0 < \frac{1}{y} < \frac{1}{x}$;

iv) $x < y$ if and only if $-y < -x$;

v) $1 \varepsilon P$;

vi) $x \varepsilon R$ and $x \neq 0$ imply $x^2 \varepsilon P$.

1.6.21 __The Archimedean property.__ The real numbers R satisfy the Archimedean property for order:

P3 if $a,b \varepsilon R$ and $a > 0$, then there exists a positive integer n such that $\underbrace{a + a + \ldots + a}_{n} > b$.

1.6.3 __Definition.__ A sequence $\{a_n\}_{n=1}^{\infty}$ of real numbers is called a Cauchy sequence if for every $\varepsilon > 0$, there exists an $N(\varepsilon)$ such that $|a_n - a_m| < \varepsilon$ whenever $m,n \geq N(\varepsilon)$.

1.6.31 __Theorem.__ Every Cauchy sequence of real numbers has a limit in R.

This is called the completeness property. An example of an incomplete Archimedean ordered field is the field of all rational numbers. An example of an ordered field not having the Archimedean property follows.

1.6.4 __Example.__ Let $\tilde{Q}$ be the set of all rational functions; a general member is of the form $\dfrac{a_o + a_1x + a_2x^2 + \cdots + a_kx^k}{b_o + b_1x + b_2x^2 + \cdots + b_mx^m}$

where the a_i and b_i are real numbers and $b_m \neq 0$ ($a_k \neq 0$ unless $k = 0$). Let us say that a rational function is positive if $a_k b_m > 0$. One can verify that $\tilde{Q}$ is an ordered field. Consider the rational functions 1 and x. Clearly $1 > 0$. Now there is no n such that $1 \cdot n > x$ since for all $n \in N$, $x - 1 \cdot n > 0$. Hence $\tilde{Q}$ is non-Archimedean.

1.6.5 Theorem. The real number field R is, up to an order-preserving algebraic isomorphism, the only complete, Archimedean ordered field. That is, if S is any field with these properties, then there is a one-to-one mapping π carrying R onto S such that $\pi(x + y) = \pi(x) + \pi(y)$, $\pi(xy) = \pi(x)\pi(y)$, and $\pi(x)$ is positive if and only if x is positive.

We shall not prove this theorem.

1.6.6 Definition. Let $A \subset R$. If there exists a number b such that $b \geq a$ for all $a \in A$, then A is said to be bounded above and b is called an upper bound for A. Similarly, if there exists a number b' such that $b' \leq a$ for all $a \in A$, b' is called a lower bound for A.

1.6.61 Theorem. Every non-void subset of R that is bounded $\left\{\begin{matrix}\text{above}\\ \text{below}\end{matrix}\right\}$ admits a $\left\{\begin{matrix}\text{least upper}\\ \text{greater lower}\end{matrix}\right\}$ bound.

1.6.62 Definition. The least upper bound of a set A will be denoted l.u.b.A or sup A (for "supremum"). The greatest lower bound of A will be denoted g.l.b.A or inf A ("infimum"). If A is not bounded above, we shall write $\sup A = +\infty$. If A is not bounded below, we shall write $\inf A = -\infty$.

Although one often thinks of $+\infty$, ∞, and $-\infty$ as merely formal symbols, we shall find it convenient to think of them as objects also. As such, it is clear that they are not members of R. In particular, if $A \subset R \cup \{-\infty, \infty\}$, then $\inf A$ and $\sup A$ can be defined in a manner similar to that of 1.6.62; here $-\infty < a < \infty$ for all $a \in R$.

1.6.63 <u>Definition</u>. Let $\{a_n\}_{n=1}^{\infty}$ be any sequence of real numbers. Then we define $\inf\{\sup\{a_p, a_{p+1}, \ldots\}\}$ to be the limit superior of $\{a_n\}_{n=1}^{\infty}$; we denote this element $\limsup a_n$ or $\overline{\lim\limits_{n\to\infty}}\, a_n$. Analogously we define $\liminf a_n$ or $\underline{\lim\limits_{n\to\infty}}\, a_n$ to be $\sup\{\inf\{a_p, a_{p+1}, \ldots\}\}$.

1.7 <u>Topology of R</u>. We now consider certain properties of the real number system, of vital importance for integration theory, that have to do with limit points, open sets, and closed sets.

1.7.1 <u>Definition</u>. Let $A \subset R$. A point $x \in R$ is called a limit point of A if for every positive number ε, there is a point $a \in A$ such that $0 < |x - a| < \varepsilon$. A point $x \in A$ that is not a limit point of A is called an isolated point of A.

1.7.11 Example. Let $A = [0,1[\cup \{2\}$. 2 is an isolated point of A. Every point of $[0,1]$ is a limit point of A.

1.7.2 Definition. A set $A \subset R$ is said to be open if for every $a \in A$ there is an open interval I such that $a \in I \subset A$.

1.7.21 Examples. The void set 0 and the real line R are open sets. Every open interval $]a,b[$ for $a,b \in R$ is an open set. The sets $]-\infty,a[$ and $]a,+\infty[$ for $a \in R$ are open sets.

1.7.22 Remark. Every union of open sets is an open set. Every finite intersection of open sets is open. Proofs of these simple facts may be supplied by the reader. Infinite intersections of open sets may fail to be open; for example:

$$\bigcap_{n=1}^{\infty}]-\tfrac{1}{n}, \tfrac{1}{n}[= \{0\}.$$

1.7.23 Remark. It is obvious from the definition of open sets that every non-void open set is the union of a family of open intervals. This assertion can be made considerably more precise, as follows:

1.7.3 Theorem. Let G be a non-void open subset of R. Then G can be written in one and only one way as the union of a countable family of pairwise disjoint open intervals.

Proof. Let x be an arbitrary point of G. Let $\alpha_x = \inf \{t: t \in R,]t,x] \subset G\}$ and $\beta_x = \sup \{t: t \in R, [x,t[\subset G\}$. Since G is open and $x \in G$, it is clear that α_x and β_x exist. We first assert that $]\alpha_x,\beta_x[\subset G$, and begin by proving that $]\alpha_x,x] \subset G$.

Case I. $-\infty < \alpha_x$. For every positive integer n, there is a number t_n such that $\alpha_x \leq t_n < \alpha_x + \frac{1}{n}$ and $]t_n,x] \subset G$. Now $]\alpha_x,x] = \bigcup_{n=1}^{\infty}]\alpha_x + \frac{1}{n},x] \subset \bigcup_{n=1}^{\infty}]t_n,x] \subset G$.

Case II. $\alpha_x = -\infty$. Then for every positive integer n there is a t_n such that $t_n < -n$ and $]t_n,x] \subset G$. Thus $]\alpha_x,x] =]-\infty,x] = \bigcup_{n=1}^{\infty}]-n,x] \subset \bigcup_{n=1}^{\infty}]t_n,x] \subset G$. Likewise, we have $[x,\beta_x[\subset G$, and hence $]\alpha_x,\beta_x[\subset G$.

We next show that $\alpha_x \notin G$, $\beta_x \notin G$. Assume that $\beta_x \in G$. Since G is open, there is a number $\delta > 0$ such that $]\beta_x - \delta, \beta_x + \delta[\subset G$. Hence $[x,\beta_x[\cup [\beta_x,\beta_x + \delta[= [x,\beta_x + \delta[\subset G$, and this contradicts the definition of β_x. Therefore $\beta_x \notin G$; likewise, $\alpha_x \notin G$.

G is thus the union of open intervals whose endpoints do not belong to G. We will show that given $x,y \in G$, $]\alpha_x,\beta_x[$ and $]\alpha_y,\beta_y[$ are disjoint or identical. Observe that $]\alpha_x,\beta_x[\cap]\alpha_y,\beta_y[\neq 0$ if and only if there is a number u such that $\alpha_x < u < \beta_x$ and $\alpha_y < u < \beta_y$, that is, if and only if $\max(\alpha_x,\alpha_y) < \min(\beta_x,\beta_y)$. Assume that $\beta_x \neq \beta_y$. It is merely a notational matter to suppose that $\beta_x < \beta_y$. Clearly $y \neq \beta_x$ since $y \in G$ and $\beta_x \notin G$. Suppose $\beta_x < y$. Since $]\alpha_y,y] \subset G$ and $\alpha_y < \beta_x < y$, we have $\beta_x \in G$, a contradiction. Suppose $y < \beta_x$. Since $[y,\beta_y[\subset G$ and $y < \beta_x < \beta_y$ we have $\beta_x \in G$, again a contradiction. Hence $\beta_x = \beta_y$. Likewise $\alpha_x = \alpha_y$. Hence $G = \bigcup_{\lambda \in \Lambda} I_\lambda$ is the union of pair-wise disjoint open intervals I_λ. Every I_λ contains a rational number r_λ. The function f, where $f(I_\lambda) = r_\lambda$, is a one-to-one map of $\{I_\lambda\}_{\lambda\in\Lambda}$ into the set of rational numbers. Thus $\overline{\overline{\Lambda}} = \overline{\overline{\{I_\lambda\}_{\lambda\in\Lambda}}} \leq \overline{\overline{\{\text{rational numbers}\}}} = \aleph_0$; that is, $\{I_\lambda\}_{\lambda\in\Lambda}$ is countable.

Suppose finally that G is written in any way at all as $\bigcup_{\lambda\in\Lambda} I_\lambda$, where the sets I_λ are pairwise disjoint open intervals. Let $I_\lambda =]a_\lambda, b_\lambda[$. Then we have $a_\lambda \notin G$. If $a_\lambda = -\infty$, this is obvious. If $a_\lambda > -\infty$ and $a_\lambda \in G$, then there is a $\mu \in \Lambda$, $\mu \neq \lambda$, such that $a_\lambda \in I_\mu =]a_\mu, b_\mu[$. Hence we have $a_\mu < a_\lambda < b_\mu$, and also $I_\lambda \cap I_\mu \supset]a_\lambda, \min(b_\lambda, b_\mu)[\neq 0$. That is, the intervals $\{I_\lambda\}_{\lambda\in\Lambda}$ fail to be pairwise disjoint. Likewise we have $b_\lambda \notin G$. It is now immediate that for all $u \in I_\lambda$, the equalities $b_\lambda = \beta_u$, $a_\lambda = \alpha_u$ obtain. That is, the sets I_λ are exactly the sets $]\alpha_u, \beta_u[$. Thus the decomposition of G into pairwise disjoint open intervals is unique, and this completes the proof.

1.7.31 <u>Remark</u>. The simple structure of open sets in R is not shared by open sets in Euclidean spaces of dimension > 1. A subset A of R^2, for example, is said to be open if for all $(x_1,x_2) \in A$ there is a $\delta > 0$ such that $[(y_1 - x_1)^2 + (y_2 - x_2)^2] < \delta$ implies $(y_1,y_2) \in A$. Open circles thus take the place of open intervals. Plainly there are open subsets of R^2 -- for example, the set

$\{(x_1,x_2): \ 0 < x_1 < 1, \ 0 < x_2 < 1\}$ -- that are not the union of a countable family of pairwise disjoint open circles.

1.7.4 Definition. A subset A of R is said to be closed if A' is open.

1.7.41 Theorem. A set $A \subset R$ is closed if and only if it contains all of its own limit points.

1.7.42 Remark. The intersection of any family of closed sets is closed. The union of a finite family of closed sets is closed.

1.7.43 Remark. Let A be a subset of R. Let A^- be the intersection of all closed sets containing A. Then A^- is closed and is the smallest closed set containing A. A^- is called the closure of A. A^- is the union of A and all limit points of A. $A = A^-$ if and only if A is closed. $(A \cup B)^- = A^- \cup B^-$. $A^- \cap B^- \supset (A \cap B)^-$; the equality does not hold in general. For, consider the case where A is the set of rationals and B is the set of irrationals. We also have $A^{--} = A^-$.

1.7.44 Remark. Let $A \subset R$. Then $A^{'-'}$ is the largest open set contained in A. $A^{'-'}$ is called the interior of A. The interior of A is the union of all open sets contained in A.

1.7.45 Definition. A set $A \subset R$ is said to be perfect if A is closed and has no isolated points.

1.7.46 Remark. A non-void perfect subset of R has cardinal number c.

1.7.5 Definition. Let $A \subset R$. A real-valued function f with domain A is said to be continuous (on A) if for every $a \in A$ and every $\varepsilon > 0$, there is a $\delta(\varepsilon,a) > 0$ such that $|f(x) - f(a)| < \varepsilon$ for all $x \in A \cap]a - \delta, a + \delta[$.

1.7.51 Remark. It is well known, and easy to prove that sums, products, and uniform limits of continuous functions on any set $A \subset R$ are continuous. A continuous non-constant function defined on an interval has its range on an interval. However, on the Cantor set for example, there are continuous functions with arbitrary finite ranges.

1.7.6 Exercises.

1.7.61 Exercise. Prove that 0 and R are the only subsets of R that are both open and closed.

1.7.62 Exercise. A set that is the intersection of a countable number of open sets is called a G_δ set. A set that is the union of a countable number of closed sets is called an F_σ set. Prove that every closed subset of R is a G_δ set and that every open subset of R is an F_σ set.

1.7.63 Exercise. A real-valued function f with domain $A \subset R$ is $\begin{Bmatrix}\text{upper}\\ \text{lower}\end{Bmatrix}$ semi-continuous $\begin{Bmatrix}\text{u.s.c.}\\ \text{l.s.c.}\end{Bmatrix}$ if for every $a \in A$ and every $\varepsilon > 0$, there is a $\delta(\varepsilon,a) > 0$ such that $\begin{Bmatrix} f(x) - f(a) < \varepsilon \\ -\varepsilon < f(x) - f(a) \end{Bmatrix}$ for all $x \in]a - \delta, a + \delta[\cap A$.

Prove that a real-valued function f with domain R is upper semi-continuous if and only if $\begin{cases} f^{-1}(]-\infty,t[) & \text{is open} \\ f^{-1}([t,+\infty[) & \text{is close} \end{cases}$ for all $t \in R$. Prove an analogous statement for l.s.c. functions. Find functions that are u.s.c. and l.s.c. but discontinuous. Prove that if $\{f_\lambda\}_{\lambda \in \Lambda}$ is a family of real-valued l.s.c. functions with a common domain A and with a common finite upper bound, then $f = \sup_{\lambda \in \Lambda} f_\lambda$ is l.s.c.

1.7.64 Exercise. Let f be a real-valued function with domain either R or a closed interval. Prove that the set of points where f is discontinuous is an F_σ set.

1.7.65 Final Exercise # 4. Let A be any non-void, bounded, perfect subset of R. Prove that there is a continuous function ϕ with domain the Cantor set and range equal to A. Suppose that A also has the property that if $a < b$ and $a,b \in A$, there exist numbers c,d such that $a < c < d < b$ and $]c,d[\subset A'$ (such a perfect set is said to be totally disconnected). Prove that in this case the function ϕ can be made one-to-one as well as continuous.

1.8 Compactness.

1.8.1 Definition. Let X be any set, $A \subset X$, and $\{B_\iota\}_{\iota \in I}$ any family of subsets of X. If $\bigcup_{\iota \in I} B_\iota \supset A$, then $\{B_\iota\}_{\iota \in I}$ is said to form a covering of A. If $X = R$, each B_ι is open, and $\{B_\iota\}_{\iota\in I}$ covers A, then $\{B_\iota\}_{\iota\in I}$ is said to form an open covering of A.

1.8.11 Definition. A subset A of R is said to have the Heine-Borel (-Lebesgue) property if every open covering of A admits a finite subfamily that also covers A (i.e., a finite subcovering).

1.8.2 Definition. Let $A \subset R$. A point $p \in R$ is called a complete limit point of A if for every $\delta > 0$, $]p - \delta, p + \delta[\cap A \cap \{p\}' \overline{\overline{=}} \overline{\overline{A}}$.

1.8.21 Definition. A set $A \subset R$ is said to have the Bolzano-Weierstrass (-Aleksandrov-Uryson) property if every infinite subset of A admits a complete limit point lying in A.

1.8.3 Definition. A subset A of R is said to be sequentially compact if every sequence with range contained in A admits a subsequence converging to a limit that lies in A.

1.8.4 Theorem. The following properties of a subset A of R are equivalent:

i) A has the Heine-Borel property;

ii) A has the Bolzano-Weierstrass property;

iii) A is sequentially compact;

iv) A is closed and bounded. → compact.

Proof: (i) implies (ii). Suppose that (i) holds and (ii) fails for a set A. Let $B \subset A$ be an infinite subset of

A admitting no complete limit point in A. Then for every $p \in A$, there is an open interval I_p containing p such that $\overline{\overline{I_p \cap B}} < \overline{\overline{B}}$. $\{I_p\}_{p \in A}$ is an open covering of A. By (i), there is a finite family $\{I_{p_1}, \ldots, I_{p_n}\}$ such that $\bigcup_{j=1}^{n} I_{p_j} \supset A$. Now $\bigcup_{j=1}^{n} [I_{p_j} \cap B] = A \cap B = B$. Since $\overline{\overline{I_{p_j} \cap B}} < \overline{\overline{B}}$ for $j = 1, 2, \ldots, n$, $m = \max\left\{\overline{\overline{I_{p_1} \cap B}}, \ldots, \overline{\overline{I_{p_n} \cap B}}\right\} < \overline{\overline{B}}$. Consequently $\overline{\overline{B}} = \overline{\overline{\bigcup_{j=1}^{n} [I_{p_j} \cap B]}} \leq \overline{\overline{I_{p_1} \cap B}} + \ldots + \overline{\overline{I_{p_n} \cap B}} \leq n \cdot m$. Since n is finite and $m < \overline{\overline{B}}$, we have $n \cdot m < n \cdot \overline{\overline{B}} = \overline{\overline{B}}$, and thus $\overline{\overline{B}} < \overline{\overline{B}}$. This contradiction proves (ii).

(ii) implies (iii). Suppose that A has the Bolzano-Weierstrass property. Let ϕ be any sequence with range contained in A. If $B = \phi(\{1, 2, \ldots\}) \subset A$ is finite, then there is some element $b \in B$ for which $\phi^{-1}(b)$ is infinite. Clearly there is a subsequence ϕ' of ϕ such that every $\phi'(n) = b$. The sequence ϕ' obviously converges to b. Suppose next that B is infinite. Then B has a complete limit point $t \in A$ by (ii). That is, $]t - \delta, t + \delta[$ contains an infinite subset of B for all $\delta > 0$. Let $\phi(n) = a_n$. We now define a subsequence $\{a_{n_1}, a_{n_2}, \ldots, a_{n_k}, \ldots\}$ of ϕ converging to t. Let a_{n_1} be the first element of $\{a_1, \ldots, a_n, \ldots\}$ such that $|a_{n_1} - t| < 1$. Having defined $a_{n_1}, \ldots, a_{n_{k-1}}$, let a_{n_k} be the first element of $\{a_1, \ldots, a_n, \ldots\}$

such that $n_k > n_{k-1}$ and $|a_{n_k} - t| < \frac{1}{k}$. It is clear that $\lim_{k\to\infty} a_{n_k} = t$, so that ϕ admits a subsequence with limit in A.

(iii) implies (iv). Suppose that (iv) fails, i.e., A is non-closed or unbounded. If A is unbounded, say above, then for all positive integers n, there is an $a_n \varepsilon A$ such that $a_n > n$. Then the sequence $\{a_n\}_{n=1}^{\infty}$ has no convergent subsequence. Suppose that A is not closed. Then A' is not open. Hence there exists a $p \varepsilon A'$ such that every open interval containing p also contains points of A. Thus p is a limit point of A not in A. For every positive integer n, there is an $a_n \varepsilon A \cap]p-\frac{1}{n}, p+\frac{1}{n}[$. Clearly $\{a_n\}_{n=1}^{\infty}$ converges to p, and so every subsequence of $\{a_n\}_{n=1}^{\infty}$ converges to p. Thus no subsequence of $\{a_n\}_{n=1}^{\infty}$ converges to a point of A. Hence A is not sequentially compact.

(iv) implies (i). Let $A \subset R$ be closed and bounded. Let $a = \inf A$, $b = \sup A$. Since A is bounded, we have $a, b \varepsilon R$; since A is closed, we have $a \varepsilon A$, $b \varepsilon A$. We first consider the case where $A = [a,b]$. Let $\{G_\iota\}_{\iota \varepsilon I}$ be any open covering of A. Let $\{I_\lambda\}_{\lambda \varepsilon \Lambda}$ be the set of all component intervals of the G_ι's (see 1.7.3). Plainly $\{I_\lambda\}_{\lambda \varepsilon \Lambda}$ is an open covering of A. It clearly suffices to prove that $\{I_\lambda\}_{\lambda\varepsilon\Lambda}$ admits a finite subcovering. Let $C = \{x: x \varepsilon [a,b]$ and there exists a finite subfamily $\{I_{\lambda_1}, I_{\lambda_2}, \ldots, I_{\lambda_n}\} \subset \{I_\lambda\}_{\lambda\varepsilon\Lambda}$ such that $[a,x] \subset I_{\lambda_1} \cup \ldots \cup I_{\lambda_n}\}$. We see that $C \neq 0$, since $a \varepsilon C$. Let $c = \sup C$.

We now show that $c \varepsilon C$. Let $\mu \varepsilon \Lambda$ be such that $c \varepsilon I_\mu$. By the properties of suprema, there exists $x \varepsilon C \cap I_\mu$. Let $\{I_{\lambda_1}, \ldots, I_{\lambda_m}\}$ be a finite subcover of $[a,x]$. Now $\{I_{\lambda_1}, \ldots, I_{\lambda_m}, I_\mu\}$ has the property that $I_{\lambda_1} \cup \ldots \cup I_{\lambda_m} \cup I_\mu \supset [a,x] \cup [x,c] = [a,c]$. Thus $c \varepsilon C$. We next show that $c = b$. For, suppose that $c < b$. There is a $y > c$ such that $y \varepsilon I_\mu$. Then $\{I_{\lambda_1}, \ldots, I_{\lambda_m}, I_\mu\}$ covers $[a,y]$; that is, $y \varepsilon C$. This contradicts $c = \sup C$. Hence $[a,b]$ is covered by a finite subfamily of $\{I_\lambda\}_{\lambda\varepsilon\Lambda}$.

Now let A be an arbitrary closed subset of $[a,b]$, where $a = \inf A$ and $b = \sup A$. Suppose $\{G_\iota\}_{\iota\varepsilon I}$ is an open covering of A. Observe that $\{G_\iota\}_{\iota\varepsilon I} \cup \{A'\}$ is an open covering of $[a,b]$. Since $[a,b]$ has the Heine-Borel property, $[a,b]$ admits a finite subcovering $\{G_1, \ldots, G_n, A'\}$. It follows at once that $A \subset G_1 \cup \ldots \cup G_n$, and thus A has the Heine-Borel property.

1.8.5 Definition. Let $A \subset R$ have any of the four properties listed in 1.8.4. Then A is said to be compact.

1.8.6 Exercises.

1.8.61 Exercise. Let A be a compact subset of R, and let $\mathfrak{F}$ be any family of closed subsets of R such that $F_1 \cap F_2 \cap \ldots \cap F_n \cap A \neq 0$ for all finite $\{F_1, \ldots, F_n\} \subset \mathfrak{F}$. Prove that $(\bigcap_{F \in \mathfrak{F}} F) \cap A \neq 0$. Let B be non-compact. Prove that there is a sequence of sets $F_1 \supset F_2 \supset \ldots \supset F_n \supset \ldots$, where each F_n is a closed subset of R, such that $F_n \cap B \neq 0$ for $n = 1, 2, \ldots$, and $(\bigcap_{n=1}^{\infty} F_n) \cap B = 0$.

1.8.62 Exercise. Let $A \subset R$. Prove that every continuous real-valued function on A is bounded if and only if every bounded continuous real-valued function assumes its least upper bound.

1.8.63 Exercise. Prove that $A \subset R$ is compact if and only if every real-valued continuous function on A is bounded.

1.8.64 Exercise. Let A be a compact subset of R. Prove that if f is a continuous real-valued function with domain A, then $f(A)$ is compact.

1.8.65 Exercise. Let A be a compact subset of R and f be a one-to-one continuous real-valued function with domain A. Prove that f^{-1} is continuous.

Chapter 2.

MEASURES ON THE LINE

2.1 Preliminaries. The theory of integration is concerned with finding averages of functions. The Riemann integral defined for all continuous functions on [0, 1], for example, is a classical means of averaging functions. Denote the class of all continuous real-valued functions on [0, 1] by the symbol $\mathfrak{C}([0, 1])$. If we write $I(f) = \int_0^1 f(x)dx$, we can then set down a number of average-like properties possessed by the Riemann integral in the following terms:

$$I(f + g) = I(f) + I(g);$$

$$I(\alpha f) = \alpha I(f);$$

$$I(1) = 1;$$

$$I(f) \geq 0 \quad \text{if} \quad f \geq 0;$$

$$f \geq 0 \quad \text{and} \quad I(f) = 0 \quad \text{imply that} \quad f = 0.$$

Here f, g are arbitrary functions in $\mathfrak{C}([0,1])$, α is any real number, and addition of functions and multiplication of a function by a number are defined in the usual way. The Riemann integral is an example of what is called a linear functional. The notion of linear functional is intimately connected, although far from identical, with the notion of integral, and we shall therefore take up the notion of linear functional here.

2.1.1 Definition. A linear space is a non-void set S with the following properties. First, there is an addition defined in S under which S is an Abelian group. That is, for all $x,y \in S$, the sum $x + y$ is defined and is an element of S. Furthermore:

i) $x + (y + z) = (x + y) + z$ for all $x,y,z \in S$;

ii) there is a zero, 0, such that $0 + x = x$ for all $x \in S$;

iii) for every $x \in S$, there is an element $-x$ such that $(-x) + x = 0$;

iv) $x + y = y + x$ for all $x,y \in S$.

Secondly, for every $\alpha \in R$ (or K), and every $x \in S$, there is an element $\alpha x \in S$, called the product of α and x, with the following properties:

v) $\alpha(x + y) = \alpha x + \alpha y$ for all $x,y \in S$ and all $\alpha \in R$ (or K);

vi) $(\alpha + \beta)x = \alpha x + \beta x$ for all $x \in S$ and all $\alpha,\beta \in R$ (or K);

vii) $(\alpha\beta)x = \alpha(\beta x)$ for all $x \in S$ and all $\alpha,\beta \in R$ (or K);

viii) $1x = x$ for all $x \in S$.

The operation $(\alpha,x) \to \alpha x$ is called scalar multiplication, and the field R (or K) is called the field of scalars. If the relevant field is R, S is called a real linear space or a linear space over R. If the relevant field is K, S is called a complex linear space or a linear space over K. The term "vector space" is sometimes used instead of "linear space".

2.1.11 Example. Let A be any non-void subset of R, and let $\mathfrak{C}(A)$ (or $\mathfrak{C}_K(A)$) be the set of all real-valued (complex-valued) continuous functions with domain A. For $f, g \in \mathfrak{C}(A)$, let $f + g$ be the function such that $(f + g)(x) = f(x) + g(x)$ for all $x \in A$, and for $f \in \mathfrak{C}(A)$ and $\alpha \in R$ (or K), let αf be the function such that $(\alpha f)(x) = \alpha(f(x))$. Then $\mathfrak{C}(A)$ (or $\mathfrak{C}_K(A)$) is a linear space on R (or K).

2.1.12 Example. Let X be a non-void set. The set of all real-valued functions with domain X (where addition and scalar multiplication are defined pointwise) is a linear space over R. The set of all bounded real-valued functions on X is also a linear space over R, and is of course a linear subspace of the space of all real-valued functions on X.

2.1.2 Definition. Let S be a real or complex linear space. A function L with domain S and range contained in R (or K) is called a linear functional if

i) $L(x + y) = L(x) + L(y)$ for all $x, y \in S$ (additivity);

ii) $L(\alpha x) = \alpha L(x)$ for all $x \in S$ and $\alpha \in R$ (or K) (homogeneity).

2.1.21 Example. Let $S = \mathfrak{C}([0, 1])$ and $L(f)$ be the Riemann integral of f for all $f \in \mathfrak{C}([0, 1])$. Then plainly L is a linear functional on the linear space $\mathfrak{C}([0, 1])$. It also has the additional positivity properties described above.

The Riemann integral is not the only positive linear functional on $\mathfrak{C}([0, 1])$. In fact, for each $a \in [0,1]$, let the functional E_a on $\mathfrak{C}([0,1])$ be defined as follows: $E_a(f) = f(a)$. Then E_a is a linear functional on $\mathfrak{C}([0,1])$ having the positivity property ($E_a(f) \geq 0$ if $f \geq 0$) but not the strict positivity property (strict positivity means $f \geq 0$ and $E_a(f) = 0$ imply that $f = 0$).

Let $A = \{a_1, \ldots, a_n, \ldots\}$ be any countable subset of $[0,1]$ and let $\{\beta_1, \ldots, \beta_n, \ldots\}$ be any sequence of real numbers such that $\sum_{n=1}^{\infty} |\beta_n| < \infty$. Now let $L(f) = \sum_{n=1}^{\infty} \beta_n f(a_n)$. L is a linear functional on $\mathfrak{C}([0,1])$.

If further each $\beta_n > 0$ and A is a dense subset of $[0,1]$, then L has the strict positivity property. For suppose that $f \geq 0$ and $f \neq 0$. Then $f(a_{n_o}) \neq 0$ for some n_o. Then $f(a_{n_o}) > 0$ and we have $L(f) \geq \beta_{n_o} f(a_{n_o}) > 0$.

2.1.22 Example. For very simple linear spaces, the class of all linear functionals can be computed without difficulty. Consider for example the space $\mathfrak{C}(\{1, 2, \ldots, m\})$. The set $\{1, 2, \ldots, m\}$ has no limit points and therefore every function on $\{1, 2, \ldots, m\}$ is continuous. For every $j = 1, 2, \ldots, m$, let ϕ_j be the function on $\{1, 2, \ldots, m\}$ such that

$$\phi_j(k) = \begin{Bmatrix} 1 & \text{if} & k = j \\ 0 & \text{if} & k \neq j \end{Bmatrix} = \delta_{jk},$$

where δ is the Kronecker delta-function. Then every function f with domain $\{1, 2, \ldots, m\}$ can be written as

$$f = \sum_{j=1}^{m} f(j)\phi_j.$$

If L is any linear functional on $\mathfrak{C}(\{1, 2, \ldots, m\})$, then we must have

$$L(f) = \sum_{j=1}^{m} f(j)L(\phi_j),$$

so that L is completely determined by its values for the functions ϕ_j. These values can of course be quite arbitrary. Hence we have computed all possible linear functionals on $\mathfrak{C}(\{1, 2, \ldots, m\})$. In geometric terms, we can say that the functional L puts a "weight" of amount $L(\phi_j)$ at the point j, and that L is a sort of integral over $\{1, 2, \ldots, m\}$ with respect to this weight.

2.1.23 Example. Consider the space $\mathfrak{C}(\{1, 2, 3, \ldots\})$. This is simply the space of all real sequences, bounded or unbounded, since the set $\{1, 2, 3, \ldots\}$ has no limit points. It is a very complicated matter to compute all of the linear functionals on this space. We content ourselves with pointing out a small class of them. Let $\{\beta_1, \beta_2, \ldots, \beta_m\}$ be any finite sequence of real numbers. For all $f \in \mathfrak{C}(\{1, 2, 3, \ldots\})$, let

$$L(f) = \beta_1 f(1) + \ldots + \beta_m f(m).$$

It is clear that L is a linear functional.

2.1.24 Example. Let $\ell_1(\{1, 2, 3, \ldots\})$ be the subspace of $\mathfrak{C}(\{1, 2, 3, \ldots\})$ consisting of all f such that

$$\sum_{n=1}^{\infty} |f(n)| < \infty.$$

This is a very small subspace of $\mathfrak{C}(\{1, 2, 3, \ldots\})$ and accordingly it is easier to find linear functionals on it. For example, if g is any bounded sequence, and we have

$$L_g(f) = \sum_{n=1}^{\infty} g(n)f(n),$$

then it is easy to see that L_g is a linear functional on $\ell_1(\{1, 2, 3, \ldots\})$.

2.1.25 Example. Let $\mathfrak{S}$ be the set of all real-valued functions with domain $[0, \infty[$ for which $\lim_{x\to\infty} f(x)$ exists and is a real number. Set $L(f) = \lim_{x\to\infty} f(x)$. Then L is a linear functional on $\mathfrak{S}$.

2.1.26 Example. Let $\mathfrak{S}$ be the space of all real functions on $]0,1[$ that have derivatives everywhere. Take any point $a \in]0,1[$, and let $D_a(f) = f'(a)$. D_a is a linear functional on $\mathfrak{S}$.

These linear functionals have been studied extensively

by Laurent Schwartz,* and also by Sobolev, Gel'fand, and others.

2.1.3 Definition. Let X be any set and A be any subset of X. Let χ_A be the real-valued function with domain X such that $\chi_A(x) = \begin{Bmatrix} 1 & x \in A \\ 0 & x \notin A \end{Bmatrix}$. χ_A is called the characteristic function of the set A (relative to X).

2.1.31 Remarks. Let $\mathfrak{F}$ be a linear space of real-valued functions (addition and scalar multiplication are defined pointwise) with domain X. Let L be a linear functional on $\mathfrak{F}$ such that $L(f) \geq 0$ for all $f \geq 0$, $f \in \mathfrak{F}$.

Suppose that $\chi_B \in \mathfrak{F}$ for some $B \subset X$. Let $\lambda(B) = L(\chi_B)$. Clearly λ is a function defined for all such sets; we call λ a set-function. Let $\mathfrak{B}$ be the family of subsets of X for which λ is defined. $\mathfrak{B}$ is non-void since $0 \in \mathfrak{B}$; it is clear that $\lambda(0) = 0$. Suppose that $B_1, B_2 \in \mathfrak{B}$ and $B_1 \cap B_2 = 0$. Then $\lambda(B_1 \cup B_2) = L(\chi_{B_1 \cup B_2}) = L(\chi_{B_1} + \chi_{B_2}) = L(\chi_{B_1}) + L(\chi_{B_2}) = \lambda(B_1) + \lambda(B_2)$. A set-function λ having this property is said to be finitely additive. Suppose $B_1, B_2 \in \mathfrak{B}$ and $B_1 \subset B_2$. Since $B_2 = B_1 \cup (B_2 \cap B_1')$ and $B_1 \cap (B_2 \cap B_1') = 0$ we have $\lambda(B_1) + \lambda(B_2 \cap B_1') = \lambda(B_2)$ or $\lambda(B_2) - \lambda(B_1) = \lambda(B_2 \cap B_1')$.

2.1.32 Example. Let $\mathfrak{F}$ consist of all bounded Riemann integrable real-valued functions on [0,1]. If f is a bounded real-

* Théorie des Distributions. Paris, Hermann, 1950-51. 2 volumes.

valued function on $[0,1]$ with only a countable number of discontinuities, then $f \varepsilon \mathfrak{F}$. Thus, for example, $\chi_{\{c\}} \varepsilon \mathfrak{F}$ if $0 \leq c \leq 1$ and $\chi_{[a,b[} \varepsilon \mathfrak{F}$ if $0 \leq a < b \leq 1$. Also $I(\chi_{\{a\}}) = \lambda(\{a\}) = 0$ and $I(\chi_{[a,b[}) = \lambda([a,b[) = b - a$. Consider the family of all half-open intervals of the form $[a,b[$, $\{1\}$, 0, together with all finite unions of these sets. This is a family of subsets of $[0,1]$ that is closed under finite unions, finite intersections, and complementation. Note that λ is defined for all of these sets.

The familiar Darboux sums for the Riemann integral of $f \varepsilon \mathfrak{F}$ can now be treated as follows. Choose x_0, x_1, ..., x_n such that $0 = x_0 < x_1 < \ldots < x_{n-1} < x_n = 1$. Now $\sum_{i=1}^{n} \inf\{f(x): x_{i-1} \leq x < x_i\} \chi_{[x_{i-1},x_i[} + f(1)\chi_{\{1\}} \leq f \leq$

$$\sum_{i=1}^{n} \sup\{f(x): x_{i-1} \leq x < x_i\} \chi_{[x_{i-1},x_i[} + f(1)\chi_{\{1\}}.$$

Hence $I(\sum_{i=1}^{n} \inf\{f(x): x_{i-1} \leq x < x_i\}\chi_{[x_{i-1},x_i[} + f(1)\chi_{\{1\}}) \leq$

$I(f) \leq I(\sum_{i=1}^{n} \sup\{f(x): x_{i-1} \leq x < x_i\}\chi_{[x_{i-1},x_i[} + f(1)\chi_{\{1\}})$,

that is, $\sum_{i=1}^{n} \inf \{f(x): x_{i-1} \leq x < x_i\} \lambda([x_{i-1},x_i[) \leq$

$I(f) \leq \sum_{i=1}^{n} \sup \{f(x): x_{i-1} \leq x < x_i\} \lambda([x_{i-1},x_i[)$.

The common limit of the left and right side sums in the above inequalities, taken over all $\{x_0, x_1, \ldots, x_n\}$ is the Riemann integral $I(f)$. Hence the set-function λ defines the linear functional I.

Further, suppose that ϕ is a monotonic function on $[0,1]$ with continuity from the left at every point. Let $\lambda([a,b[) = \phi(b) - \phi(a)$ for $0 \leq a < b \leq 1$ and $\lambda(\{a\}) = \phi(a + 0) - \phi(a)$ for $0 \leq a \leq 1$. One can now construct functionals from these set-functions that closely resemble the Riemann integral. They are called Riemann-Stieltjes integrals, and will be dealt with from another point of view in Chapter 4.

2.1.4 Exercises.

2.1.41 Exercise. Let A be a compact subset of R. Let L be a linear functional on $\mathfrak{C}(A)$ such that $f \geq 0$ implies $L(f) \geq 0$. Prove that $f \leq g$ implies $L(f) \leq L(g)$. Prove that $-\alpha \cdot 1 \leq f \leq \alpha \cdot 1$ $(\alpha \geq 0)$ implies $|L(f)| \leq \alpha L(1)$. Prove finally that for every $\varepsilon > 0$, there is a $\delta > 0$ such that $|f(x) - g(x)| < \delta$ for all $x \in A$ implies $|L(f) - L(g)| < \varepsilon$.

2.1.42 Exercise. Let $A = \{x_1, x_2, x_3, \ldots, x_0\}$, where the x_n's are all distinct and $x_n \to x_0$. Let L be a linear functional on $\mathfrak{C}(A)$ such that $f \geq 0$ implies $L(f) \geq 0$. Prove that $L(f) = \sum_{n=0}^{\infty} \alpha_n f(x_n)$, where $\alpha_n \geq 0$ $(n = 0, 1, 2, \ldots)$ and $\sum_{n=0}^{\infty} \alpha_n < \infty$.

2.2. Definition of a measure.

2.2.1 Definition. Let X be any set. Let $\mathfrak{a}$ be a non-void family of subsets of X. Suppose that $A, B \in \mathfrak{a}$ implies

$A \cup B \in \mathcal{A}$, and $A \cap B' \in \mathcal{A}$. Then $\mathcal{A}$ is said to be a ring of sets. If $\mathcal{A}$ is a ring of sets and $A \in \mathcal{A}$ implies $A' \in \mathcal{A}$, then $\mathcal{A}$ is said to be an algebra of sets. If $\mathcal{A}$ is a ring and $\{A_n\}_{n=1}^{\infty} \subset \mathcal{A}$ implies $\bigcup_{n=1}^{\infty} A_n \in \mathcal{A}$, then $\mathcal{A}$ is said to be a σ-ring of sets. If $\mathcal{A}$ is an algebra and a σ-ring, it is said to be a σ-algebra of sets. When there will be no confusion, a ring of sets will simply be called a ring, an algebra of sets an algebra, etc.

2.2.11 Remark. If $\mathcal{A}$ is a ring of sets and $A, B \in \mathcal{A}$, then $A \cap B \in \mathcal{A}$.

2.2.12 Examples.

i) All finite subsets of an arbitrary set X form a ring; this ring is an algebra if and only if X is finite. Then it is also a σ-algebra.

ii) All countable subsets of an arbitrary set X form a σ-ring; this ring is a σ-algebra if and only if X is countable.

iii) Let $X = R$ and consider all finite unions of intervals $[a,b[$ where $-\infty < a < b < +\infty$ together with 0. Every set of this sort has a unique representation of the form $[a_1,b_1[\cup \ldots \cup [a_k,b_k[$, where $-\infty < a_1$, $b_i < a_{i+1}$ $(i = 1, 2, \ldots, k-1)$, $b_k < \infty$. This family of subsets of R is a ring but not an algebra.

iv) Let $X = [0,1[$, and consider all subsets of $[0,1[$

of the type described in iii). This is an algebra that is not a σ-algebra.

2.2.13 <u>Theorem</u>. Let X be any set, $\mathcal{B}$ any non-void family of subsets of X. Then there is a smallest [ring; algebra; σ-ring; σ-algebra] of sets containing $\mathcal{B}$.

<u>Proof</u>. We prove the theorem for "ring"; the other proofs are analogous. There exists a ring of subsets of X containing $\mathcal{B}$ --namely, the set of all subsets of X. Let $\{R_\lambda\}_{\lambda \varepsilon \Lambda}$ be the family of all rings of subsets of X containing $\mathcal{B}$. Let $R = \bigcap_{\lambda \varepsilon \Lambda} R_\lambda$. Clearly $R \supset \mathcal{B}$. We see that R is a ring as follows. $A, B \varepsilon R$ implies $A, B \varepsilon R_\lambda$ for all $\lambda \varepsilon \Lambda$ implies that $A \cup B \varepsilon R_\lambda$ and $A \cap B' \varepsilon R_\lambda$ for all $\lambda \varepsilon \Lambda$. Hence $A \cup B$ and $A \cap B' \varepsilon R$. Therefore R is a ring and must be the smallest ring containing $\mathcal{B}$.

2.2.131 <u>Conventions</u>. For $a \varepsilon R$ we define $a + \infty = \infty + a = \infty$; $\infty + \infty = \infty$; $a \cdot \infty = \infty$ if $a > 0$; and $0 \cdot \infty = 0$. We also agree that $\sum_{n=1}^{\infty} x_n = \infty$ if for some k, $x_k = \infty$, and all x_n are real or $+\infty$.

2.2.2 <u>Definition</u>. Let X be any set and $\mathcal{B}$ be a ring of subsets of X. A set-function μ defined for all $B \varepsilon \mathcal{B}$ is called a finitely additive measure if

i) $0 \leq \mu(B) \leq \infty$ for all $B \varepsilon \mathcal{B}$;

ii) $\mu(0) = 0$;

iii) $\mu(A \cup B) = \mu(A) + \mu(B)$ for all $A, B \varepsilon \mathcal{B}$ such that $A \cap B = 0$.

If iii) is replaced by

iii') $\mu(\bigcup_{n=1}^{\infty} B_n) = \sum_{n=1}^{\infty} \mu(B_n)$ for all sequences of sets

$\{B_n\}_{n=1}^{\infty}$ such that $B_n \varepsilon \mathcal{B}$ for all n, $\bigcup_{n=1}^{\infty} B_n \varepsilon \mathcal{B}$,

and $B_n \cap B_m = 0$ if $m \neq n$;

then μ is said to be countably additive.

2.2.21 Example. Let X be any non-void set and let $a \varepsilon X$. Let $\mathcal{B}$ be the set of all subsets of X. Let ε_a be defined by $\varepsilon_a(T) = \begin{cases} 1 & \text{if } a \varepsilon T \\ 0 & \text{if } a \not\varepsilon T \end{cases}$, for all $T \subset X$. That ε_a satisfies i) and ii) is obvious. If $\varepsilon_a(\bigcup_{n=1}^{\infty} B_n) = 1$, then $\varepsilon_a(B_k) = 1$ for just one k and $\varepsilon_a(B_{k'}) = 0$ for $k \neq k'$. If $\varepsilon_a(\bigcup_{n=1}^{\infty} B_n) = 0$, then $\varepsilon_a(B_k) = 0$ for all k. Thus, in either case we see that iii') is satisfied.

2.2.22 Example. Let X, $\mathcal{B}$, and ε_a be as defined in 2.2.21. Let $\{\alpha_n\}_{n=1}^{\infty}$ be any sequence of positive real numbers, and $\{a_n\}_{n=1}^{\infty}$ be a sequence of points in X. For all $T \subset X$, let $\mu(T) = \sum_{n=1}^{\infty} \alpha_n \varepsilon_{a_n}(T)$. μ is a countably additive measure on $\mathcal{B}$.

2.2.23 Example. Let X and $\mathcal{B}$ be as defined in 2.2.21. Let $\mu(0) = 0$ and $\mu(T) = +\infty$ if $T \neq 0$. This otherwise uninteresting countably additive measure is a fruitful source of counter-examples.

2.2.24 Example. Let X be any set and let $\mathcal{B}$ be the ring of finite subsets of X. Let f be any function on X such that $0 \leq f(x) \leq \infty$ for all $x \in X$. We now define $\mu(\{x_1, \ldots, x_n\}) = \sum_{k=1}^{n} f(x_k)$. μ is trivially countably additive, since $\bigcup_{n=1}^{\infty} B_n$ is finite only if all but a finite number of B_n's are void.

2.2.25 Example. Let $X = [0,1[$ and $\mathcal{B}$ be the algebra of all finite unions of intervals of the form $[a,b[$, where $0 \leq a < b \leq 1$; see Example 2.2.12. Let f by any monotone increasing function on $[0,1[$; that is, $f(a) \leq f(b)$ if $0 \leq a < b < 1$. Define $\mu_f(\bigcup_{k=1}^{m} [a_k,b_k[) = \sum_{k=1}^{m} [f(b_k) - f(a_k)]$. Then μ_f is always finitely additive; μ_f is countably additive if and only if f is left continuous at all a, $0 < a < 1$.

2.2.3 Theorem. (Ulam) Let X be any set such that $\overline{\overline{X}} \leq c$. Then there is no measure μ defined for all subsets of X such that

i) $\mu(T) = 0$ or 1 for all $T \subset X$;

ii) $\mu(\{x\}) = 0$ for all $x \in X$;

iii) μ is countably additive;

iv) $\mu(X) = 1$.

Proof. Let $\overline{\overline{X}} = c$. Since the properties demanded of μ are purely set-theoretic, they are invariant under one-to-one correspondences. Therefore we may suppose that $X = [0,1]$. Suppose that μ is defined for all subsets of $[0,1]$ and satisfies properties i), ii), iii), and iv). We have $1 = \mu([0,1]) = \mu([0,\frac{1}{2}[) + \mu(\{\frac{1}{2}\}) + \mu(]\frac{1}{2},1])$, where $\mu(\{\frac{1}{2}\}) = 0$. Thus either $\mu([0,\frac{1}{2}[) = 1$ or $\mu(]\frac{1}{2},1]) = 1$. Let $I_1 = \begin{Bmatrix} [0,\frac{1}{2}] & \text{if} & \mu([0,\frac{1}{2}[) = 1 \\ [\frac{1}{2},1] & \text{if} & \mu(]\frac{1}{2},1]) = 1 \end{Bmatrix}$.

Suppose that $I_1, \ldots, I_k$ have been defined so that each $I_j = [a_j, a_j + \frac{1}{2^j}]$, $\mu(I_j) = 1$ and $I_{j+1} \subset I_j$. As above $1 = \mu([a_k, a_k + \frac{1}{2^k}]) = \mu([a_k, a_k + \frac{1}{2^{k+1}}[) + \mu(\{a_k + \frac{1}{2^{k+1}}\}) + \mu(]a_k + \frac{1}{2^{k+1}}, a_k + \frac{1}{2^k}])$, where $\mu(\{a_k + \frac{1}{2^{k+1}}\}) = 0$.

Therefore either $\mu([a_k, a_k + \frac{1}{2^{k+1}}[) = 1$ or $\mu(]a_k + \frac{1}{2^{k+1}}, a_k + \frac{1}{2^k}]) = 1$. We now define

$$I_{k+1} = \begin{Bmatrix} [a_k, a_k + \frac{1}{2^{k+1}}] & \text{if} & \mu([a_k, a_k + \frac{1}{2^{k+1}}[) = 1 \\ [a_k + \frac{1}{2^{k+1}}, a_k + \frac{1}{2^k}] & \text{if} & \mu(]a_k + \frac{1}{2^{k+1}}, a_k + \frac{1}{2^k}]) = 1 \end{Bmatrix}.$$

We thus have a sequence of closed sets $\{I_n\}_{n=1}^{\infty}$ such that $I_1 \supset I_2 \supset \ldots \supset I_k \supset \ldots$, the length of I_k is $\frac{1}{2^k}$, and $\mu(I_k) = 1$. We conclude (see 1.8.61) that $\bigcap_{k=1}^{\infty} I_k = \{p\}$ where $p \in [0,1]$. We have $I_1 = \{p\} \cup (I_1 \cap I_2') \cup (I_2 \cap I_3') \cup \ldots \cup (I_n \cap I_{n+1}') \cup \ldots$. Therefore $\mu(I_1) = \mu(\{p\}) + \sum_{n=1}^{\infty} \mu(I_n \cap I_{n+1}')$. Since $\mu(I_n) = 1$ and $\mu(I_{n+1}) = 1$ and $I_n = I_{n+1} \cup (I_n \cap I_{n+1}')$, we have $\mu(I_n \cap I_{n+1}') = 0$. Thus we have $1 = \mu(\{p\}) + 0$ or $\mu(\{p\}) = 1$. Thus ii) fails and we have a contradiction.

Suppose now that $0 < \bar{\bar{X}} < c$. We may suppose that X is a subset of $[0,1]$. Suppose further that there is a

μ defined for all subsets of X and satisfying properties i), ii), iii), and iv). We define a measure μ^* for all subsets of $[0,1]$ as follows: $\mu^*(A) = \mu(A \cap X)$. It is evident that μ^* also satisfies properties i), ii), iii), and iv) and is defined for all subsets of $[0,1]$. We have just shown that this is impossible.

2.2.4 Theorem. Let X be any infinite set. Then there is a finitely additive measure ω defined for all subsets of X such that $\omega(A) = 0$ or 1 for all $A \subset X$, $\omega(\{p\}) = 0$ for all $p \varepsilon X$, and $\omega(X) = 1$.

The discussion which follows provides motivation for the proof. Suppose we have such an ω. Let $\mathcal{U} = \{A\colon\ A \subset X,\ \omega(A) = 1\}$. Let $\{p_1, \ldots, p_n\} \subset X$. Then $1 = \omega(X) = \omega(\{p_1, \ldots, p_n\}') + \omega(\{p_1\}) + \ldots + \omega(\{p_n\})$. Thus $1 = \omega(\{p_1, \ldots, p_n\}') + 0$ or $\omega(\{p_1, \ldots, p_n\}') = 1$ Hence $\mathcal{U}$ contains $\{p_1, \ldots, p_n\}'$ for all finite subsets $\{p_1, \ldots, p_n\}$ of X.

Suppose that $A \subset X$. Then $\omega(A) + \omega(A') = \omega(X) = 1$. Hence either $\omega(A) = 1$ and $\omega(A') = 0$ or conversely. That is, either $A \varepsilon \mathcal{U}$ and $A' \not\varepsilon \mathcal{U}$ or $A' \varepsilon \mathcal{U}$ and $A \not\varepsilon \mathcal{U}$.

Note that if $\omega(E) = 0$ and $D \subset E$, then $\omega(D) = 0$. This follows immediately from the equation $0 = \omega(E) = \omega(D) + \omega(E \cap D')$ since ω is non-negative. Suppose that $A,B \varepsilon \mathcal{U}$. Then $\omega((A \cap B)') = \omega(A' \cup B') = \omega((A' \cap B) \cup (A' \cap B') \cup (A \cap B')) = \omega(A' \cap B) + \omega(A' \cap B'$

$+ \omega(A \cap B') = 0$ since $A' \cap B \subset A'$, $A' \cap B' \subset A'$, and $A \cap B' \subset B'$ where $\omega(A') = \omega(B') = 0$. Thus $\omega(A \cap B) = 1$ and $A \cap B \in \mathcal{U}$.

Summing up, we see that $\mathcal{U}$ satisfies the following conditions.

i) $\mathcal{U}$ contains all sets with finite complement.

ii) $A,B \in \mathcal{U}$ implies $A \cap B \in \mathcal{U}$.

iii) $0 \notin \mathcal{U}$.

iv) For every $B \subset X$, we have $B \in \mathcal{U}$ or $B' \in \mathcal{U}$, but not both.

2.2.41 Exercise. Suppose that X is an infinite set and that $\mathcal{U}$ is a family of subsets of X with properties i), ii), iii), and iv) above. Let $\omega(A) = \begin{cases} 1 & \text{if } A \in \mathcal{U} \\ 0 & \text{if } A' \in \mathcal{U} \end{cases}$. Prove that ω is a finitely additive $0-1$ measure such that $\omega(X) = 1$ and $\omega(\{p\}) = 0$ for all $p \in X$.

Proof of Theorem 2.2.4. The foregoing shows that we can find a measure ω of the kind required if and only if we can find a family $\mathcal{U}$ of subsets of X satisfying i), ii), iii), iv).

Let $\mathfrak{X}$ be the collection of all families $\mathcal{B}$ of subsets of X such that

i) $\mathcal{B}$ contains all sets with finite complement.

ii) $A,B \in \mathcal{B}$ implies $A \cap B \in \mathcal{B}$.

iii) $0 \notin \mathcal{B}$.

Let $\mathfrak{F}$ be the family of all subsets A of X such that A' is finite. Clearly $\mathfrak{F} \in \mathfrak{X}$ so that $\mathfrak{X}$ is non-void.

Suppose $\mathcal{B}_1$, $\mathcal{B}_2 \varepsilon \mathcal{K}$. The relation $\mathcal{B}_1 \subset \mathcal{B}_2$ means as usual that every set in $\mathcal{B}_1$ is also in $\mathcal{B}_2$. We thus have a partial ordering $\subset$ for $\mathcal{K}$.

Suppose that $\{\mathcal{B}_\lambda\}_{\lambda \varepsilon \Lambda}$ is a non-void completely ordered subset of $\mathcal{K}$; that is, for all $\lambda, \lambda^* \varepsilon \Lambda$, either $\mathcal{B}_\lambda \supset \mathcal{B}_{\lambda}^*$ or $\mathcal{B}_{\lambda}^* \supset \mathcal{B}_\lambda$. Let $\mathcal{C} = \bigcup_{\lambda \varepsilon \Lambda} \mathcal{B}_\lambda = \{A\colon\ A \subset X,\ A \varepsilon \mathcal{B}_\lambda$ for some $\lambda \varepsilon \Lambda\}$. Clearly $\mathcal{C}$ is an upper bound for $\{\mathcal{B}_\lambda\}_{\lambda \varepsilon \Lambda}$; we will show that $\mathcal{C} \varepsilon \mathcal{K}$. To verify property i), suppose that A' is finite. Then $A \varepsilon \mathcal{B}_\lambda$ for all $\lambda \varepsilon \Lambda$ and thus $A \varepsilon \mathcal{C}$. We now check property ii). Suppose that $A, B \varepsilon \mathcal{C}$. Then $A \varepsilon \mathcal{B}_\lambda$ and $B \varepsilon \mathcal{B}_{\lambda}^*$ for some $\lambda, \overset{*}{\lambda} \varepsilon \Lambda$. We may suppose that $\mathcal{B}_\lambda \subset \mathcal{B}_{\lambda}^*$. Then $A, B \varepsilon \mathcal{B}_{\lambda}^*$, and therefore $A \cap B \varepsilon \mathcal{B}_{\lambda}^* \subset \mathcal{C}$. This shows property ii), and property iii) is clear. Thus $\mathcal{C} \varepsilon \mathcal{K}$.

We now apply Theorem 1.5.7 to the partially ordered set $\mathcal{K}$. Theorem 1.5.7 implies that there exists a maximal family $\mathcal{U} \varepsilon \mathcal{K}$. That is, $\mathcal{U}$ has properties i), ii), and iii), and no strictly larger family of subsets of X has properties i), ii), and iii). Thus if $\mathcal{Y}$ is a family of subsets of X, $\mathcal{Y} \supsetneqq \mathcal{U}$, and $\mathcal{Y}$ has properties i) and ii), then $\mathcal{Y}$ fails to have property iii).

Choose any $D \subset X$, $D \notin \mathcal{U}$. Let $\mathcal{Y} = \mathcal{U} \cup \{D\} \cup \{A \cap D\}_{A \varepsilon \mathcal{U}}$. It is not difficult to see that $\mathcal{Y}$ satisfies properties i) and ii), and $\mathcal{Y} \supsetneqq \mathcal{U}$. Thus $\mathcal{Y}$ fails to have property iii); that is, $0 \varepsilon \mathcal{Y}$. Therefore

$A \cap D = 0$ for some $A \in \mathcal{U}$. Then $D' \supset A$ for some $A \in \mathcal{U}$. This inclusion implies that $D' \in \mathcal{U}$. For let $\mathcal{W} = \mathcal{U} \cup \{D'\} \cup \{D' \cap B\}_{B \in \mathcal{U}}$; properties i) and ii) for $\mathcal{W}$ are clear. $\mathcal{W}$ satisfies property iii) also. Otherwise, we would have $D' \cap B = 0$ for some $B \in \mathcal{U}$. Since $D' \supset A$, we have $A \cap B = 0$ for $A, B \in \mathcal{U}$. Thus $0 \in \mathcal{U}$, a contradiction. Thus $\mathcal{W} \in \mathfrak{K}$ and $\mathcal{W} \supset \mathcal{U}$; therefore $\mathcal{W} = \mathcal{U}$. Hence $D' \in \mathcal{U}$. Thus we see that $\mathcal{U}$ also has property iv): For every $D \subset X$, either $D \in \mathcal{U}$ or $D' \in \mathcal{U}$.

This completes the proof since we have found a family $\mathcal{U}$ of subsets of X satisfying properties i), ii), iii), and iv).

2.2.5 Remarks. A family of subsets $\mathcal{E}$ of a set X is called a filter (H. Cartan) if it satisfies properties ii) and iii) from the foregoing proof and also

v) $A \in \mathcal{E}$ and $X \supset B \supset A$ imply that $B \in \mathcal{E}$.

Every family of subsets of X with properties ii) and iii) and maximal with respect to possessing properties ii) and iii) also has property iv) and property v). Such families of subsets are called ultrafilters. If an ultrafilter also has property i), then it is called a free ultrafilter (Hewitt). An ultrafilter that is not free consists of all subsets of X that contain some fixed point $p \in X$, and is called a fixed ultrafilter. Ultrafilters have been used in algebra and functional analysis since at least the middle 1920's (Tarski), and were heavily exploited by M. H. Stone.

It is a remarkable fact that the number of distinct ultrafilters for an infinite set X is precisely equal to

$$2^{(2^{\overline{\overline{X}}})}.$$

Since this number is the number of distinct families of subsets of X, we see that the number of ultrafilters on X is as large as it can possibly be. The proof of this equality, which is of course a purely set-theoretic assertion, depends upon the theory of compact Hausdorff spaces. For $\overline{\overline{X}} = \aleph_0$, the theorem is due to B. Pospíšil, for general $\overline{\overline{X}}$, to E. Hewitt.

2.3 Lebesgue measure.

2.3.1 Preliminaries. We now turn to the problem of extending the idea of length. The set $t + A = \{t + x: x \in A\}$, $t \in R$, is called a translate of the set A. The set $-A = \{-x: x \in A\}$ is the reflection of A about the origin. We seek a set-function λ defined for as many subsets of R as possible with the following properties:

$\lambda(]a,b[) = b - a$;

$\lambda([a,b]) = b - a$;

$\lambda(\bigcup_{n=1}^{\infty} A_n) = \sum_{n=1}^{\infty} \lambda(A_n)$ if the A_n's are pairwise disjoint;

$\lambda(t + A) = \lambda(A)$ for all $t \in R$;

$\lambda(-A) = \lambda(A)$.

Peano and Jordan attempted to produce such a measure. Consider a bounded set X. We define the Jordan measure λ_J of X by $\lambda_J(X) = \inf \left\{ \sum_{k=1}^{n} (b_k - a_k) : X \subset]a_1,b_1[\cup \ldots \cup]a_n,b_n[\text{ where the }]a_k,b_k[\text{ are pairwise disjoint} \right\}$. Clearly this is always a well-defined number. This measure turns out to be quite unsatisfactory; we will show that λ_J fails to be finitely additive even for fairly simple sets. Let $Q = \{x: x \text{ rational}, 0 \leq x \leq 1\}$. Suppose that $Q \subset (]a_1,b_1[\cup \ldots \cup]a_n,b_n[)$. Then $[0,1] = Q^- \subset (]a_1,b_1[\cup \ldots \cup]a_n,b_n[)^- = [a_1,b_1] \cup \ldots \cup [a_n,b_n]$. It can be proved (see 2.3.27 <u>infra</u>, with some trivial modifications) that $\sum_{k=1}^{n} (b_k - a_k) > 1$. Thus $\lambda_J(Q) \geq 1$. On the other hand, for any $\varepsilon > 0$, $Q \subset]-\varepsilon, 1+\varepsilon[$. Thus $\lambda_J(Q) = 1$. Let $S = [0,1] \cap Q'$. In a similar fashion we see that $\lambda_J(S) = 1$. Then $\lambda_J(Q \cup S) = \lambda_J([0,1]) = 1$ and $\lambda_J(Q) + \lambda_J(S) = 2$. Hence λ_J fails to be finitely additive on any family of sets containing Q, S, and $[0,1]$.

By making an apparently slight but actually vital change in the above definition, H. Lebesgue produced a very useful measure having the desired properties listed above.

2.3.2 <u>Definition</u>. The Lebesgue outer-measure of a set X is defined by

$$\lambda(X) = \inf \left\{ \sum_{n=1}^{\infty} (b_n - a_n) : X \subset]a_1,b_1[\cup \ldots \cup]a_n,b_n[\cup \ldots \right.$$

where the $]a_n,b_n[$ are pairwise disjoint$\}$. By convention we have $\infty - a_n = \infty$ and $b_n - (-\infty) = \infty$.

2.3.21 Remark. Lebesgue measure is not the only possible measure with the properties described in 2.3.1. For example, S. Kakutani and J. C. Oxtoby* have produced a remarkable extension of Lebesgue measure, which has properties that at first sight seem hardly credible. It would appear that this measure of Kakutani and Oxtoby has not yet been fully exploited by any means. On the other hand, it can be shown (see 2.6 *infra*) that no countably additive, translation-invariant extension of Lebesgue measure exists for all subsets of R.

2.3.211 Theorem. i) $\lambda(0) = 0$;

ii) $0 \leq \lambda(X) \leq \infty$ for all $X \subset R$;

iii) $X \subset Y$ implies that $\lambda(X) \leq \lambda(Y)$.

The proof of this theorem is very simple and is omitted. We next state and prove an elementary, but very useful, theorem on double infinite series.

2.3.22 Theorem. Let $\{\alpha_{mn}\}_{m=1}^{\infty}{}_{n=1}^{\infty}$ be a non-negative function defined on $\{1, 2, \ldots, n, \ldots\} \times \{1, 2, \ldots, n, \ldots\}$ where $0 \leq \alpha_{mn} \leq \infty$ for all m, n. Then $\sum_{m=1}^{\infty}(\sum_{n=1}^{\infty} \alpha_{mn}) = \sum_{n=1}^{\infty}(\sum_{m=1}^{\infty} \alpha_{mn}) = \sup\{\alpha_{m_1n_1} + \ldots + \alpha_{m_kn_k} :$ $\{m_1n_1, \ldots, m_kn_k\}$ is a finite subset of the domain of $\alpha\}$.

* See S. Kakutani and J. C. Oxtoby, "A non-separable translation invariant extension of the Lebesgue measure space". Annals of Math. (2), 1950, pp. 580-590.

<u>Proof</u>. Let $A = \sum_{m=1}^{\infty} (\sum_{n=1}^{\infty} \alpha_{mn})$ and let B be $\sup \{\alpha_{m_1n_1} + \ldots + \alpha_{m_kn_k}\}$. Suppose that $A = \infty$. If some $\alpha_{mn} = \infty$, then since $B \geq \alpha_{mn}$, we have $B = \infty = A$. If all the α_{mn} are finite and for some m, we have $\sum_{n=1}^{\infty} \alpha_{mn} = \infty$, then $B \geq \sup \left\{ \sum_{n=1}^{k} \alpha_{mn} \right\} = \sum_{n=1}^{\infty} \alpha_{mn}$. Therefore, $B = \infty = A$. Finally suppose that $\sum_{n=1}^{\infty} \alpha_{mn} < \infty$ for all m and that $A = \infty$. Let T be an arbitrary positive number. There exists a positive integer M such that $\sum_{m=1}^{M} (\sum_{n=1}^{\infty} \alpha_{mn}) > 2T$. Further there exist positive integers N_m for $m = 1, 2, \ldots, M$ such that $\sum_{n=N_m+1}^{\infty} \alpha_{mn} < \frac{T}{M}$. Then we have $\sum_{n=1}^{\infty} \alpha_{mn} = \sum_{n=1}^{N_m} \alpha_{mn} + \sum_{n=N_m+1}^{\infty} \alpha_{mn} < \sum_{n=1}^{N_m} \alpha_{mn} + \frac{T}{M}$. Summing these inequalities over $m = 1, 2, \ldots, M$, we have $2T < \sum_{m=1}^{M} (\sum_{n=1}^{\infty} \alpha_{mn}) \leq \sum_{m=1}^{M} (\sum_{n=1}^{N_m} \alpha_{mn}) + \sum_{m=1}^{M} \frac{T}{M} = \sum_{m=1}^{M} (\sum_{n=1}^{N_m} \alpha_{mn}) + T$. Therefore $T < \sum_{m=1}^{M} (\sum_{n=1}^{N_m} \alpha_{mn}) \leq B$. Since T was arbitrary, we have once again $B = \infty = A$.

Suppose next that A is finite. For every $\varepsilon > 0$, there exists a positive integer M such that $\sum_{m=1}^{M} (\sum_{n=1}^{\infty} \alpha_{mn}) + \frac{\varepsilon}{2} > A$. There exist positive integers N_m for $m = 1, 2, \ldots, M$ such that $\sum_{n=1}^{N_m} \alpha_{mn} + \frac{\varepsilon}{2M} > \sum_{n=1}^{\infty} \alpha_{mn}$.

Then we have

$$B + \frac{\varepsilon}{2} \geq \sum_{m=1}^{M} \sum_{n=1}^{N_m} \alpha_{mn} + \frac{\varepsilon}{2} = \sum_{m=1}^{M} \left(\sum_{n=1}^{N_m} \alpha_{mn} + \frac{\varepsilon}{2M} \right) > \sum_{m=1}^{M} \left(\sum_{n=1}^{\infty} \alpha_{mn} \right) >$$

$A - \frac{\varepsilon}{2}$. Thus $B + \varepsilon > A$ for all $\varepsilon > 0$. Therefore $B \geq A$ if A is finite.

To prove the reverse inequality $B \leq A$, we observe that $\alpha_{m_1 n_1} + \ldots + \alpha_{m_k n_k} \leq \sum_{\ell=1}^{k} \left(\sum_{n=1}^{\infty} \alpha_{m_\ell n} \right) \leq \sum_{m=1}^{\infty} \left(\sum_{n=1}^{\infty} \alpha_{mn} \right) = A$.

Therefore $B = \sup \left\{ \alpha_{m_1 n_1} + \ldots + \alpha_{m_k n_k} \right\} \leq A$.

Similarly we see that $A^* = \sum_{n=1}^{\infty} \left(\sum_{m=1}^{\infty} \alpha_{mn} \right) = B$.

Therefore $A = A^* = B$.

2.3.221 Exercise. Let X be any non-void set, $\{X_\lambda\}_{\lambda \in \Lambda}$ a family of pairwise disjoint non-void sets such that $\bigcup_{\lambda \in \Lambda} X_\lambda = X$. Suppose that f is a function defined on X where $0 \leq f(x) \leq \infty$. What is the analog of 2.3.22?

2.3.222 Exercise. Let $\{\alpha_n\}_{n=1}^{\infty}$ be a sequence, $0 \leq \alpha_n \leq \infty$. Let ϕ be a one-to-one mapping of $\{1, 2, 3, \ldots\}$ onto itself. Then $\lim_{n\to\infty} (\alpha_1 + \ldots + \alpha_n) = \lim_{n\to\infty} (\alpha_{\phi(1)} + \ldots + \alpha_{\phi(n)}) = \sup \left\{ \alpha_{n_1} + \ldots + \alpha_{n_k} : \{n_1, \ldots, n_k\} \text{ is a finite subset of } \{1, 2, \ldots\} \right\}$.

2.3.23 Theorem. Let $-\infty < a < b < \infty$. Then $\lambda(]a,b[) = b - a$.

Proof. Clearly $\lambda(]a,b[) \leq b - a$ because $]a,b[\subset]a,b[$. Suppose that $]a,b[\subset \bigcup_{n=1}^{\infty}]\alpha_n,\beta_n[$ where the $]\alpha_n,\beta_n[$ are pairwise disjoint. Consider any $x \in]a,b[$. For a unique n_o, we have $x \in]\alpha_{n_o}, \beta_{n_o}[$. We have $\beta_{n_o} \geq b$, for suppose that $\beta_{n_o} < b$. Since $a < x < \beta_{n_o}$, we would have $\beta_{n_o} \in]a,b[\subset \bigcup_{n=1}^{\infty}]\alpha_n, \beta_n[$. On the other hand, from theorem 1.7.3, $\beta_{n_o} \notin \bigcup_{n=1}^{\infty}]\alpha_n, \beta_n[$. Thus $\beta_{n_o} \geq b$. Similarly $\alpha_{n_o} \leq a$. Now $b - a \leq \beta_{n_o} - \alpha_{n_o} \leq \sum_{n=1}^{\infty} (\beta_n - \alpha_n)$. Therefore $b - a \leq \inf \left\{ \sum_{n=1}^{\infty} (\beta_n - \alpha_n) \right\} = \lambda(]a,b[)$. Hence $\lambda(]a,b[) = b - a$.

2.3.24 Theorem. For $t \in R$, $\lambda(]t, \infty[) = \infty$ and $\lambda(]-\infty, t[) = \infty$.

Proof. We prove that $\lambda(]t, \infty[) = \infty$. Suppose that $]t, \infty[\subset \bigcup_{n=1}^{\infty}]\alpha_n, \beta_n[$. Pick an $x \in R$, $t < x < \infty$. For a unique n_o, $x \in]\alpha_{n_o}, \beta_{n_o}[$. Then $\beta_{n_o} = \infty$, for if β_{n_o} were finite, we would have $\beta_{n_o} \notin \bigcup_{n=1}^{\infty}]\alpha_n, \beta_n[$ whereas $t < x < \beta_{n_o} < \infty$ so that $\beta_{n_o} \in]t, \infty[$; hence we have a contradiction. Since $\beta_{n_o} = \infty$, it follows that

$$\lambda(]t, \infty[) = \inf \left\{ \sum_{n=1}^{\infty} (\beta_n - \alpha_n) \right\} = \infty.$$

2.3.25 Theorem. Let G be any open subset of $R, G = \bigcup_{n=1}^{\infty}]\alpha_n, \beta_n[$, where the $]\alpha_n, \beta_n[$ are pairwise disjoint. Then

$$\lambda(G) = \sum_{n=1}^{\infty} (\beta_n - \alpha_n).$$

Proof. For the case where G is bounded, we refer the reader to Theorem 2, page 57, Natanson. For unbounded G (for which $\lambda(G)$ may still be finite, of course), the proof is simple and is omitted.

2.3.26 Theorem. Suppose that $-\infty < a < b < \infty$. Then $\lambda([a,b]) = b - a$.

Proof. Since $]a,b[\subset [a,b]$, we have $\lambda([a,b]) \geq b - a$, by 2.3.211. For every $\varepsilon > 0$, the inclusion $[a,b] \subset]a - \frac{\varepsilon}{2}, b + \frac{\varepsilon}{2}[$ obviously holds. Thus we have $\lambda([a,b]) \leq b - a + \varepsilon$. Therefore $\lambda([a,b]) \leq b - a$, so that $\lambda([a,b]) = b - a$

2.3.27 Lemma. Let $-\infty < a < b < \infty$. Suppose that $\{I_\lambda\}_{\lambda \varepsilon \Lambda}$ is a family of open intervals such that $[a,b] \subset \bigcup_{\lambda \varepsilon \Lambda} I_\lambda$. Then

$$b - a < \sum_{\lambda \varepsilon \Lambda} (\beta_\lambda - \alpha_\lambda),$$

where $I_\lambda =]\alpha_\lambda, \beta_\lambda[$, and Σ means the supremum of all finite partial sums.

Proof. Since $[a,b]$ is closed and bounded, 1.8.4 implies that a finite number, say m, of the intervals $]\alpha_\lambda, \beta_\lambda[$ suffice to cover $[a,b]$. Let $\mathcal{I}$ denote this family of m intervals. There is some interval in $\mathcal{I}$, which we call $]\alpha_1, \beta_1[$, such that $\alpha_1 < a < \beta_1$. If we have $\beta_1 > b$, we stop. If we have $\beta_1 \leq b$, we choose an interval $]\alpha_2, \beta_2[$ in $\mathcal{I}$ such that $\alpha_2 < \beta_1 < \beta_2$. In general, if $]\alpha_1, \beta_1[, \ldots,]\alpha_k, \beta_k[$ have been chosen so that $\alpha_1 < a < \beta_1$ and $\alpha_i < \beta_{i-1} < \beta_i$ for $i = 2, 3, \ldots, k$, we have two possibilities. If $\beta_k > b$, we stop. If $\beta_k \leq b$, we can find an interval $]\alpha_{k+1}, \beta_{k+1}[$ in $\mathcal{I}$ such that $\alpha_{k+1} < \beta_k < \beta_{k+1}$. Since the intervals in $\mathcal{I}$ cover $[a,b]$, and there are only m intervals in $\mathcal{I}$,

our construction must stop with some n, $n \leq m$. That is, we have: $\beta_n > b$; $\beta_{n-1} \leq b$; $\beta_1 < \beta_2 < \ldots < \beta_n$; $\alpha_2 < \beta_1$, $\alpha_3 < \beta_2$, ..., $\alpha_n < \beta_{n-1}$. Then we see that
$$\sum_{i=1}^{m} (\beta_i - \alpha_i) \geq \sum_{i=1}^{n} (\beta_i - \alpha_i) > \sum_{i=1}^{n-1} (\alpha_{i+1} - \alpha_i) + \beta_n - \alpha_n =$$
$\beta_n - \alpha_1 > b - a$. Since $\sum_{i=1}^{n} (\beta_i - \alpha_i) \leq \sum_{\lambda \in \Lambda} (\beta_\lambda - \alpha_\lambda)$, the lemma is proved.

2.3.28 Theorem. Let $\{G_n\}_{n=1}^{\infty}$ be a countable family of pairwise disjoint open sets. Then $\lambda(\bigcup_{n=1}^{\infty} G_n) = \sum_{n=1}^{\infty} \lambda(G_n)$.

Proof. For each n, we have $G_n = \bigcup_{k=1}^{\infty}]\alpha_{n,k}, \beta_{n,k}[$, where the $]\alpha_{n,k}, \beta_{n,k}[$ are pairwise disjoint. Then $\bigcup_{n=1}^{\infty} G_n = \bigcup_{n=1}^{\infty} \bigcup_{k=1}^{\infty}]\alpha_{n,k}, \beta_{n,k}[$ and all of the intervals $]\alpha_{n,k}, \beta_{n,k}[$ are pairwise disjoint (over all n and k). Therefore, by 2.3.25 and 2.3.22, we have $\lambda(\bigcup_{n=1}^{\infty} G_n) =$
$$\sum_{n,k=1}^{\infty} (\beta_{n,k} - \alpha_{n,k}) = \sum_{n=1}^{\infty} \sum_{k=1}^{\infty} (\beta_{n,k} - \alpha_{n,k}) = \sum_{n=1}^{\infty} \lambda(G_n).$$

2.3.29 Theorem. Let $\{G_n\}_{n=1}^{\infty}$ be any family of open sets. Then $\lambda(\bigcup_{n=1}^{\infty} G_n) \leq \sum_{n=1}^{\infty} \lambda(G_n)$. (We express this relation by saying that λ is countably subadditive on the family of all open sets.)

Proof. Let $H = \bigcup_{n=1}^{\infty} G_n$.

Case I. Suppose that $H =]a,b[$, $-\infty < a < b < \infty$. Let η be a positive real number, $\eta < \frac{b-a}{2}$. Then $[a + \eta, b - \eta] \subset]a,b[$ and $[a + \eta, b - \eta]$ is compact.

Using the notation established in 2.3.28, we have $[a+\eta, b-\eta] \subset \bigcup_{n=1}^{\infty} G_n = \bigcup_{n,k=1}^{\infty}]\alpha_{n,k}, \beta_{n,k}[$. By 2.3.27 and 2.3.22, we have $b - a - 2\eta < \sum_{n,k=1}^{\infty} (\beta_{n,k} - \alpha_{n,k}) = \sum_{n=1}^{\infty} \lambda(G_n)$. Since η was arbitrary, we see that $\lambda(H) = b - a \leq \sum_{n=1}^{\infty} \lambda(G_n)$.

Case II. Suppose that $H =]t,\infty[$, $]-\infty,t[$, or $]-\infty, \infty[$. We prove the inequality for $H =]t,\infty[$. Let N be an arbitrary positive number. Then $]t,t+N[\subset \bigcup_{n=1}^{\infty} G_n$ and, by Case I, we have $N \leq \sum_{n=1}^{\infty} \lambda(G_n)$. Since N is arbitrary, it follows that $\sum_{n=1}^{\infty} \lambda(G_n) = \infty = \lambda(H)$. The other sub-cases are handled similarly.

Case III. Suppose that H is an arbitrary open set. Then $H = \bigcup_{p=1}^{\infty}]a_p,b_p[$ where the $]a_p,b_p[$ are pairwise disjoint. For each p, we have $]a_p,b_p[\subset \bigcup_{n=1}^{\infty} (G_n \cap]a_p,b_p[)$. From Cases I and II, we infer that $b_p - a_p \leq \sum_{n=1}^{\infty} \lambda(G_n \cap]a_p,b_p[)$. We add these inequalities over all p. Then by 2.3.22, 2.3.28, and 2.3.211 we have

$$\lambda(H) = \sum_{p=1}^{\infty} (b_p - a_p) \leq \sum_{p=1}^{\infty} \left(\sum_{n=1}^{\infty} \lambda(G_n \cap]a_p,b_p[) \right) =$$

$$\sum_{n=1}^{\infty} \left(\sum_{p=1}^{\infty} \lambda(G_n \cap]a_p,b_p[) \right) = \sum_{n=1}^{\infty} \lambda\left(\bigcup_{p=1}^{\infty} (G_n \cap]a_p,b_p[) \right) =$$

$$\sum_{n=1}^{\infty} \lambda\left\{ \left(\bigcup_{p=1}^{\infty}]a_p,b_p[\right) \cap G_n \right\} = \sum_{n=1}^{\infty} \lambda(H \cap G_n) \leq \sum_{n=1}^{\infty} \lambda(G_n).$$

This completes the proof of 2.3.29.

2.3.291 <u>Exercise</u>. Prove that every countable set has λ-measure 0.

2.3.292 <u>Exercise</u>. Prove that $\lambda(C) = 0$, where C is the Cantor set.

2.3.293 <u>Final Exercise #5</u>. Prove that every non-void perfect set in R contains a non-void perfect subset of λ-measure 0.

2.3.294 <u>Final Exercise #6.</u> Exhibit a perfect set S such that $S^{'-'} = 0$ and $\lambda(S) > 0$.

2.3.3 <u>Theorem</u>. Let $\{X_n\}_{n=1}^{\infty}$ be any sequence of subsets of R. Then $\lambda(\bigcup_{n=1}^{\infty} X_n) \leq \sum_{n=1}^{\infty} \lambda(X_n)$, that is, λ is countably subadditive on all subsets of R.

<u>Proof</u>. If $\sum_{n=1}^{\infty} \lambda(X_n) = \infty$, the inequality is clear. Suppose that $\sum_{n=1}^{\infty} \lambda(X_n) < \infty$. Choose $\varepsilon > 0$. For each n there is an open set G_n containing X_n such that $\lambda(G_n) < \lambda(X_n) + \frac{\varepsilon}{2^n}$. We add these inequalities over all n, and note that $\bigcup_{n=1}^{\infty} G_n$ is an open set containing $\bigcup_{n=1}^{\infty} X_n$. Then we have by 2.3.2 and 2.3.29,

$$\lambda(\bigcup_{n=1}^{\infty} X_n) \leq \lambda(\bigcup_{n=1}^{\infty} G_n) \leq \sum_{n=1}^{\infty} \lambda(G_n) < \sum_{n=1}^{\infty} (\lambda(X_n) + \frac{\varepsilon}{2^n}) = \sum_{n=1}^{\infty} \lambda(X_n) + \varepsilon.$$

Since this is true for all $\varepsilon > 0$, the theorem is proved.

2.3.31 <u>Definition</u>. Let X be any set, and μ a set-function defined for all subsets of X. Suppose that:

i) $0 \leq \mu(A) \leq \infty$ for all $A \subset X$;

ii) $\mu(0) = 0$;

iii) $\mu(A) \leq \mu(B)$ if $A \subset B \subset X$;

iv) $\mu(\bigcup_{n=1}^{\infty} A_n) \leq \sum_{n=1}^{\infty} \mu(A_n)$ for all sequences of subsets of X.

Then μ is called a Carathéodory outer measure.* The following merely reiterates previously proven facts.

2.3.32 <u>Theorem</u>. λ is a Carathéodory outer measure on all subsets of R.

2.3.4 <u>Definition</u>. Let μ be a Carathéodory outer measure on all subsets of X. A subset A of X is said to be μ-measurable if $\mu(T) = \mu(T \cap A) + \mu(T \cap A')$ for all $T \subset X$.

2.3.41 <u>Theorem</u>. Let μ be a Carathéodory outer measure on X. Then every set $N \subset X$ such that $\mu(N) = 0$ is μ-measurable, and $\mu(T) = \mu(T \cap N')$ for all $T \subset X$.

<u>Proof</u>. Let T be any subset of X. Then $\mu(T \cap N) = 0$, since $T \cap N \subset N$. Also, $\mu(T) \leq \mu(T \cap N) + \mu(T \cap N') = \mu(T \cap N') \leq \mu(T)$. Thus $\mu(T) = \mu(T \cap N) + \mu(T \cap N') = \mu(T \cap N')$; the first equality shows that N is measurable, completing the proof.

<u>Note</u>. In 2.3.42-2.3.45 inclusive, X and μ are as in

---

* This notion was introduced by C. Carathéodory in an article entitled "Über das lineare Mass von Punktmengen-eine Verallgemeinerung des Längen Begriffs", in Nachrichten Ges. Wiss. Göttingen 1914, 404-426.

2.3.31, and μ-measurability is as in 2.3.41.

2.3.42 Theorem. If A is a μ-measurable subset of X, then A' is μ-measurable.

This theorem follows at once from Definition 2.3.4.

2.3.43 Theorem. Let $\{A_n\}_{n=1}^{\infty}$ be a sequence of pairwise disjoint μ-measurable subsets of X. Then we have

(i) $\mu(Y) = \sum_{n=1}^{\infty} \mu(Y \cap A_n) + \mu(Y \cap (\bigcup_{n=1}^{\infty} A_n)')$ for all $Y \subset X$.

Proof. By countable subadditivity, we have $\mu(Y) \leq \sum_{n=1}^{\infty} \mu(Y \cap A_n) + \mu(Y \cap (\bigcup_{n=1}^{\infty} A_n)')$. If $\mu(Y) = \infty$, (i) follows immediately. Hence we may suppose $\mu(Y) < \infty$. We first prove

(ii) $\mu(Y) = \sum_{n=1}^{p} \mu(Y \cap A_n) + \mu(Y \cap (\bigcup_{n=1}^{p} A_n)')$.

We prove this for all positive integers p by induction on p. For $p = 1$, equation (ii) becomes $\mu(Y) = \mu(Y \cap A_1) + \mu(Y \cap A_1')$. This is true for all $Y \subset X$ since A_1 is μ-measurable. Suppose that (ii) is known to be true for a positive integer p and all possible subsets $Y \subset X$. Then, since A_{p+1} is μ-measurable, we have $\mu(Y) = \mu(Y \cap A_{p+1}) + \mu(Y \cap A'_{p+1}) =$

$\mu(Y \cap A_{p+1}) + \sum_{n=1}^{p} \mu(Y \cap A'_{p+1} \cap A_n) + \mu(Y \cap A'_{p+1} \cap (\bigcup_{n=1}^{p} A_n)')$.

(We apply the inductive hypothesis to the set $Y \cap A'_{p+1}$.) Since we have $A_n \subset A'_{p+1}$ for

$n \neq p+1$, the above equation reduces to

$$\mu(Y) = \mu(Y \cap A_{p+1}) + \sum_{n=1}^{p} \mu(Y \cap A_n) + \mu(Y \cap A'_{p+1} \cap (\bigcup_{n=1}^{p} A_n)').$$

Using DeMorgan's Law, we arrive at

$$\mu(Y) = \sum_{n=1}^{p+1} \mu(Y \cap A_n) + \mu(Y \cap (\bigcup_{n=1}^{p+1} A_n)'),$$

which proves (ii) for all positive integers p.

The sequence of numbers $\left\{\mu(Y \cap (\bigcup_{n=1}^{p} A_n)')\right\}_{p=1}^{\infty}$ is a non-increasing sequence bounded below by the number $\mu(Y \cap (\bigcup_{n=1}^{\infty} A_n)')$. It thus has a limit, which is greater than or equal to $\mu(Y \cap (\bigcup_{n=1}^{\infty} A_n)')$. Taking limits in the equality (ii), we obtain,

$$\mu(Y) = \lim_{p\to\infty} \sum_{n=1}^{p} \mu(Y \cap A_n) + \lim_{p\to\infty} \mu(Y \cap (\bigcup_{n=1}^{p} A_n)') \geq$$

$\sum_{n=1}^{\infty} \mu(Y \cap A_n) + \mu(Y \cap (\bigcup_{n=1}^{\infty} A_n)')$. Since the reversed inequality has already been established, this completes the proof.

2.3.44 <u>Theorem</u>. If A and B are μ-measurable, then $A \cap B'$ is μ-measurable.

<u>Proof</u>. It suffices to prove that if $P \subset A \cap B'$ and $Q \subset (A \cap B')'$, then $\mu(P \cup Q) = \mu(P) + \mu(Q)$. Since $Q = (Q \cap B) \cup (Q \cap B')$ and B is μ-measurable, we have $\mu(P) + \mu(Q) = \mu(P) + \mu((Q \cap B) \cup (Q \cap B')) = \mu(P) + \mu(Q \cap B)$ $\mu(Q \cap B')$. Now since $P \subset A$, $Q \cap B' \subset A'$, and A is μ-measurable, we have $\mu(P) + \mu(Q \cap B') + \mu(Q \cap B) =$ $\mu(P \cup (Q \cap B')) + \mu(Q \cap B)$. Again $P \cup (Q \cap B') \subset B'$

and $Q \cap B \subset B$ so that $\mu(P \cup (Q \cap B')) + \mu(Q \cap B) = \mu(P \cup (Q \cap B') \cup (Q \cap B)) = \mu(P \cup Q)$. Combining these equalities, we have $\mu(P) + \mu(Q) = \mu(P \cup Q)$, i.e., $A \cap B'$ is measurable.

2.3.45 Theorem. The family of μ-measurable sets is a σ-algebra of subsets of X and μ is countably additive on this σ-algebra.

Proof. Let $\{A_n\}_{n=1}^{\infty}$ be a sequence of μ-measurable subsets of X. Then $\bigcup_{n=1}^{\infty} A_n = A_1 \cup (A_2 \cap A_1') \cup (A_3 \cap A_2' \cap A_1') \cup \ldots \cup (A_n \cap A_{n-1}' \cap \ldots \cap A_1') \cup \ldots$. By 2.3.44, each set of the form $B_n = (A_n \cap A_{n-1}' \cap \ldots \cap A_1')$ is μ-measurable. Furthermore, the sets B_n are pairwise disjoint.

Let $Y \subset X$. By 2.3.43 (i) and countable subadditivity, we have $\mu(Y) = \sum_{n=1}^{\infty} \mu(Y \cap B_n) + \mu(Y \cap (\bigcup_{n=1}^{\infty} B_n)') \geq \mu(Y \cap (\bigcup_{n=1}^{\infty} B_n)) + \mu(Y \cap (\bigcup_{n=1}^{\infty} B_n)')$. By countable subadditivity we have $\mu(Y) \leq \mu(Y \cap (\bigcup_{n=1}^{\infty} B_n)) + \mu(Y \cap (\bigcup_{n=1}^{\infty} B_n)')$. Thus we have $\mu(Y) = \mu(Y \cap (\bigcup_{n=1}^{\infty} B_n)) + \mu(Y \cap (\bigcup_{n=1}^{\infty} B_n)')$. This implies that $\bigcup_{n=1}^{\infty} B_n$ is μ-measurable. Thus $\bigcup_{n=1}^{\infty} A_n = \bigcup_{n=1}^{\infty} B_n$ is μ-measurable. This fact and 2.3.42 imply that the family of μ-measurable sets is a σ-algebra (2.2.1).

Upon setting $Y = \bigcup_{k=1}^{\infty} B_k$ in equation (i) of 2.3.43 we obtain $\mu(\bigcup_{n=1}^{\infty} B_n) = \sum_{n=1}^{\infty} \mu((\bigcup_{k=1}^{\infty} B_k) \cap B_n) + \mu((\bigcup_{k=1}^{\infty} B_k) \cap (\bigcup_{n=1}^{\infty} B_n)') = \sum_{n=1}^{\infty} \mu(B_n) + \mu(0) = \sum_{n=1}^{\infty} \mu(B_n)$. Thus μ is countably additive on the σ-algebra of all μ-measurable subsets of X.

2.3.46 Theorem. Every closed interval $[a,b]$, $-\infty < a < b < \infty$, is a λ-measurable subset of R.

Proof. We will show that for all $Y \subset R$,
$\lambda(Y) = \lambda([a,b] \cap Y) + \lambda([a,b]' \cap Y)$.

Case I. Suppose that Y is an open subset of R such that $a \notin Y$, $b \notin Y$. We have $Y = \bigcup_{n=1}^{\infty}]\alpha_n,\beta_n[$ where the $]\alpha_n,\beta_n[$ are pairwise disjoint. For each n, either $]\alpha_n,\beta_n[\subset]-\infty,a[$, $]\alpha_n,\beta_n[\subset]a,b[$, or $]\alpha_n,\beta_n[\subset]b,\infty[$. Let $M = \{n:]\alpha_n,\beta_n[\subset]a,b[\}$. Then by 2.3.25, $\lambda(Y) = \sum_{n=1}^{\infty}(\beta_n - \alpha_n) = \sum_{n\in M}(\beta_n - \alpha_n) + \sum_{n\notin M}(\beta_n - \alpha_n) = \lambda([a,b] \cap Y) + \lambda([a,b]' \cap Y)$.

Case II. Suppose that Y is any open subset of R. Let $N = \{a,b\}$ and note that N' is an open set. By Theorem 2.3.41 and Case I, we have $\lambda(Y) = \lambda(Y \cap N') = \lambda([a,b] \cap Y \cap N') + \lambda([a,b]' \cap Y \cap N') = \lambda([a,b] \cap Y) + \lambda([a,b]' \cap Y)$.

Case III. Suppose that Y is any subset of R. By countable subadditivity $\lambda(Y) \leq \lambda([a,b] \cap Y) + \lambda([a,b]' \cap Y)$ for $Y \subset R$. If $\lambda(Y) = \infty$, the reverse inequality is clear. If $\lambda(Y) < \infty$, choose $\varepsilon > 0$ and an open set $G \supset Y$ such that $\lambda(G) < \lambda(Y) + \varepsilon$. By Case II and the monotonicity of λ, we have $\lambda([a,b] \cap Y) + \lambda([a,b]' \cap Y) \leq \lambda([a,b] \cap G) + \lambda([a,b]' \cap G) = \lambda(G) <$

$\lambda(Y) + \varepsilon$. Since ε was arbitrary, we conclude that $\lambda([a,b] \cap Y) + \lambda([a,b]' \cap Y) \leq \lambda(Y)$. Thus for any subset $Y \subset R$, $\lambda(Y) = \lambda([a,b] \cap Y) + \lambda([a,b]' \cap Y)$.

2.3.461 Notation. Let $\mathfrak{M}_\lambda = \{Y\colon\ Y \subset R,\ Y \text{ is } \lambda\text{-measurable}\}$, and let $\mathcal{B}$ be the smallest σ-algebra of subsets of R, containing all open sets. $\mathcal{B}$ is called the family of Borel sets in R.

2.3.47 Theorem. The relation $\mathcal{B} \subsetneq \mathfrak{M}_\lambda$ obtains, and hence λ is countable additive on the σ-algebra $\mathcal{B}$.

Proof. We first prove that every open set is λ-measurable. The set $]\alpha,\beta[$ is λ-measurable for all $\alpha,\beta \in R$ since $]\alpha,\beta[= \bigcup_{n=1}^{\infty} [\alpha + \frac{1}{n}, \beta - \frac{1}{n}]$; recall that $\mathfrak{M}_\lambda$ is a σ-algebra. The set $]\alpha, \infty[$ is λ-measurable for all $\alpha \in R$ since $]\alpha, \infty[= \bigcup_{n=1}^{\infty} [\alpha + \frac{1}{n}, \alpha + n]$. Likewise $]-\infty,\beta[$ is λ-measurable. R is obviously λ-measurable. Since every open set is a countable union of sets of these types, Theorem 2.3.45 implies that every open set is λ-measurable.

Since the set of all λ-measurable sets is a σ-algebra containing all open sets, it is clear that $\mathcal{B} \subset \mathfrak{M}_\lambda$. Every Borel set can be obtained from sets in the countable family $\{]\alpha,\beta[\colon\ \alpha,\beta \text{ rational}\}$ by a countable number of applications of complementation and forming countable unions. This implies (we omit the details) that $\overline{\overline{\mathcal{B}}} = c$. Now we observe that the Cantor set, C, has λ-measure zero and hence all subsets of C have λ-measure zero. Therefore all subsets of C are λ-measurable. Thus $2^c \leq \overline{\overline{\mathcal{M}_\lambda}} \leq \overline{\overline{\{Y: Y \subset R\}}} = 2^c$; that is, there are 2^c λ-measurable subsets of R. Thus we see that $\mathcal{B} \neq \mathcal{M}_\lambda$.

2.3.471 Remark. The argument just used to show that $\mathcal{B} \neq \mathcal{M}_\lambda$ is a crude cardinal number argument. One can actually construct subsets of R (so-called analytic sets) that are not in $\mathcal{B}$ but are in $\mathcal{M}_\lambda$. See Saks, Theory of the Integral, 2nd ed., pp. 47-51.

2.3.48 Theorem. λ is invariant under translations and reflections about the origin, for all subsets of R. That is, $\lambda(A + t) = \lambda(A)$ and $\lambda(-A) = \lambda(A)$ for all $A \subset R$ and $t \in R$.

Suppose that A and B are subsets of R and that $A = \bigcup_{n=1}^{\infty} A_n$ and $B = \bigcup_{n=1}^{\infty} B_n$ where the A_n's are pairwise disjoint λ-measurable sets and the B_n's are pairwise disjoint λ-measurable sets. Suppose further that for all n, $A_n = (-1)^{\sigma_n} B_n + t_n$, where $\sigma_n = 0$ or 1 and $t_n \in R$. Then $\lambda(A) = \lambda(B)$.

Proof. Since $A \subset G$ if and only if $(-1)^\sigma A + t \subset (-1)^\sigma G +$ ($\sigma = 0$ or 1, $t \in R$), it suffices to show that $\lambda(G + t)$ $\lambda(G)$ and $\lambda(-G) = \lambda(G)$ for all open sets $G \subset R$ and $t \in R$. If G is open, $G = \bigcup_{n=1}^{\infty}]a_n, b_n[$. Then $G + t = \bigcup_{n=1}^{\infty}]a_n + t, b_n + t[$ and $-G = \bigcup_{n=1}^{\infty}]-b_n, -a_n[$ which together with 2.3.25 implies that $\lambda(G + t) = \lambda(G) = \lambda(-G)$.

The second statement of the theorem is easy to verify. We omit the proof.

Up to now we have proved that certain classes of subsets of R are λ-measurable. This leads to the question: Are all subsets of R λ-measurable? The answer to this question is no; an example of a non-measurable set is given in Natanson, pages 76-78. We give below another example of a non-measurable set. Our construction is actually equivalent to that given by Natanson, which goes back to Vitali. The details, however, are different.

2.3.49 Theorem. There exists a subset of R that is not λ-measurable.

Proof. In this proof we will use the notation [a] for the greatest integer less than or equal to a. We also use the fact that $[a + n] = [a] + n$ for $a \in R$, $n \in N$.

Let H be a Hamel basis for R over the rationals Q such that $1 \in H$. Let $A = \{x_1r_1 + x_2r_2 + \dots + x_mr_m - [x_1r_1 + \dots + x_mr_m]: r_1, r_2, \dots, r_m \in Q,\ x_1, x_2, \dots, x_m \in H \cap \{1\}'\}$. Note that $A \subset [0,1[$. We will show that A is not λ-measurable.

For $s \in Q$, we define $A_s = \{x + s - [x + s]: x \in A\}$. We now show that $\bigcup_{\substack{0 \le s < 1 \\ s \in Q}} A_s = [0,1[$. The inclusion $\bigcup_{\substack{0 \le s < 1 \\ s \in Q}} A_s \subset [0,1[$ is clear. Suppose that $y \in [0,1[$. Since H is a Hamel basis, there are elements $x_1, \dots, x_m \in H \cap \{1\}'$ and rational numbers $r_1, \dots, r_m, s$ such that $y = r_1x_1 + \dots + r_mx_m + s \cdot 1$. The relation

$y \in [0,1[$ implies that $[r_1x_1 + \ldots + r_mx_m + s] = 0$. Thus $y = r_1x_1 + \ldots + r_mx_m + s - [r_1x_1 + \ldots + r_mx_m+s] = r_1x_1 + \ldots + r_mx_m - [r_1x_1 + \ldots + r_mx_m] + s - [x_1r_1 + \ldots + x_mr_m - [x_1r_1 + \ldots + x_mr_m] + s] = x + s - [x + s]$ where $x \in A$. Thus $y \in A_s$. To show $y \in \bigcup_{\substack{0 \leq s < 1 \\ s \in Q}} A_s$, it now suffices to show that $A_s = A_{s-[s]}$. But we have $A_{s-[s]} = \{x + s - [s] - [x + s - [s]]: x \in A\} = \{x + s - [s] - [x + s] + [s]: x \in A\} = \{x + s - [x + s]: x \in A\} = A_s$. Hence $\bigcup_{0 \leq s < 1, s \in Q} A_s = [0,1[$.

We now show that if $s, s^* \in Q$, $0 \leq s < 1$, $0 \leq s^* < 1$, and $s \neq s^*$, then $A_s \cap A_{s^*} = 0$. Suppose that $t \in A_s \cap A_{s^*}$. Then $t = x + s - [x + s] = x^* + s^* - [x^* + s^*]$, where $x, x^* \in A$. We have $x = u - [u]$ and $x^* = u^* - [u^*]$, where $u = r_1z_1 + \ldots r_mz_m$, $u^* = r_1^*z_1^* + \ldots + r_n^*z_n^*$, with $z_i, z_i^* \in H \cap \{1\}'$ and $r_i, r_i^* \in Q$. Thus we have

$0 = x - x^* + s - s^* + [x^* + s^*] - [x + s] = u - [u] - u^* + [u^*] + s - s^* + [x^* + s^*] - [x + s] = r_1z_1 + \ldots + r_mz_m - r_1z_1^* \ldots - r_nz_n^* + [x^* + s^*] - [x + s] + s - s^* - [u] + [u^*]$.

Since H is linearly independent, each coefficient of members of H must be 0. In particular, $[x^* + s^*] - [x + s] + s - s^* - [u] + [u^*]$, the coefficient of 1, is zero. Since $s - s^* = [u] - [u^*] - [x^* + s^*] + [x + s]$, an integer, and $0 \leq |s - s^*| < 1$, we see that $s - s^* = 0$ or $s = s^*$. This is a contradiction.

Finally, we show that A is not λ-measurable. For, assume that A is λ-measurable. For all $s \in Q$, $0 \leq s < 1$, we see that $\lambda(A_s) = \lambda(A)$. In fact, $A_s = \{(A + s) \cap [0,1[\} \cup \{(A + s) \cap [1,2[- 1\}$. The two sets in curly brackets are clearly congruent under translations to a dissection of A into two disjoint sets, and these sets are λ-measurable if A is. Theorem 2.3.48 implies that $\lambda(A) = \lambda(A_s)$. We have $[0,1[= \bigcup_{\substack{s\in Q\\0\leq s<1}} A_s$, a countable union of pairwise disjoint measurable sets. Thus $1 = \lambda([0,1[) = \sum_{\substack{s\in Q\\0\leq s<1}} \lambda(A_s) = \begin{Bmatrix} 0 & \text{if } \lambda(A) = \lambda(A_s) = 0 \\ \infty & \text{if } \lambda(A) = \lambda(A_s) > 0 \end{Bmatrix}$.

Hence A is not λ-measurable.

Remark. In the above proof, we could not replace A by the set $B = \{x_1r_1 + \ldots + x_mr_m\colon\ x_i \in H \cap \{1\}'$ and $r_i \in Q\}$, for this would lead only to $\infty = \lambda(R) = \lambda(\bigcup_{\substack{s\in Q\\0\leq s<1}} B_s) = \sum_{\substack{s\in Q\\0\leq s<1}} \lambda(B_s) = \begin{Bmatrix} 0 \\ \infty \end{Bmatrix}$, which is not a contradiction.

However, B is not λ-measurable. This follows from Exercise 2.3.491 below, since $B + B \subset B$.

2.3.491 Exercise. (Steinhaus) Let A be a measurable set of positive measure. Then $A + A = \{x + y\colon\ x,y \in A\}$ contains an interval.

2.3.492 Final Exercise # 7. Let $A \subset R$. Define $\lambda_*(A) = \sup \{\lambda(F)\colon F \subset A$ and F is closed and bounded$\}$.

i) Let $\lambda(A) < \infty$. Prove that A is λ-measurable if and only if $\lambda(A) = \lambda_*(A)$.

ii) Let $A \subset R$. Prove that $\lambda_*(A) = \sup \{\lambda(F): F \subset A$ and F closed$\}$.

2.4 Additional properties of measures. Throughout 2.4, X is any set, $\mathcal{A}$ is a σ-algebra of subsets of X, μ is a set-function on $\mathcal{A}$ such that $\mu(0) = 0$, $0 \leq \mu(A) \leq \infty$ for all $A \in \mathcal{A}$, and $\mu(\bigcup_{n=1}^{\infty} A_n) = \sum_{n=1}^{\infty} \mu(A_n)$ where the A_n's are pairwise disjoint members of $\mathcal{A}$ (countable additivity).

2.4.1 Theorem. Suppose $A, B \in \mathcal{A}$, $A \subset B$. Then $\mu(A) \leq \mu(B)$.

Proof. This follows easily from the equality $\mu(B) = \mu(A) + \mu(B \cap A')$.

2.4.2 Theorem. Let $\{A_n\}_{n=1}^{\infty} \subset \mathcal{A}$ and $A_n \subset A_{n+1}$ for $n = 1, 2, \ldots$. Then $\mu(\bigcup_{n=1}^{\infty} A_n) = \lim_{n\to\infty} \mu(A_n)$.

Proof. Clearly $\bigcup_{n=1}^{\infty} A_n = A_1 \cup (A_2 \cap A_1') \cup \ldots \cup (A_{n+1} \cap A_n') \cup \ldots$. Using countable additivity we obtain $\mu(\bigcup_{n=1}^{\infty} A_n) = \mu(A_1) + \sum_{n=1}^{\infty} \mu(A_{n+1} \cap A_n') = \mu(A_1) + \lim_{N\to\infty} \sum_{n=1}^{N} \mu(A_{n+1} \cap A_n') =$

$\lim_{N\to\infty} [\mu(A_1) + \sum_{n=1}^{N} \mu(A_{n+1} \cap A_n')] = \lim_{N\to\infty} \mu(A_{N+1})$. This is the desired equality.

2.4.21 Remark. A result strictly analogous to Theorem 2.4.2 for intersections of measurable sets cannot be proved. To see this, let $X = R$, $\lambda = \mu$, and $\mathcal{A} = \mathcal{M}_\lambda$, the Lebesgue measurable sets. Let $A_n = [n, \infty[$. Then $\lambda(A_n) = \infty$ for $n = 1, 2, 3, \ldots$, so that $\lim_{n\to\infty} \lambda(A_n) = \infty$. On the other hand, $\lambda(\bigcap_{n=1}^{\infty} A_n) = \lambda(0) = 0$. However, we do obtain the following result.

2.4.3 Theorem. If $\mu(A_1) < \infty$ and $A_1 \supset A_2 \supset \ldots \supset A_n \supset \ldots$, then $\lim_{n\to\infty} \mu(A_n) = \mu(\bigcap_{n=1}^{\infty} A_n)$.

Proof. $\{A_1 \cap A_n'\}_{n=1}^{\infty}$ is an increasing sequence of measurable sets. Applying 2.4.2, we get $\mu(A_1) - \lim_{n\to\infty} \mu(A_n) =$

$$\lim_{n\to\infty} (\mu(A_1) - \mu(A_n)) = \lim_{n\to\infty} \mu(A_1 \cap A_n') = \mu(\bigcup_{n=1}^{\infty} (A_1 \cap A_n')) =$$

$$\mu(A_1 \cap (\bigcup_{n=1}^{\infty} A_n')) = \mu(A_1 \cap (\bigcap_{n=1}^{\infty} A_n)') = \mu(A_1) - \mu(\bigcap_{n=1}^{\infty} A_n).$$

Thus $\lim_{n\to\infty} \mu(A_n) = \mu(\bigcap_{n=1}^{\infty} A_n)$.

2.4.4 Theorem. Let $\{A_n\}_{n=1}^{\infty}$ be any sequence of sets in $\mathcal{A}$.

Then

i) $\mu(\bigcup_{k=1}^{\infty} (\bigcap_{n=k}^{\infty} A_n)) \leq \underline{\lim}_{k\to\infty} \mu(A_k)$.

We also have

ii) $\mu(\bigcap_{k=1}^{\infty} (\bigcup_{n=k}^{\infty} A_n)) \geq \overline{\lim}_{k\to\infty} \mu(A_k)$

provided that $\mu(\bigcup_{k=1}^{\infty} A_k) < \infty$.

Proof. Clearly $\bigcap_{n=1}^{\infty} A_n \subset \bigcap_{n=2}^{\infty} A_n \subset \ldots \subset \bigcap_{n=k}^{\infty} A_n \subset \ldots$.

Theorem 2.4.2 implies that $\mu(\bigcup_{k=1}^{\infty} (\bigcap_{n=k}^{\infty} A_n)) = \lim_{k\to\infty} \mu(\bigcap_{n=k}^{\infty} A_n)$.

We also have $\mu(A_k) \geq \mu(\bigcap_{n=k}^{\infty} A_n)$ for all k. This implies that $\lim_{k\to\infty} \mu(\bigcap_{n=k}^{\infty} A_n) \leq \underline{\lim}_{k\to\infty} \mu(A_k)$, from which equation (i) follows.

(ii) is proved in like manner.

2.4.41 Corollary. Suppose that $\bigcap_{k=1}^{\infty} (\bigcup_{n=k}^{\infty} A_n) = \bigcup_{k=1}^{\infty} (\bigcap_{n=k}^{\infty} A_n) = B$ and $\mu(\bigcup_{k=1}^{\infty} A_k) < \infty$. Then $\lim_{k\to\infty} \mu(A_k)$ exists and is equal to $\mu(B)$.

Proof. The assertion follows from the inequality,

$\overline{\lim}_{k\to\infty} \mu(A_k) \leq \mu(B) \leq \underline{\lim}_{k\to\infty} \mu(A_k)$.

2.4.5 Discussion. Let X, $\mathcal{A}$, and μ be as previously. For all $T \subset X$, let $\mu^*(T) = \inf \{ \mu(A) : A \in \mathcal{A}, A \supset T \}$. μ^* is a Carathéodory outer measure and the σ-algebra $\mathfrak{M}_{\mu^*}$ of μ^*-measurable sets always contains $\mathcal{A}$ and $\mu^*(A) = \mu(A)$ for $A \in \mathcal{A}$.

μ^* on $\mathfrak{M}_{\mu^*}$ is called the completion of μ, and is an extension of μ to a possibly larger σ-algebra of sets, retaining countable additivity.

2.4.6 Discussion. Suppose that X is a set, $\mathcal{A}$ an algebra of subsets of X, and μ a set-function on $\mathcal{A}$ such that:

$\mu(0) = 0$;

$0 \leq \mu(A) \leq \infty$ for all $A \in \mathcal{A}$;

$\mu(\bigcup_{n=1}^{\infty} A_n) = \sum_{n=1}^{\infty} \mu(A_n)$ whenever $\bigcup_{n=1}^{\infty} A_n \in \mathcal{A}$ and the A_n's are pairwise disjoint. This measure can always be extended to a σ-algebra (E. Hopf's extension theorem). The extension is defined by $\mu^*(T) = \inf \left\{ \sum_{n=1}^{\infty} \mu(A_n) : A_n \in \mathcal{A} \text{ and } T \subset \bigcup_{n=1}^{\infty} A_n \right\}$. As before, μ^* is a Carathéodory outer measure. μ^* agrees with μ on $\mathcal{A}$, and all sets in $\mathcal{A}$ are μ^*-measurable.

If μ is finitely additive but not countably additive, then μ^* is still a Carathéodory outer measure and all elements of $\mathcal{A}$ are μ^*-measurable, but $\mu^*(A) < \mu(A)$ for some $A \in \mathcal{A}$.

For example, let $X = [0,1[$ and $\mathcal{A}$ be all subsets of $[0,1[$ that are finite unions of half-open intervals $[\alpha,\beta[$. Define $\lambda([a_1,b_1[\cup \ldots \cup [a_k,b_k[) = (b_1 - a_1) + \ldots + (b_k - a_k)$. $\mathcal{A}$ is an algebra but not a σ-algebra. λ is countably additive, since λ is Lebesgue measure for all members of $\mathcal{A}$. It is a bit tricky to prove ab initio that λ is countably additive on $\mathcal{A}$.

2.4.7 Final Exercise #8. Let X be any set, $\mathcal{A}$ a σ-algebra of subsets of X. Let γ be a set-function defined on $\mathcal{A}$ such that:

$\gamma(A) \in R$ for all $A \in \mathcal{A}$;

$\gamma(\bigcup_{n=1}^{\infty} A_n) = \sum_{n=1}^{\infty} \gamma(A_n)$ if each $A_n \in \mathcal{A}$ and the A_n are pairwise disjoint.

For each $A \in \mathcal{A}$, let $\gamma^+(A) = \sup\{\gamma(B): B \in \mathcal{A}, B \subset A\}$ and $\gamma^-(A) = \inf\{\gamma(B): B \in \mathcal{A}, B \subset A\}$. Prove the following facts.

i) $\gamma(0) = 0$.

ii) $\gamma^+(A)$ and $\gamma^-(A)$ are finite for all $A \in \mathcal{A}$.

iii) γ^+ and γ^- are countably additive set-functions on $\mathcal{A}$.

iv) sup $\{ |\gamma(A)| : A \in \mathcal{A} \} \leq \gamma^+(X) - \gamma^-(X)$.

v) $\gamma(A) = \gamma^+(A) + \gamma^-(A)$ for all $A \in \mathcal{A}$.

vi) there exists a $B \in \mathcal{A}$ such that $\gamma^+(B) = 0$ and $\gamma^-(B') = 0$.

2.5 Vitali's Theorem.

2.5.1 Definition. Let E be a bounded set in R. Let $\delta(E) = \sup E - \inf E$. $\delta(E)$ is the diameter of E. For E containing at least two points, let $r(E) = \frac{\lambda(E)}{\delta(E)}$.

2.5.2 Definition. A family $\mathcal{V}$ of bounded sets in R each containing at least two points, is said to cover $A \subset R$ in the sense of Vitali if for all $a \in A$, there is a sequence $\{E_n\}_{n=1}^{\infty}$ of sets such that $E_n \in \mathcal{V}$ for all n and:

i) $a \in E_n$ for all n;

ii) $\lim_{n\to\infty} \delta(E_n) = 0$;

iii) $r(E_n) \geq \alpha > 0$ for some α and for all n (α depends upon a).

2.5.3 Theorem. (Vitali) Let $A \subset R$, and let $\mathcal{V}$ be a family of closed bounded sets covering A in the sense of Vitali. Then there exists a sequence $\{E_n\}_{n=1}^{\infty}$ such that $E_n \in \mathcal{V}$, the E_n are pairwise disjoint, and $\lambda(A \cap (\bigcup_{n=1}^{\infty} E_n)') = 0$.

Proof. We give the remarkable proof of this theorem discovered by S. Banach.* Case I. Suppose that A is bounded,

* See Fund. Math. 6 (1924), pp. 170-188.

$A \subset [-t,t]$ for some $t > 0$, and that there is a positive number α such that $r(E) \geq \alpha > 0$ for all $E \in \mathcal{V}$. Let E_1 be any set in $\mathcal{V}$ where $E_1 \subset [-t-1, t+1]$. Suppose that $E_1, E_2, \ldots, E_p \in \mathcal{V}$ have already been chosen so that the E_i are pairwise disjoint. If $A \subset E_1 \cup \ldots \cup E_p$, then we stop. If $A \not\subset E_1 \cup \ldots \cup E_p$, there exists an $x \in A \cap (E_1 \cup \ldots \cup E_p)'$ and there exists a $\gamma > 0$ such that $]x-\gamma, x+\gamma[\subset (E_1 \cup \ldots \cup E_p)'$ where we may suppose that $\gamma < 1$. There is an $E \in \mathcal{V}$ such that $x \in E \subset]x-\gamma, x+\gamma[$. Thus $E \subset (E_1 \cup \ldots \cup E_p)' \cap [-t-1, t+1]$. Let $\Delta_p = \sup\{\delta(E): E \in \mathcal{V}$ and $E \subset (E_1 \cup \ldots \cup E_p)' \cap [-t-1, t+1]\}$. Δ_p is finite since $\delta(E) \leq 2t+2$ for all $E \subset [-t-1, t+1]$. Let E_{p+1} be any set in $\mathcal{V}$ such that

i) $E_{p+1} \subset (E_1 \cup \ldots \cup E_p)' \cap [-t-1, t+1]$;

ii) $\delta(E_{p+1}) > \frac{1}{2} \Delta_p$.

Hence we have defined a sequence $\{E_n\}_{n=1}^{?}$ of pairwise disjoint sets in $\mathcal{V}$, where ? is a positive integer or $+\infty$.

If the sequence is finite, the theorem is obvious. If the sequence is infinite, let $B = A \cap (\bigcup_{n=1}^{\infty} E_n)'$. We will show that $\lambda(B) = 0$. To do this, let us assume that $\lambda(B) > 0$. For each n, let $J_n = [\inf E_n, \sup E_n]$. Let $\tilde{J}_n$ be the closed interval with the same center as

J_n and five times as long; it is clear that $\tilde{J}_n =$ $[3 \cdot \inf E_n - 2 \cdot \sup E_n, 3 \cdot \sup E_n - 2 \cdot \inf E_n]$. Since $r(E_n) \geq \alpha > 0$ and $\lambda(J_n) = \delta(J_n) = \delta(E_n)$, we have $\alpha \leq r(E_n) = \frac{\lambda(E_n)}{\delta(E_n)} = \frac{\lambda(E_n)}{\lambda(J_n)}$. Thus $\lambda(J_n) \leq \frac{1}{\alpha} \lambda(E_n)$. Therefore, by elementary analysis and countable additivity of λ, we have $\sum_{n=1}^{\infty} \lambda(\tilde{J}_n) = 5 \sum_{n=1}^{\infty} \lambda(J_n) \leq \frac{5}{\alpha} \sum_{n=1}^{\infty} \lambda(E_n) =$ $\frac{5}{\alpha} \lambda(\bigcup_{n=1}^{\infty} E_n) \leq \frac{5}{\alpha} \lambda([-t - 1, t + 1]) = \frac{5}{\alpha}(2t + 2) < \infty$. Let N be a positive integer such that $\sum_{n=N+1}^{\infty} \lambda(\tilde{J}_n) < \lambda(B)$. There exists an $x_o \in B$ such that $x_o \notin \tilde{J}_{N+1} \cup \tilde{J}_{N+2} \cup$ $\ldots$, since the inclusion $B \subset \bigcup_{n=N+1}^{\infty} \tilde{J}_n$ implies that $\lambda(B) \leq \lambda(\bigcup_{n=N+1}^{\infty} \tilde{J}_n) \leq \sum_{n=N+1}^{\infty} \lambda(\tilde{J}_n)$. By the definition of B, we have $x_o \notin E_1 \cup \ldots \cup E_N$. Since $(E_1 \cup \ldots \cup E_N)'$ is open, there is an $E \in \mathcal{V}$ such that $x_o \in E \subset (E_1 \cup \ldots \cup$ $E_N)' \cap [-t - 1, t + 1]$. If $E \cap (E_1 \cap \ldots \cap E_n) = 0$ for all n, then $\delta(E) \leq \Delta_n < 2\delta(E_{n+1}) \leq 2\delta(J_{n+1}) = 2\lambda(J_{n+1})$ for all n; since $\lambda(J_n) \to 0$ as $n \to \infty$, we would have $\delta(E) = 0$, a violation of hypotheses. Thus for some n, we have $E \cap E_n \neq 0$. Let n_o be the least positive integer such that $E \cap E_{n_o} \neq 0$. Clearly $n_o > N$, since $E \subset (E_1 \cup \ldots \cup E_N)'$. It follows that $E \subset (E_1 \cup \ldots \cup$ $E_{n_o-1})' \cap]-t - 1, t + 1[$. Consequently $\delta(E) \leq \Delta_{n_o-1}$. We have $E \cap J_{n_o} \supset E \cap E_{n_o} \neq 0$. Since $x_o \notin \tilde{J}_{n_o}$, we have

$E \cap \tilde{J}_{n_o}' \neq 0$. Let a be the center of J_{n_o} and $2u$ be its diameter. Then clearly $J_{n_o} = [a-u, a+u]$ and $\tilde{J}_{n_o} = [a-5u, a+5u]$. From this and the facts that $E \cap J_{n_o} \neq 0$ and $E \cap \tilde{J}_{n_o}' \neq 0$, we see that $\delta(E) \geq 4u = 2\delta(J_{n_o}) = 2\delta(E_{n_o}) > \Delta_{n_o-1}$. This contradicts the inequality $\delta(E) \leq \Delta_{n_o-1}$. We conclude that $\lambda(B) = 0$. Hence the theorem is proved under the hypotheses of Case I.

Case II. Suppose that A is <u>any</u> subset of R, and that for each $a \in A$, there is a sequence $\{B_n\}_{n=1}^{\infty}$, $B_n \in \mathcal{V}$, where

i) $a \in B_n$ for all n;

ii) $\lim_{n\to\infty} \delta(B_n) = 0$;

iii) $r(B_n) \geq \alpha(a) > 0$ for all n where $\alpha(a)$ depends upon a.

For every positive integer p, let $A_p = \{a\colon a \in A,\ |a| < p$, and there is a sequence $\{B_n\}_{n=1}^{\infty}$, $B_n \in \mathcal{V}$, where $r(B_n) > \frac{1}{p}$ for all n, $a \in B_n$ for all n, and $\lim_{n\to\infty} \delta(B_n) = 0\}$. It is evident that $A_1 \subset A_2 \subset \cdots \subset A_p \subset \cdots$ and now we show that $\bigcup_{p=1}^{\infty} A_p = A$. For any $a \in A$ let p be such that $|a| < p$ and q be such that $\alpha(a) > \frac{1}{q}$. Then clearly $a \in A_{\max(p,q)}$. Thus $A \subset \bigcup_{p=1}^{\infty} A_p$; the reverse inclusion is trivial.

Consider $A_1 \subset]-1,1[$. By Case I, there is a sequence $\{E_n\}_{n=1}^{\infty}$ of pairwise disjoint sets of $\mathcal{V}$ such that

$E_n \subset]-2,2[$ and $\lambda(A_1 \cap (\bigcup_{n=1}^{\infty} E_n)') = 0$, or else there is a finite sequence $E_1, \ldots, E_{p_1}$ of pairwise disjoint sets of $\mathcal{V}$ such that $A_1 \subset E_1 \cup \ldots \cup E_{p_1}$. In the latter case let $\mathcal{T}_1 = \{E_1, \ldots, E_{p_1}\}$. In the first case, we observe that $\sum_{n=1}^{\infty} \lambda(E_n) \leq 4 < \infty$. Therefore for any $\varepsilon > 0$, there is a positive integer M such that $\sum_{n=M+1}^{\infty} \lambda(E_n) < \varepsilon$. By the subadditivity of λ on all subsets and countable additivity on measurable subsets, we have $\lambda(A_1 \cap (E_1 \cup \ldots \cup E_M)') \leq \lambda(A_1 \cap (\bigcup_{n=1}^{\infty} E_n)') + \lambda(\bigcup_{n=M+1}^{\infty} E_n) < \varepsilon$. We now pick M_1 corresponding to $\varepsilon = 1$ and let $\mathcal{T}_1 = \{E_1, \ldots, E_{M_1}\}$. We thus have $\lambda(A_1 \cap (E_1 \cup \ldots \cup E_{M_1})') < 1$

Suppose $\mathcal{T}_1, \ldots, \mathcal{T}_p$ have been defined to be finite families of sets in $\mathcal{V}$ such that $\bigcup_{i=1}^{p} \mathcal{T}_i$ consists of pairwise disjoint sets. Let $T_i = \bigcup_{B \varepsilon \mathcal{T}_i} B$. Consider $\tilde{A}_{p+1} = A_{p+1} \cap (T_1 \cup \ldots \cup T_p)'$. Note that each T_i is a finite union of closed sets and hence closed. Thus $(T_1 \cup \ldots \cup T_p)'$ is open. Let $\mathcal{V}_{p+1}$ be the family of all sets $E \varepsilon \mathcal{V}$ such that $E \subset]-p-1, p+1[\cap (T_1 \cup \ldots \cup T_p)'$. Evidently, $\mathcal{V}_{p+1}$ covers $\tilde{A}_{p+1}$ in the sense of Vitali. Exactly as with A_1, we find pairwise disjoint sets $E_1^{(p+1)}, \ldots, E_{M_{p+1}}^{(p+1)}$ such that $E_i^{(p+1)} \varepsilon \mathcal{V}_{p+1} \subset \mathcal{V} (i = 1, 2, \ldots, M_{p+1})$ and $\lambda(\tilde{A}_{p+1} \cap (E_1^{(p+1)} \cup \ldots \cup E_{M_{p+1}}^{(p+1)})',$

$\frac{1}{p+1}$. We now define $\mathcal{T}_{p+1} = \left\{E_1^{(p+1)}, \ldots, E_{M_{p+1}}^{(p+1)}\right\}$. The family of sets $\bigcup_{p=1}^{\infty} \mathcal{T}_p$ is a countable family of pairwise disjoint sets in $\mathcal{V}$. Let $T = \bigcup_{j=1}^{\infty} T_j$. We now show that $\lambda(A \cap T') = 0$. For each p and an arbitrary q we have $\lambda(A_p \cap T') = \lambda(A_p \cap (\bigcup_{j=1}^{\infty} T_j)') \leq \lambda(A_{p+q} \cap (T_1 \cup \ldots \cup T_{p+q})') < \frac{1}{p+q}$. Since q is arbitrary, we have $\lambda(A_p \cap T') = 0$. Since $A_1 \cap T' = \bigcup_{n=1}^{\infty} (A_n \cap T')$, we conclude that $\lambda(A \cap T') = 0$.

2.5.4 __Theorem.__ Let $\mathcal{V}$ and A be as in 2.5.3 with the added restriction that A be bounded. Then for every $\varepsilon > 0$ there exists $E_1, \ldots, E_m \in \mathcal{V}$ such that $\lambda(A \cap (E_1 \cup \ldots \cup E_m)') < \varepsilon$.

The proof is contained in the proof of 2.5.3.

2.5.5 __Theorem.__ Let $B \subset R$ be the union of intervals (open or closed). Then B is Lebesgue measurable.

__Proof.__ Let $\mathcal{V}$ be the family of all bounded closed intervals containing at least two points that are contained in B. Clearly $\mathcal{V}$ covers B in the sense of Vitali. Thus there is a sequence $\{E_n\}_{n=1}^{\infty}$, $E_n \in \mathcal{V}$, where $\lambda(B \cap (E_1 \cup \ldots \cup E_n \cup \ldots)') = 0$. Now $B = (E_1 \cup \ldots \cup E_n \cup \ldots) \cup (B \cap (E_1 \cup \ldots \cup E_n \cup \ldots)')$ and hence is the union of two λ-measurable sets. Thus B is Lebesgue measurable.

2.5.6 Final Exercise # 9. For a real-valued function f defined in an open interval containing x, let

$$D^+f(x) = \overline{\lim_{h\downarrow 0}} \frac{f(x+h)-f(x)}{h}, \qquad D_+f(x) = \underline{\lim_{h\downarrow 0}} \frac{f(x+h)-f(x)}{h},$$

$$D^-f(x) = \overline{\lim_{h\uparrow 0}} \frac{f(x+h)-f(x)}{h}, \qquad D_-f(x) = \underline{\lim_{h\uparrow 0}} \frac{f(x+h)-f(x)}{h}.$$

If $D^+f(x) = D_+f(x)$, we write $f'_+(x) = D^+f(x)$. If $D^-f(x) = D_-f(x)$, we write $f'_-(x) = D^-f(x)$. If $f'_+(x) = f'_-(x)$, then we write $f'(x) = f'_+(x)$, and f is said to be differentiable at x.

Let f be a real-valued function non-decreasing in $]\alpha,\beta[$, i.e., $f(x_1) \leq f(x_2)$ if $\alpha < x_1 < x_2 < \beta$.

i) For rational numbers u and v such that $u < v$, let $E(u,v) = \{x: \alpha < x < \beta, D_+f(x) < u < v < D^+f(x)\}$. Prove from 2.5.3 or 2.5.4 that $\lambda(E(u,v)) = 0$ for all u,v.

ii) Prove that $D_+f(x) = D^+f(x)$ for almost all x in $]\alpha,\beta[$.

iii) Note that similarly $D_-f(x) = D^-f(x)$ for almost all x in $]\alpha,\beta[$.

iv) Define $F(u,v)$ like $E(u,v)$ to show that $f'_+(x) \geq f'_-(x)$ almost everywhere in $]\alpha,\beta[$.

v) Prove that f is differentiable almost everywhere in $]\alpha,\beta[$.

2.6 Analogues of Lebesgue measure.

2.6.1 Theorem. There is no set-function γ defined for all subsets of R such that

i) $0 \leq \gamma(X) \leq +\infty$ for all $X \subset R$;

ii) $\gamma(X + a) = \gamma(X)$ for all $X \subset R$ and $a \in R$;

iii) $\gamma(\bigcup_{n=1}^{\infty} X_n) = \sum_{n=1}^{\infty} \gamma(X_n)$ for all pairwise disjoint sequences $\{X_n\}_{n=1}^{\infty}$ of subsets of R.

iv) $\gamma([0,1[) = 1$.

Proof. In 2.3.49, the sets A_s all have the same γ-measure. We saw then that $[0,1[= \bigcup_{\substack{s \in Q \\ 0 \leq s < 1}} A_s$ where the A_s are pairwise disjoint. As before we have $1 = \gamma([0,1[) = \sum_{\substack{s \in Q \\ 0 \leq s < 1}} \gamma(A_s) = \begin{Bmatrix} 0 \\ \infty \end{Bmatrix}$.

2.6.11 Remark. A measure on R with properties i), ii), iv), of 2.6.1, and finite additivity, can be constructed. To do this, we need a famous theorem of functional analysis called the Hahn-Banach theorem.

2.6.2 Theorem. (Hahn-Banach) Let L be a real linear space and M be any proper subspace of L. Let p be a real-valued function on L such that

i) $p(\alpha x) = \alpha p(x)$ if $\alpha \geq 0$ and $x \in L$;

ii) $p(x + y) \leq p(x) + p(y)$ for all $x, y \in L$.

Let f be a linear functional defined only on M and such that $f(x) \leq p(x)$ for all $x \in M$. Then there is a linear functional F defined on L such that $F(x) \leq p(x)$ for all $x \in L$ and $F(x) = f(x)$ for all $x \in M$

(F is an extension of the functional f).

Proof. Step I. Let x_o be any element of $L \cap M'$. Let $M_{x_o} = \{y + \alpha x_o:\ y \in M,\ \alpha \in R\}$. We show that M_{x_o} is a linear subspace of L. It is evident from Definition 2.1.1 that we need only show that M_{x_o} is closed under addition and subtraction, and that if $\beta \in R$ and $z \in M_{x_o}$, then $\beta z \in M_{x_o}$. Now we have $(y_1 + \alpha_1 x_o) + (y_2 + \alpha_2 x_o) = (y_1 + y_2) + (\alpha_1 + \alpha_2)x_o \in M_{x_o}$ and $-(y + \alpha x_o) = (-y) + (-\alpha)x_o \in M_{x_o}$ so that M_{x_o} is closed under addition and subtraction. Now for $\beta \in R$, $y + \alpha x_o \in M_{x_o}$, we have $\beta(y + \alpha x_o) = \beta y + (\beta\alpha)x_o \in M_{x_o}$, since $\beta y \in M$ and $(\beta\alpha) \in R$. We now show that in the representation $y_1 + \alpha_1 x_o$ of an element of M_{x_o}, y_1 and α_1 are unique. If $y_1 + \alpha_1 x_o = y_2 + \alpha_2 x_o$, then $y_1 - y_2 = (\alpha_2 - \alpha_1)x_o$. If $\alpha_2 - \alpha_1 \neq 0$, then $x_o = \dfrac{y_1 - y_2}{\alpha_2 - \alpha_1} \in M$, contradicting the choice of x_o. Thus $\alpha_2 - \alpha_1 = 0$ and $y_1 - y_2 = 0$. Thus $\alpha_1 = \alpha_2$ and $y_1 = y_2$. Hence every element of M_{x_o} can be written in just one way in the form $y + \alpha x_o$, $y \in M$, $\alpha \in R$.

Consider $y', y'' \in M$. We have $f(y') - f(y'') = f(y' - y'') \leq p(y' - y'') = p[(y' + x_o) + (-y'' - x_o)] \leq p(y' + x_o) + p(-y'' - x_o)$. It follows that $-p(-y'' - x_o) - f(y'') \leq p(y' + x_o) - f(y')$. Consequently, we have

$\sup_{y \in M} [-p(-y - x_0) - f(y)] \leq \inf_{y \in M} [p(y + x_0) - f(y)]$.

Let $F(x_0)$ be any number such that $\sup_{y \in M} [-p(-y - x_0) - f(y)] \leq F(x_0) \leq \inf_{y \in M} [p(y + x_0) - f(y)]$. For all $y + \alpha x_0$, let $F(y + \alpha x_0) = f(y) + \alpha F(x_0)$. It is easy to see that F is linear and that F is an extension of f. We now show that $F(y + \alpha x_0) \leq p(y + \alpha x_0)$ for all $y + \alpha x_0 \varepsilon M_{x_0}$. If $\alpha = 0$, we have $F(y) = f(y) \leq p(y)$. If $\alpha > 0$, we have $F(x_0) \leq p(\frac{y}{\alpha} + x_0) - f(\frac{y}{\alpha}) = p(\frac{y + \alpha x_0}{\alpha}) - \frac{1}{\alpha} f(y) = \frac{1}{\alpha} p(y + \alpha x_0) - \frac{1}{\alpha} f(y)$. Multiplying through by α, we have $\alpha F(x_0) \leq p(y + \alpha x_0) - f(y)$, and thus $F(y + \alpha x_0) = f(y) + \alpha F(x_0) \leq p(y + \alpha x_0)$. If $\alpha < 0$, we have $F(x_0) \geq -p(-\frac{y}{\alpha} - x_0) - f(\frac{y}{\alpha}) = -p(-\frac{1}{\alpha}(y + \alpha x_0)) - \frac{1}{\alpha} f(y) = \frac{1}{\alpha} p(y + \alpha x_0) - \frac{1}{\alpha} f(y)$. Multiplying through by α, which is negative, we have $p(y + \alpha x_0) - f(y) \geq \alpha F(x_0)$ and hence $F(y + \alpha x_0) = f(y) + \alpha F(x_0) \leq p(y + \alpha x_0)$.

Hence we have proved that if f is a linear functional defined on a proper subspace M of L such that $f(x) \leq p(x)$ for all $x \varepsilon M$, then f can be extended linearly over a subspace of L that strictly contains M, while still being bounded above by p.

Step II. Let $Ж_p$ be the set of all linear functionals G such that

i) G is defined on a subspace N of L containing M;

ii) G is linear on N;

iii) G is an extension of f;

iv) $G(x) \leq p(x)$ for all $x \in N$.

For $G, G' \in \mathcal{K}_p$ we write $G \prec G'$ if G' is an extension of G. It is easy to see that $\prec$ is a partial ordering of $\mathcal{K}_p$. Clearly $f \in \mathcal{K}_p$, so that $\mathcal{K}_p$ is non-void. Suppose that $\{G_\iota\}_{\iota \in I}$ is a non-void completely ordered subset of $\mathcal{K}_p$; i.e., for all $\iota, \iota' \in I$, either $G_\iota \prec G_{\iota'}$ or $G_{\iota'} \prec G_\iota$. For each G_ι, let N_ι be the subspace on which G_ι is defined. It is clear that $G_{\iota'} \prec G_\iota$ implies that $N_{\iota'} \subset N_\iota$; thus $\{N_\iota\}_{\iota \in I}$ is completely ordered by inclusion. Let $N = \bigcup_{\iota \in I} N_\iota$; we show that N is a linear subspace. Let $x, y \in N$ and $\alpha, \beta \in R$. For some $\iota', \iota \in I$, $x \in N_\iota$, $y \in N_{\iota'}$. We may suppose that $N_\iota \subset N_{\iota'}$. Then $x, y \in N_{\iota'}$ and thus $\alpha x + \beta y \in N_{\iota'} \subset N$.

We now define a functional H on N. For all $x \in N$, let $H(x) = G_\iota(x)$, for any $\iota \in I$ such that $x \in N_\iota$. The functional H is well-defined, for suppose that $x \in N_\iota$, $x \in N_{\iota'}$. We may suppose that $N_\iota \subset N_{\iota'}$. Then $G_\iota \prec G_{\iota'}$ and $G_\iota(x) = G_{\iota'}(x)$. Let $x, y \in N$ and $\alpha, \beta \in R$. As above, there is an $\iota \in I$ such that $x, y \in N_\iota$. Thus $H(\alpha x + \beta y) = G_\iota(\alpha x + \beta y) = \alpha G_\iota(x) + \beta G_\iota(y) = \alpha H(x) + \beta H(y)$. Thus H is linear on N. H extends f since all the G_ι's do so, and for all $x \in N$, we have $H(x) = G_\iota(x) \leq p(x)$, where $x \in N_\iota$. Thus $H \in \mathcal{K}_p$;

evidently $H \succ G_\iota$ for all $\iota \varepsilon I$. Thus we have shown that every completely ordered subset of $\mathfrak{H}_p$ admits an upper bound in $\mathfrak{H}_p$.

By Theorem 1.5.7, $\mathfrak{H}_p$ contains a maximal element; that is, there exists a subspace $N \supset M$ and a linear functional H defined on N such that $H(x) \leq p(x)$ for all $x \varepsilon N$, H extends f, and no proper extension of H has all of these properties. By step I, it is clear that $N = L$; for otherwise H could be extended to an $H' \underset{\neq}{\succ} H$ with $H' \varepsilon \mathfrak{H}_p$, contradicting the maximality of H.

2.6.21 Theorem. Let L be a real linear space and p a real-valued functional on L such that $p(\alpha x) = \alpha p(x)$ whenever $\alpha \geq 0$, and $p(x + y) \leq p(x) + p(y)$. Then there exists a linear functional f on L such that $f(x) \leq p(x)$ for all $x \varepsilon L$.

Proof. We have $p(0) = p(0 \cdot x) = 0p(x) = 0$. Let $M = \{0\}$; clearly M is a linear subspace of L. Let $g(0) = 0$. Then g is linear on M and $g(x) \leq p(x)$ for all $x \varepsilon M$. By 2.6.2, there is a linear extension f of g on L such that $f(x) \leq p(x)$ for all $x \varepsilon L$.

2.6.3 Definition. Let $\mathfrak{B}(R)$ be the set of all bounded real-valued functions on R with addition and scalar multiplication defined point-wise. $\mathfrak{B}(R)$ is easily seen to be a linear space over R.

2.6.31 Definitions. For f any real-valued function and $t \in R$, let f_t be the function on R such that $f_t(x) = f(t+x)$ for all $x \in R$. The function f_t is called a translate of f and the mapping $f \to f_t$ is called translation.

For $\alpha \in R$, the symbol α will be used where needed to denote the function f such that $f(x) = \alpha$ for all x in the domain of f.

2.6.4 Theorem. Let $f \in \mathfrak{B}(R)$ and $\{a_1, \ldots, a_m\}$ be any finite sequence in R. We define $M_{a_1,\ldots,a_m}(f) =$ $\lim_{t\to\infty} [\sup \{\frac{1}{m} \sum_{i=1}^{m} f_{a_i}(x) : x \geq t\}]$, and $p(f) = \inf \{M_{a_1,\ldots,a_m}($ $\{a_1, \ldots, a_m\}$ is a finite sequence in $R\}$. Then

i) $\inf \{f(x): x \in R\} \leq p(f) \leq \sup \{f(x): x \in R\}$;

ii) $p(f) = \lim_{t\to\infty} f(t)$ if this limit exists;

iii) $p(\alpha f) = \alpha p(f)$ for all $f \in \mathfrak{B}(R)$ and $\alpha \geq 0$;

iv) $p(f+g) \leq p(f) + p(g)$ for all $f,g \in \mathfrak{B}(R)$;

v) $p(f_a - f) = p(f - f_a) = 0$ for all $f \in \mathfrak{B}(R)$ and $a \in R$.

Before proving this we state without proof three elementary lemmas.

2.6.41 Lemma. Let $A \subset R$, $A \neq 0$, and let $\alpha \geq 0$. Then $\sup \{\alpha x: x \in A\} = \alpha \sup A$.

2.6.42 Lemma. Let X be any set, and let F and G be real-valued functions on X. Then $\sup \{F(x) + G(x): x \in X\} \leq \sup \{F(x): x \in X\} + \sup \{G(x): x \in X\}$.

2.6.43 Lemma. For X and F as in 2.6.42 we have

$$\sup \{F(x): x \in X\} = -\inf \{-F(x): x \in X\}.$$

Proof of 2.6.4. To prove i), let $u = \inf \{f(x): x \in R\}$ and $v = \sup \{f(x): x \in R\}$. For any $\{a_1, \ldots, a_m\} \subset R$,

$$u = \lim_{t\to\infty} [\sup \{\frac{1}{m} \sum_{i=1}^{m} u\}] \leq \lim_{t\to\infty} [\sup\{\frac{1}{m} \sum_{i=1}^{m} f_{a_i}(x): x \geq t\}]$$

$$\leq \lim_{t\to\infty} [\sup \{\frac{1}{m}\sum_{i=1}^{m} v\}] = v.$$ Thus

clearly $u \leq p(f) \leq v$.

To prove ii), suppose that $\lim_{t\to\infty} f(t)$ exists and is equal to L; clearly L must be finite. Fix $\varepsilon > 0$. Then there is a T such that $|f(t) - L| < \varepsilon$ for $t \geq T$. For $i = 1, \ldots, m$, we have $-\varepsilon < f(x + a_i) - L < \varepsilon$ whenever $x + a_i \geq T$. Thus $L - \varepsilon < \frac{1}{m} \sum_{i=1}^{m} f(x + a_i) < L + \varepsilon$ whenever $x \geq \max [T - a_1, \ldots, T - a_m]$. Consequently,

$$L - \varepsilon \leq \lim_{t\to\infty} [\sup \{\frac{1}{m} \sum_{i=1}^{m} f_{a_i}(x): x \geq t\}] \leq L + \varepsilon.$$

Since ε is arbitrary, we have $M_{a_1,\ldots,a_m}(f) = L$. Thus $p(f) = L = \lim_{t\to\infty} f(t)$.

iii) follows immediately from 2.6.41.

We next prove iv). Let $\varepsilon > 0$. Choose $\{a_1, \ldots, a_m\}$ and $\{b_1, \ldots, b_n\}$ such that $M_{a_1,\ldots,a_m}(f) < p(f) + \frac{\varepsilon}{2}$ and $M_{b_1,\ldots,b_n}(g) < p(g) + \frac{\varepsilon}{2}$. Let

$$A = \lim_{t\to\infty} [\sup \{\frac{1}{mn} \sum_{i=1}^{m} \sum_{j=1}^{n} f_{a_i+b_j}(x): x \geq t\}]$$ and

$B = \lim_{t\to\infty} [\sup \{\frac{1}{mn} \sum_{i=1}^{m} \sum_{j=1}^{n} g_{a_i+b_j}(x): \; x \geq t\}]$. Using 2.6.42, we see that $A = \lim_{t\to\infty} [\sup\{\frac{1}{n} \sum_{j=1}^{n} \frac{1}{m} \sum_{i=1}^{m} f_{a_i}(x + b_j): x \geq t\}]$ $\leq \lim_{t\to\infty} [\frac{1}{n} \sum_{j=1}^{n} \sup \{\frac{1}{m} \sum_{i=1}^{m} f_{a_i}(x): \; x \geq t + b_j\}] =$ $\frac{1}{n} \sum_{j=1}^{n} \lim_{t\to\infty} [\sup \{\frac{1}{m} \sum_{i=1}^{m} f_{a_i}(x): \; x \geq t + b_j\}] =$ $\frac{1}{n} \cdot n\, M_{a_1,\ldots,a_m}(f) = M_{a_1,\ldots,a_m}(f) < p(f) + \frac{\varepsilon}{2}$. Similarly $B < p(g) + \frac{\varepsilon}{2}$. Using 2.6.42 again, we have $p(f + g) \leq$ $\lim_{t\to\infty} [\sup\{\frac{1}{mn} \sum_{i=1}^{m} \sum_{j=1}^{n} f_{a_i+b_j}(x) + \frac{1}{mn} \sum_{i=1}^{m} \sum_{j=1}^{n} g_{a_i+b_j}(x):$ $x \geq t\}] \leq A + B < p(f) + p(g) + \varepsilon$. Thus $p(f + g) \leq$ $p(f) + p(g)$ for all $f, g \in \mathfrak{B}(R)$.

Finally we prove v). We have $M_{0,a,2a,\ldots,(n-1)a}(f_a - f)$ $\lim_{t\to\infty} [\sup\{\frac{1}{n} (f(a+x) - f(x) + f(2a + x) - f(a + x) + \ldots +$ $f(na + x) - f((n - 1)\cdot a + x)): \; x \geq t\}] = \lim_{t\to\infty} [\sup$ $\{\frac{1}{n} (f(na + x) - f(x)): x \geq t\}] \leq \lim_{t\to\infty} [\frac{1}{n} \cdot 2 \sup \{f(x):$ $x \in R\}] = \frac{1}{n}\, 2 \sup \{f(x): \; x \in R\}$. Thus $p(f_a - f) \leq 0$, since $\frac{1}{n}\, 2 \sup \{f(x): \; x \in R\}$ can be made arbitrarily close to 0. We also have $p(f - f_a) = p((f_a)_{-a} - f_a) \leq 0$ or $-p(f - f_a) \geq 0$. Note that for all $h \in \mathfrak{B}(R)$, $-p(-h) \leq$ $p(h)$; this follows from the inequality $0 = p(0) =$ $p[h + (-h)] \leq p(h) + p(-h)$. Thus $0 \leq -p(f - f_a) \leq$ $p(f_a - f) \leq 0$, from which v) follows.

2.6.44 <u>Theorem</u>. There exists a linear functional F on $\mathfrak{B}(R)$

such that

i) $\inf f \leq F(f) \leq \sup f$ for all $f \in \mathfrak{B}(R)$;

ii) $F(\alpha) = \alpha$ for all $\alpha \in R$;

iii) $F(f) = \lim_{t\to\infty} f(t)$ whenever this limit exists;

iv) $F(f_a) = F(f)$ for all $f \in \mathfrak{B}(R)$ and $a \in R$.

Proof. Let p be as in 2.6.4. By 2.6.21, there exists a linear functional F on $\mathfrak{B}(R)$ such that $F(f) \leq p(f)$ for all $f \in \mathfrak{B}(R)$. Clearly $F(-f) \leq p(-f)$ for all $f \in \mathfrak{B}(R)$. Thus by 2.6.4, i),

$$\inf f \leq -p(-f) \leq F(f) \leq p(f) \leq \sup f,$$

the first inequality following from the inequality $p(-f) \leq \sup(-f)$ and 2.6.43. This proves i). The equality ii) follows from i), since $\alpha = \inf \alpha \leq F(\alpha) \leq \sup \alpha = \alpha$. To prove iii), write $\lim_{t\to\infty} f(t) = L$. By 2.6.4, ii), we have $p(f) = L$, $p(-f) = -L$, and $-p(-f) = L$. Since $-p(-f) \leq F(f) \leq p(f)$, iii) follows.

From 2.6.4, v), we infer that $0 = -p(f - f_a) \leq F(f_a - f) \leq p(f_a - f) = 0$. Thus we have iv).

2.6.5 Theorem. There exists a set-function γ defined for all subsets of R such that:

i) $0 \leq \gamma(A) \leq 1$ for all $A \subset R$;

ii) $\gamma(A) = 1$ if $[\alpha, \infty[\subset A$ for some $\alpha \in R$;

iii) $\gamma(A) = 0$ if A is bounded above;

iv) $\gamma(A \cup B) = \gamma(A) + \gamma(B)$ if $A \cap B = 0$;

v) $\gamma(A + b) = \gamma(A)$ for all $A \subset R$ and $b \in R$.

<u>Proof</u>. Let F be a linear functional on $\mathcal{B}(R)$ as described in 2.6.44. For each $A \subset R$, let χ_A be the characteristic function of A. Clearly each $\chi_A \in \mathcal{B}(R)$. For each $A \subset R$, let $\gamma(A) = F(\chi_A)$. Condition i) follows from 2.6.44, i); conditions ii) and iii) follow from 2.6.44, iii).

If $A \cap B = 0$, then $\chi_{A \cup B} = \chi_A + \chi_B$. Thus $\gamma(A \cup B) = F(\chi_{A \cup B}) = F(\chi_A + \chi_B) = F(\chi_A) + F(\chi_B) = \gamma(A) + \gamma(B)$. This proves condition iv). We verify condition v) as follows. We have

$$\chi_{A+b}(x) = \begin{Bmatrix} 1 & \text{if} & x \in A + b \\ 0 & \text{if} & x \notin A + b \end{Bmatrix} = \begin{Bmatrix} 1 & \text{if} & x - b \in A \\ 0 & \text{if} & x - b \notin A \end{Bmatrix} = \chi_A(x - b).$$

Thus $\chi_{A+b} = (\chi_A)_{-b}$. Hence
$\gamma(A + b) = F(\chi_{A+b}) = F((\chi_A)_{-b}) = F(\chi_A) = \gamma(A)$.

2.6.6 <u>Definition</u>. A real-valued function f on R is said to be periodic with period a if for all $x \in R$, $f(x + a) = f(x)$. A subset A of R is said to be periodic with period a if the function χ_A has period a.

2.6.61 <u>Theorem</u>. There exists a set-function δ defined for all subsets of R such that

i) $0 \leq \delta(A) \leq \infty$ for all $A \subset R$;

ii) $\delta(A \cup B) = \delta(A) + \delta(B)$ if $A \cap B = 0$;

iii) $\delta([0,1]) = 1$;

iv) $\delta(A + b) = \delta(A)$ for all $A \subset R$ and $b \in R$.

<u>Proof</u>. We will merely outline the proof; the details are

similar to those in the proofs of 2.6.4 - 2.6.5.

Let $\mathscr{P}(R)$ be the set of all bounded real-valued functions on R with period 1. Define $M_{a_1,\ldots,a_m}(f) = \sup \left\{ \frac{1}{m} \sum_{i=1}^{m} f_{a_i}(x) : x \in R \right\}$. For each $f \in \mathscr{P}(R)$, let $p(f) = \inf \left\{ M_{a_1,\ldots,a_m}(f) : \{a_1, \ldots, a_m\} \text{ is a finite subset of } R \right\}$. The functional p satisfies conditions i) - v) of 2.6.4 where, of course, f and g are restricted to $\mathscr{P}(R)$. By 2.6.21, there is a linear functional F on $\mathscr{P}(R)$ such that $F(f) \leq p(f)$ for all $f \in \mathscr{P}(R)$. The functional F satisfies conditions i), ii), and iv) of 2.6.44. For $A \in \mathscr{P}(R)$, we let $\delta_o(A) = F(\chi_A)$. For any subset B of R, let $B_n = \bigcup_{k=-\infty}^{\infty} (B \cap [n,n+1[+ k)$. We now define $\delta(B) = \sum_{n=-\infty}^{\infty} \delta_o(B_n)$. δ satisfies conditions i) - iv) of this theorem.

2.6.7 Remarks. Let λ' be the Kakutani-Oxtoby extension of Lebesgue measure discussed in 2.3.21. λ' is countably additive and translation invariant. The set $\mathcal{H}$ of all λ'-measurable sets is much larger than the set $\mathfrak{M}_\lambda$ of λ-measurable sets; we make this remark more precise in the following.

Let γ be a measure on a set X and let $\mathfrak{M}$ be the set of γ-measurable subsets of X. We will say that $\mathfrak{B} \subset \mathfrak{M}$ is a basis for $\mathfrak{M}$ if for every $A \in \mathfrak{M}$ and $\varepsilon > 0$, there exists $G \in \mathfrak{B}$ such that $\gamma((A \cap G') \cup$

$(A' \cap G)) < \varepsilon$.

Let $\mathcal{G}_\lambda$ be the set of all open subsets of R whose component intervals have rational end-points. It is easy to see that $\mathcal{G}_\lambda$ is a basis for $\mathcal{M}_\lambda$. Furthermore, $\mathcal{G}_\lambda$ is countable. However, any subfamily of $\mathcal{K}$ that is a basis for $\mathcal{K}$ must have cardinality 2^c. That is, $\mathcal{K}$ is an enormously larger measure space than the family of Lebesgue measurable sets.

2.6.8 Remarks. Let G be any group and $\mathcal{B}(G)$ be the set of all bounded real-valued functions on G. Let f_a and ${}_af$ be defined such that $f_a(x) = f(xa)$ and ${}_af(x) = f(ax)$ for all x. f_a and ${}_af$ are called right and left translates, respectively, of f. Consider the following question: When is there a linear functional F on $\mathcal{B}(G)$ such that

i) $F(1) = 1$;

ii) $F(f) \geq 0$ if $f \geq 0$;

iii) $F(f_a) = F({}_af) = F(f)$ for all $f \in \mathcal{B}(G)$ and $a \in G$?

If $G = \{x_1, \ldots, x_n\}$ then F where $F(f) = \frac{1}{n} \sum_{i=1}^{n} f(x_i)$ is the one and only such linear functional. If G is commutative, there exist such linear functionals and if G is infinite they are not unique. On the other hand, suppose that G contains a subgroup H that is a free group with two generators (that is, there are $a,b \in H$ such that H consists of all products

$$a^{n_1}b^{m_1}a^{n_2}b^{m_2}\ldots\ldots\ldots a^{n_k}b^{m_k},$$

where the n_i's and m_i's are arbitrary integers, and such a product is the group identity only if all n_i's and m_i's are zero). Then it can be shown that $\mathfrak{B}(G)$ admits no invariant mean. This theorem goes back to J. v. Neumann (Zur allgemeinen Theorie des Masses, Fund. Math. 13 (1929), 73-116), and is discussed in detail by J. Dixmier (Les moyennes invariantes dans les semi-groupes et leurs applications, Acta Sci. Math. Szeged 12, Pars A (1950), 213-227). The class of groups G for which $\mathfrak{B}(G)$ admits an invariant mean has not been completely characterized.

Chapter 3.

THE LEBESGUE INTEGRAL

3.1 Measurable functions. In this section X will be any set and $\mathcal{M}$ will be any σ-algebra of subsets of X. If μ is a countably additive function on $\mathcal{M}$ such that $0 \leq \mu(A) \leq \infty$ for $A \in \mathcal{M}$, we refer to the triple $(X, \mathcal{M}, \mu)$ as a measure space. For many of the results of this section, no measure μ is required.

Let P be any property of points of X that holds for all $x \in X$ except for a set of μ-measure 0. Then we will say that P holds almost everywhere (a.e.) on X.

3.1.1 Definition. Let f be a function on X with values in $R \cup \{-\infty, \infty\}$. The function f is said to be $\mathcal{M}$-measurable (measurable) if $\{x: x \in X, f(x) > a\} \in \mathcal{M}$ for all $a \in R$.

3.1.11 Remark. Definition 3.1.1 may be stated in the following form: The function f is $\mathcal{M}$-measurable if for all $a \in R$, $f^{-1}(]a, \infty]) \in \mathcal{M}$. This is analogous to the following characterization of continuity: A real-valued function f on R is continuous if, for all $a, b \in R$, $a < b$, $f^{-1}(]a,b[)$ is open. Thus in some respects measurable functions resemble continuous functions. There are fundamental relations between measurability and continuity; and from one point of view, the two concepts merge.

3.1.12 Theorem. The following conditions on f are equivalent to measurability:

i) $\{x: f(x) \leq a\} \in \mathfrak{M}$ for all $a \in R$;

ii) $\{x: f(x) < a\} \in \mathfrak{M}$ for all $a \in R$;

iii) $\{x: f(x) \geq a\} \in \mathfrak{M}$ for all $a \in R$.

Furthermore R can be replaced by any dense subset in 3.1.1 and i) - iii) above.

Proof. Suppose that f is measurable. Then $\{x: f(x) \leq a\} = \{x: f(x) > a\}' \in \mathfrak{M}$ for all $a \in R$. Thus measurability implies i). Suppose that i) holds. Then $\{x: f(x) < a\} = \bigcup_{n=1}^{\infty} \{x: f(x) \leq a - \frac{1}{n}\} \in \mathfrak{M}$ for all $a \in R$. Thus i) implies ii). Suppose that ii) holds. Then $\{x: f(x) \geq a\} = \{x: f(x) < a\}' \in \mathfrak{M}$ for all $a \in R$. Thus ii) implies iii). Finally, suppose that iii) holds. Then we have $\{x: f(x) > a\} = \bigcup_{n=1}^{\infty} \{x: f(x) \geq a + \frac{1}{n}\} \in \mathfrak{M}$ for all $a \in R$, and hence f is measurable.

We will show that R can be replaced by a dense subset D in 3.1.1. The analogous refinements in 3.1.12 are proved similarly. Trivially, if f is measurable, then $\{x: f(x) > a\} \in \mathfrak{M}$ for all $a \in D$. Suppose now that $\{x: f(x) > a\} \in \mathfrak{M}$ for all $a \in D$. For an arbitrary $b \in R$, there exists a sequence $\{a_n\}_{n=1}^{\infty}$ where each $a_n \in D$, $a_{n+1} < a_n$ for $n=1, 2, \ldots$, and $\lim_{n\to\infty} a_n = b$. Then $\{x: f(x) > b\} = \bigcup_{n=1}^{\infty} \{x: f(x) > a_n\} \in \mathfrak{M}$. Since b is arbitrary, we conclude that f is measurable.

3.1.13 <u>Theorem</u>. Let f be $\mathfrak{M}$-measurable. Then $\{x: f(x) = \infty\}$ $\varepsilon\ \mathfrak{M}$ and $\{x: f(x) = -\infty\} \ \varepsilon\ \mathfrak{M}$.

<u>Proof</u>. We have $\{x: f(x) = \infty\} = \bigcap_{n=1}^{\infty} \{x: f(x) > n\} \ \varepsilon\ \mathfrak{M}$

and $\{x: f(x) = -\infty\} = \bigcap_{n=1}^{\infty} \{x: f(x) < -n\} \ \varepsilon\ \mathfrak{M}$.

3.1.14 <u>Theorem</u>. Let f be $\mathfrak{M}$-measurable and α be any real number. Then the following functions are also $\mathfrak{M}$-measurable:

i) $f + \alpha$;

ii) αf;

iii) $|f|$;

iv) f^m for $m = 1, 2, \ldots$;

v) $|f|^\beta$ for β a positive real number;

vi) $\frac{1}{f}$ if $f(x)$ is finite and different from 0 for all $x \ \varepsilon\ X$;

vii) α.

<u>Proof</u>. For each $a \ \varepsilon\ R$, $\{x: f(x) + \alpha > a\} = \{x: f(x) > a -$ $\varepsilon\ \mathfrak{M}$. Therefore $f + \alpha$ is $\mathfrak{M}$-measurable. We now show that αf is $\mathfrak{M}$-measurable. If $\alpha = 0$, then

$$\{x: \alpha f(x) > a\} = \begin{cases} X \ \varepsilon\ \mathfrak{M} & \text{if } a < 0 \\ 0 \ \varepsilon\ \mathfrak{M} & \text{if } a \geq 0 \end{cases}.$$

If $\alpha > 0$, then $\{x: \alpha f(x) > a\} = \{x: f(x) > \frac{a}{\alpha}\} \ \varepsilon\ \mathfrak{M}$.

If $\alpha < 0$, $\{x: \alpha f(x) > a\} = \{x: f(x) < \frac{a}{\alpha}\} \ \varepsilon\ \mathfrak{M}$.

We have next

$$\{x: |f(x)| > a\} = \begin{cases} X \ \varepsilon\ \mathfrak{M} \text{ if } a < 0 \\ \{x: f(x) > a\} \cup \{x: f(x) < -a\} \ \varepsilon\ \mathfrak{M} \text{ if } a \end{cases}$$

Thus $|f|$ is $\mathfrak{M}$-measurable.

The proofs of iv) - vii) are omitted.

3.1.21 Theorem. Let f and g be $\mathcal{M}$-measurable. Then the sets $\{x: f(x) > g(x)\}$, $\{x: f(x) = g(x)\}$, $\{x: f(x) < g(x)\}$, $\{x: f(x) \geq g(x)\}$, and $\{x: f(x) \leq g(x)\}$ are in $\mathcal{M}$.

Proof. we have

$$\{x: f(x) > g(x)\} = \bigcup_{u \in Q} (\{x: g(x) < u\} \cap \{x: f(x) > u\})$$

$\varepsilon\ \mathcal{M}$. The rest of the theorem follows at once from this.

3.1.22 Theorem. Let f and g be $\mathcal{M}$-measurable and suppose that $f + g$ does not assume an undefined form for any $x \in X$ (that is, $(+\infty) + (-\infty)$). Then $f + g$ is $\mathcal{M}$-measurable.

Proof. We have $\{x: f(x) + g(x) > a\} = \{x: f(x) > a - g(x)\}$. Since $a - g$ is $\mathcal{M}$-measurable, we may apply 3.1.21 to see that $\{x: f(x) > a - g(x)\} \in \mathcal{M}$. Thus $f + g$ is $\mathcal{M}$-measurable.

3.1.23 Theorem. Let f and g be $\mathcal{M}$-measurable. Then fg is $\mathcal{M}$-measurable.

Proof. Let $a < 0$. Then $\{x: f(x)g(x) > a\} = \{x: f(x)$ and $g(x)$ are finite and $\frac{1}{4}([f(x) + g(x)]^2 - [f(x) - g(x)]^2) > a\} \cup \{x: f(x) = 0\} \cup \{x: g(x) = 0\} \cup \{x: f(x) = +\infty$ and $g(x) > 0\} \cup \{x: g(x) = +\infty$ and $f(x) > 0\} \cup \{x: f(x) = -\infty$ and $g(x) < 0\} \cup \{x: g(x) = -\infty$ and $f(x) < 0\}$. Thus $\{x: f(x)g(x) > a\} \in \mathcal{M}$. A similar expression shows that $\{x: f(x)g(x) > a\} \in \mathcal{M}$ for $a \geq 0$.

3.1.24 Theorem. Let f,g be $\mathcal{M}$-measurable. Then $\min(f,g)$ and $\max(f,g)$ are $\mathcal{M}$-measurable.

Proof. Where $f(x)$ and $g(x)$ are finite, we have

$\max(f(x),g(x)) = \dfrac{|f(x) - g(x)| + f(x) + g(x)}{2}$ and

$\min(f(x),g(x)) = \dfrac{-|f(x) - g(x)| + f(x) + g(x)}{2}$. The

proof now proceeds as in 3.1.23.

3.1.3 Theorem. Let $\{f_n\}_{n=1}^{\infty}$ be any sequence of $\mathcal{M}$-measurable functions. Then $\sup f_n$, $\inf f_n$, $\overline{\lim}_{n\to\infty} f_n$, and $\underline{\lim}_{n\to\infty} f_n$ are $\mathcal{M}$-measurable.

Proof. Since, for each $a \in R$, $\{x: \sup f_n(x) > a\} = \bigcup_{n=1}^{\infty} \{x: f_n(x) > a\} \in \mathcal{M}$, $\sup f_n$ is $\mathcal{M}$-measurable.

Since $\{x: \inf f_n(x) < a\} = \bigcup_{n=1}^{\infty}\{x: f_n(x) < a\} \in \mathcal{M}$, $\inf f_n$ is $\mathcal{M}$-measurable. Since $\overline{\lim}_{n\to\infty} f_n = \inf_k \{\sup\{f_k, f_{k+1}, \ldots\}\}$ and $\underline{\lim}_{n\to\infty} f_n = \sup_k \{\inf\{f_k, f_{k+1}, \ldots\}\}$, we see that $\overline{\lim}_{n\to\infty} f_n$ and $\underline{\lim}_{n\to\infty} f_n$ are $\mathcal{M}$-measurable.

3.1.31 Theorem. Let $(X, \mathcal{M}, \mu)$ be a measure space with the property that every subset of a set of μ-measure 0 is in $\mathcal{M}$. Let $\{f_n\}_{n=1}^{\infty}$ be a sequence of $\mathcal{M}$-measurable functions on X that converge almost everywhere on X to a function F. Then F is $\mathcal{M}$-measurable.

Proof. Let $A = \{x: x \in X, f_n(x) \not\to F(x)\}$. Then $\mu(A) = 0$. Therefore A' and all subsets of A are in $\mathcal{M}$. Also by 3.1.3, we have $\{x: \overline{\lim}_{n\to\infty} f_n(x) > a\} \in \mathcal{M}$. Consequently, for all $a \in R$, $\{x: F(x) > a\} = (\{x: \overline{\lim}_{n\to\infty} f_n(x) > a\} \cap A') \cup (\{x: F(x) > a\} \cap A) \in \mathcal{M}$.

3.1.32 Remarks. Theorem 3.1.31 is true for any X and $\mathfrak{M}$ if $f_n(x) \to F(x)$ for all $x \in X$. Also, suppose $(X, \mathfrak{M}, \mu)$ is a measure space not having the property that all subsets of sets of measure 0 are measurable. Then we may adjoin these sets to $\mathfrak{M}$, give each of them measure 0, and still have a countably additive measure.

3.1.33 Theorem. Let F be $\mathfrak{M}$-measurable on $(X, \mathfrak{M}, \mu)$ where all subsets of sets of measure 0 are measurable. If G is any function such that $G(x) = F(x)$ except for a set of measure 0, then G is $\mathfrak{M}$-measurable.

The proof is like that of 3.1.31.

3.1.4 Lemma. Let $(X, \mathfrak{M}, \mu)$ be a measure space with $\mu(X) < \infty$ and let $\{f_n\}_{n=1}^{\infty}$ be a sequence of $\mathfrak{M}$-measurable functions, finite almost everywhere on X, and such that $f_n(x) \to f(x)$ almost everywhere on X, where f is finite almost everywhere. Let ε and η be any positive real numbers. Then there exists $J \in \mathfrak{M}$ and a positive integer N such that $|f_n(x) - f(x)| < \varepsilon$ for all $x \in J$ and all $n \geq N$, and $\mu(J') < \eta$.

Proof. Let $E = \{x\colon\ x \in X,\ f_n(x)$ is finite for $n = 1, 2, \ldots,\ f(x)$ is finite, and $f_n(x) \to f(x)\}$. E' is the union of a countable number of sets of measure 0 and therefore has measure 0. For each positive integer m let $E_m = \{x\colon\ x \in E,\ |f_n(x) - f(x)| < \varepsilon$ for all $n \geq m\}$. Note that each $E_m \in \mathfrak{M}$. We have $E_1 \subset E_2 \subset \ldots \subset E_m \subset \ldots$ and $E = \bigcup_{m=1}^{\infty} E_m$. Consequently, $E_1' \supset E_2' \supset \ldots \supset E_m' \supset$

. . . . Since $\mu(E_1') < \infty$, we have $\lim_{m\to\infty} \mu(E_m') = \mu(\bigcap_{m=1}^{\infty} E_m') = \mu(E') = 0$ by 2.4.3. Let N be a positive integer such that $\mu(E_N') < \eta$. Let $J = E_N$. By the definition of E_N, we have $|f_n(x) - f(x)| < \varepsilon$ for all $x \in J = E_N$ and all $n \geq N$. Clearly, $\mu(J') = \mu(E_N') < \eta$.

3.1.41 Theorem. (Lebesgue) Let $(X, \mathcal{M}, \mu)$, $\{f_n\}_{n=1}^{\infty}$, and f be as in 3.1.4. Let ε be any positive real number. Then $\lim_{n\to\infty} \mu\{x: x \in X, |f_n(x) - f(x)| \geq \varepsilon\} = 0$.

Proof. For each positive integer n, let $S_n(\varepsilon) = \{x: x \in X, |f_n(x) - f(x)| \geq \varepsilon\}$. Let η be an arbitrary positive number. By 3.1.4 there are a set $J \in \mathcal{M}$ and a positive integer N such that $|f_n(x) - f(x)| < \varepsilon$ for all $x \in J$ and $n \geq N$, and $\mu(J') < \eta$. Thus for $n \geq N$, $S_n(\varepsilon) \subset J'$. Hence $\mu S_n(\varepsilon) \leq \mu(J') < \eta$ for $n \geq N$. Since η is arbitrary, we have $\lim_{n\to\infty} \mu S_n(\varepsilon) = 0$.

3.1.42 Definition. Let $(X, \mathcal{M}, \mu)$ be an arbitrary measure space and $\{f_n\}_{n=1}^{\infty}$ be a sequence of measurable functions finite a.e. Then the sequence $\{f_n\}_{n=1}^{\infty}$ is said to converge in measure to the function f if

$\lim_{n\to\infty} \mu\{x: |f_n(x) - f(x)| \geq \varepsilon\} = 0$ for all $\varepsilon > 0$.

Remark. Theorem 3.1.41 can now be stated as follows. In a measure space with total measure finite, convergence a.e. implies convergence in measure. The hypothesis that $\mu(X) < \infty$ cannot be dropped. For consider the sequence

$\{f_n\}_{n=1}^{\infty}$ of functions on R such that $f_n(x) = \begin{Bmatrix} 1 \text{ if } x \geq n \\ 0 \text{ if } x < n \end{Bmatrix}$. ($X = R$, μ is Lebesgue measure, and $\mathfrak{M}$ is the family of Lebesgue measurable sets.) Then $f_n \to 0$ everywhere but $\lim_{n\to\infty} \mu\{x: |f_n(x) - 0| \geq \frac{1}{2}\} = \infty$.

We also have the following properties of convergence in measure:

i) if $f_n \to f(\text{meas})$ and $f_n \to g(\text{meas})$, then $f = g$ a.e.;

ii) if $f_n \to f(\text{meas})$ and $g_n \to g(\text{meas})$, then $f_n + g_n \to f + g(\text{meas})$;

if $\mu(X) < \infty$, then $f_n g_n \to fg(\text{meas})$.

3.1.43 Theorem. (Egorov) Let $(X, \mathfrak{M}, \mu)$, $\{f_n\}_{n=1}^{\infty}$, and f be as in 3.1.4. For every $\eta > 0$, there exists a $Q \in \mathfrak{M}$ such that $f_n(x) \to f(x)$ uniformly on Q and $\mu(Q') < \eta$.

Proof. By 3.1.4, for each positive integer m there exist a set $J_m \in \mathfrak{M}$ and a positive integer N_m such that $\mu(J_m') < \frac{\eta}{2^m}$ and $|f_n(x) - f(x)| < \frac{1}{m}$ if $n \geq N_m$ and $x \in J_m$. Let $Q = \bigcap_{m=1}^{\infty} J_m$. We have $\mu(Q') = \mu(\bigcup_{m=1}^{\infty} J_m') \leq \sum_{m=1}^{\infty} \mu(J_m') < \sum_{m=1}^{\infty} \frac{\eta}{2^m} = \eta$. Also we have $|f_n(x) - f(x)| < \frac{1}{m}$ for all $x \in Q$ if $n \geq N_m$. Thus $f_n \to f$ uniformly on Q.

3.1.5 Theorem. (F. Riesz) Let $(X, \mathfrak{M}, \mu)$ be an arbitrary measure space and let the sequence $\{f_n\}_{n=1}^{\infty}$ of measurable functions converge in measure to f. Then there exists a subsequence $\{f_{n_k}\}_{k=1}^{\infty}$ such that $\{f_{n_k}\}_{k=1}^{\infty} \to f$ almost everywhere.

<u>Proof</u>. For every $\varepsilon > 0$ we have $\lim_{n\to\infty} \mu\{x: |f_n(x) - f(x)| \geq \varepsilon\} = 0$. Choose n_1 such that $\mu\{x: |f_{n_1}(x) - f(x)| \geq 1\} < \frac{1}{2}$. Suppose $n_1, n_2, \ldots, n_k$ have been chosen. Then choose n_{k+1} such that $n_{k+1} > n_k$ and $\mu\{x: |f_{n_{k+1}}(x) - f(x)| \geq \frac{1}{k+1}\} < \frac{1}{2^{k+1}}$. Let $R_j = \bigcup_{k=j}^{\infty} \{x: |f_{n_k}(x) - f(x)| \geq \frac{1}{k}\}$ $(j = 1, 2, 3, \ldots)$. Clearly we have $R_1 \supset R_2 \supset \ldots \supset R_j \supset \ldots$. Next, let $Q = \bigcap_{j=1}^{\infty} R_j$. Since $\mu(R_1) \leq \sum_{k=1}^{\infty} \frac{1}{2^k} < \infty$, we have by 2.4.3 that

$$\mu(Q) = \lim_{j\to\infty} \mu(R_j) \leq \lim_{j\to\infty} \sum_{k=j}^{\infty} \frac{1}{2^k} = \lim_{j\to\infty} \frac{1}{2^{j-1}} = 0.$$

Hence $\mu(Q) = 0$.

Let $x \varepsilon Q' = \bigcup_{j=1}^{\infty} R'_j$. Then there exists a j_x such that $x \varepsilon R'_{j_x} = \bigcap_{k=j_x}^{\infty} \{x: |f_{n_k}(x) - f(x)| < \frac{1}{k}\}$. Therefore if $k \geq j_x$, $|f_{n_k}(x) - f(x)| < \frac{1}{k}$. Thus $f_{n_k} \to f$ on Q'; that is, $f_{n_k} \to f$ a.e.

3.1.6 <u>Exercises</u>.

3.1.61 <u>Exercise</u>. Let X be the union of a countable number of sets of finite measure. (Such a measure space is called σ-finite.) Let $\{f_n\}_{n=1}^{\infty}$ be a sequence of measurable functions finite a.e. such that $\{f_n\}_{n=1}^{\infty} \to f$ a.e. and f is finite a.e. Then $X = H \cup E_1 \cup E_2 \cup \ldots$ where $\mu(H) = 0$ and $\{f_n\}_{n=1}^{\infty} \to f$ uniformly on each E_n.

3.1.62 Final Exercise # 10. Let $X = [0,1]$ and for $A \subset X$ let $\mu(A) = \begin{cases} \bar{\bar{A}} & \text{if } \bar{\bar{A}} < \aleph_0 \\ \infty & \text{if } \bar{\bar{A}} \geq \aleph_0 \end{cases}$.

i) Let $\mathfrak{M}$ be the set of all subsets of X. Prove that μ is a countably additive measure on $(X, \mathfrak{M})$.

ii) Find a sequence of continuous functions $\{g_n\}_{n=1}^{\infty}$ on $[0,1]$ such that $\{g_n\}_{n=1}^{\infty} \to g$ everywhere but $\{g_n\}_{n=1}^{\infty} \to g$ uniformly on no proper subinterval of $[0,1]$.

iii) Prove that 3.1.61 fails for this measure space $(X, \mathfrak{M}, \mu)$ and sequence $\{g_n\}_{n=1}^{\infty}$.

Hint: Show that the E_n can be taken closed and that at least one E_n contains an interval.

3.2 Structure of measurable functions. Throughout this section $(X, \mathfrak{M}, \mu)$ will be an arbitrary measure space.

3.2.1 Definition. A simple function ϕ is a function that assumes only a finite number of values. If $\alpha_1, \ldots, \alpha_n$ are the values assumed, we may write $\phi = \sum_{k=1}^{n} \alpha_k \chi_{A_k}$, where A_k is the set on which ϕ takes the value α_k.

3.2.11 Remark. It is easy to see that sums, products, and differences of simple functions are simple, whenever they are defined. It is also evident that a simple function $\phi = \sum_{k=1}^{n} \alpha_k \chi_{A_k}$ is measurable if and only if each $A_k \in \mathfrak{M}$.

3.2.12 Theorem. Let f be a measurable function on X. Then there exists a sequence $\{\phi_n\}_{n=1}^{\infty}$ of bounded, measurable, simple functions such that $\phi_n(x) \to f(x)$ everywhere. If $f \geq 0$, we can choose the sequence $\{\phi_n\}_{n=1}^{\infty}$ such that $\phi_n \leq \phi_{n+1}$ for all n.

Proof. i) Suppose $f \geq 0$. For each positive integer n let

$$\phi_n(x) = \begin{cases} \frac{j}{2^n} & \text{if } \frac{j}{2^n} \leq f(x) < \frac{j+1}{2^n} \text{ and } j = 0, 1, \ldots, n2^n-1 \\ n & \text{if } f(x) \geq n. \end{cases}$$

It is clear that the sequence $\{\phi_n\}_{n=1}^{\infty}$ has all the properties we need.

ii) Suppose f is an arbitrary measurable function. Let $f^+ = \max(f,0)$ and $f^- = -\min(f,0)$. Then f^+ and f^- are measurable and non-negative. Furthermore $f = f^+ - f^-$. By i) there exist sequences $\{\phi_n\}_{n=1}^{\infty}$ and $\{\psi_n\}_{n=1}^{\infty}$ of bounded, simple, measurable functions such that $\phi_n \to f^+$ and $\psi_n \to f^-$. We see at once that the sequence $\{\phi_n - \psi_n\}_{n=1}^{\infty}$ has all the needed properties.

3.2.13 Theorem. (Luzin) Let f be a Lebesgue measurable (λ-measurable) function defined on $[a,b]$ that is finite a.e. Then for every $\delta > 0$, there exists a continuous function ϕ on $[a,b]$ such that $\lambda\{x: f(x) \neq \phi(x)\} < \delta$.

Proof. We refer the reader to Theorem 4, page 106, Natanson.

3.3 Definition of the Lebesgue integral.

3.3.1 Definition. A dissection of X is a finite family of pairwise disjoint sets, $\{A_k\}_{k=1}^{n}$, such that $X = \bigcup_{k=1}^{n} A_k$.

A dissection is said to be measurable if each A_k is measurable.

3.3.2 Definition. Let $(X, \mathcal{M}, \mu)$ be an arbitrary measure space and f be any non-negative function on X. Then the Lebesgue integral of f, denoted by $L(f)$, is defined as follows:

$$L(f) = \sup\left\{\sum_{k=1}^{n} \inf\,[f(x):\ x \in E_k]\mu(E_k):\ \{E_k\}_{k=1}^{n} \text{ is a measurable dissection of } X\right\}.$$

3.3.21 Examples. i) If f is a constant function, say α, then $L(f) = \alpha\mu(X)$.

ii) If $f = +\infty$ on a measurable set E of positive measure, then $L(f) = +\infty$.

iii) If $X = [a,b]$, λ is Lebesgue measure, and f is Riemann integrable on $[a,b]$, then $L(f) \geq \int_a^b f(x)dx$. To see this, consider the lower Darboux integral.

3.3.22 Exercise. Let f and g be non-negative functions on X. Prove $L(f + g) \geq L(f) + L(g)$.

3.3.3 Definition. Let $f = f^+ - f^-$ be any function on X such that either $L(f^+)$ or $L(f^-)$ is finite. Then we define $L(f) = L(f^+) - L(f^-)$.

3.3.31 Theorem. Let $f = \sum_{k=1}^{n} \alpha_k \chi_{A_k}$ be a measurable simple function such that $L(f)$ exists. Then $L(f) = \sum_{k=1}^{n} \alpha_k\mu(A_k)$.

Proof. Suppose first that $f \geq 0$. The family $\{A_k\}_{k=1}^{n}$ is a dissection of X. Since $\inf\{f(x): x \in A_k\} = \alpha_k$, we have $L(f) \geq \sum_{k=1}^{n} \alpha_k\mu(A_k)$. Now let $\{B_j\}_{j=1}^{m}$ be an arbitrary measurable dissection of X. Then

$$\sum_{j=1}^{m} \inf\{f(x): x \in B_j\} \mu(B_j) = \sum_{j=1}^{m} \sum_{k=1}^{n} \inf\{f(x): x \in B_j\} \cdot \mu(A_k \cap B_j) \leq \sum_{j=1}^{m} \sum_{k=1}^{n} \inf\{f(x): x \in A_k \cap B_j\} \mu(A_k \cap B_j) = \sum_{j=1}^{m} \sum_{k=1}^{n} \alpha_k\mu(A_k \cap B_j) = \sum_{k=1}^{n} \alpha_k\mu(A_k).$$

Thus we obtain $L(f) \leq \sum_{k=1}^{n} \alpha_k\mu(A_k)$ and hence $L(f) = \sum_{k=1}^{n} \alpha_k\mu(A_k)$ for $f \geq 0$.

The general result now follows by writing $f = f^+ - f^-$ and applying the definition of the integral.

3.3.32 Note. The statement of 3.3.31 remains true even if $\alpha_k = \alpha_m$ for some indices k, m such that $k \neq m$.

3.3.4 Theorem. Let f and g be any non-negative functions on X. If $f(x) \leq g(x)$ for all $x \in X$, then $L(f) \leq L(g)$

We omit the proof.

3.3.5 Theorem. If $f(x) = 0$ a.e. then $L(f) = 0$.

Proof. Exercise.

3.3.6 Theorem. Let f be a non-negative measurable function. If $\mu\{x: x \in X, f(x) > 0\} > 0$, then $L(f) > 0$.

Proof. We will find a set $A \in \mathfrak{M}$ and a positive number α such that $\mu(A) > 0$ and $f(x) \geq \alpha$ for all $x \in A$. Then $L(f) \geq \inf\{f(x): x \in A\} \mu(A) + \inf\{f(x): x \in A'\} \cdot \mu(A') \geq \alpha\mu(A) > 0$.

For each positive integer n, let $A_n = \{x: x \in X, f(x) \geq \frac{1}{n}\}$. We have $A_1 \subset A_2 \subset \ldots \subset A_n \subset \ldots$ and $\bigcup_{n=1}^{\infty} A_n = \{x: x \in X, f(x) > 0\}$. By 2.4.2, $\lim_{n\to\infty} \mu(A_n) = \mu(\bigcup_{n=1}^{\infty} A_n) > 0$. Thus for some positive integer n_o, we have $\mu(A_{n_o}) > 0$ and $f(x) \geq \frac{1}{n_o}$ on A_{n_o}.

3.4 Linearity of the integral. In this section, we shall find a large space of functions on which L is linear: $L(\alpha f + \beta g) = \alpha L(f) + \beta L(g)$.

3.4.1 Theorem. Let f and g be non-negative, simple, measurable functions. Then $L(f + g) = L(f) + L(g)$.

Proof. Write $f = \sum_{j=1}^{m} \alpha_j \chi_{A_j}$ and $g = \sum_{k=1}^{n} \beta_k \chi_{B_k}$. Then $f + g = \sum_{j=1}^{m} \sum_{k=1}^{n} (\alpha_j + \beta_k) \chi_{(A_j \cap B_k)}$. Thus by 3.3.32, we have $L(f + g) = \sum_{j=1}^{m} \sum_{k=1}^{n} (\alpha_j + \beta_k)\mu(A_j \cap B_k) =$

$$\sum_{j=1}^{m} \sum_{k=1}^{n} \alpha_j \mu(A_j \cap B_k) + \sum_{k=1}^{n} \sum_{j=1}^{m} \beta_k \mu(A_j \cap \beta_k) =$$

$$\sum_{j=1}^{m} \alpha_j \mu(A_j \cap (\bigcup_{k=1}^{n} B_k)) + \sum_{k=1}^{n} \beta_k \mu(B_k \cap (\bigcup_{j=1}^{m} A_j)) =$$

$$\sum_{j=1}^{m} \alpha_j \mu(A_j) + \sum_{k=1}^{n} \beta_k \mu(B_k) = L(f) + L(g).$$

3.4.11 Theorem. Let f be a non-negative, simple, measurable function. Let t be a non-negative real number. Then $L(tf) = tL(f)$.

Proof. This is obvious.

3.4.2 Theorem. Let $\{g_n\}_{n=1}^{\infty}$ be an increasing sequence of simple, measurable, non-negative functions. Let h be any simple, measurable, non-negative function such that $h(x) \leq \lim_{n\to\infty} g_n(x)$ for all $x \varepsilon X$. Then $\lim_{n\to\infty} L(g_n) \geq L(h)$.

<u>Proof</u>. Let $h = \sum_{k=1}^{m} \gamma_k \chi_{E_k}$ where $0 \leq \gamma_1 < \gamma_2 < \ldots < \gamma_m \leq +\infty$. We may suppose $\gamma_1 > 0$, for if $\gamma_1 = 0$, we can replace X by $E_2 \cup \ldots \cup E_m$ and carry out the proof on this set.

Case I. Suppose that $\gamma_m < \infty$ and $\mu(X) < \infty$. Let ε be a positive number such that $\varepsilon < \gamma_1$. For every positive integer n, let $Q_n = \{x: x \varepsilon X, g_n(x) > h(x) - \varepsilon\}$ It is evident that $\bigcup_{n=1}^{\infty} Q_n = X$ and that $Q_1 \subset Q_2 \subset \ldots \subset Q_n \subset \ldots$. Thus, by 2.4.2, $\lim_{n\to\infty} \mu(Q_n) = \mu(X)$. Hence $\lim_{n\to\infty} \mu(Q_n') = 0$. We have, by 3.3.4,
$L(g_n) \geq L(g_n \cdot \chi_{Q_n}) \geq L((h - \varepsilon)\chi_{Q_n}) = L(h \cdot \chi_{Q_n} - \varepsilon \cdot \chi_{Q_n}) = L(h \cdot \chi_{Q_n}) - \varepsilon\mu(Q_n)$. Since $h \leq h \cdot \chi_{Q_n} + \gamma_m \cdot \chi_{Q_n'}$ we have $L(h) \leq L(h \cdot \chi_{Q_n}) + \gamma_m\mu(Q_n')$. Consequently, $L(g_n) \geq L(h) - \gamma_m\mu(Q_n') - \varepsilon\mu(Q_n) \geq L(h) - \gamma_m\mu(Q_n') - \varepsilon\mu(X)$. Since ε is arbitrary and $\mu(X) < \infty$, we conclude that $L(g_n) \geq L(h) - \gamma_m\mu(Q_n')$. Thus $\lim_{n\to\infty} L(g_n) \geq \lim_{n\to\infty} \{L(h) - \gamma_m\mu(Q_n')\} = L(h) - \gamma_m \lim_{n\to\infty} \mu(Q_n') = L(h)$.

Case II. Suppose that $\mu(X) = \infty$ and $\gamma_m < \infty$. Choose ε and define Q_n as above. For $x \varepsilon Q_n$, we have $g_n(x) \geq h(x) - \varepsilon \geq \gamma_1 - \varepsilon$. Hence $g_n \geq g_n \cdot \chi_{Q_n} \geq (\gamma_1 - \varepsilon)\chi_{Q_n}$. By 3.3.4, we have $L(g_n) \geq (\gamma_1 - \varepsilon)\mu(Q_n)$

and thus, using 2.4.2, we have $\lim_{n\to\infty} L(g_n) \geq (\gamma_1 - \varepsilon)\cdot \lim_{n\to\infty} \mu(Q_n) = (\gamma_1 - \varepsilon)\mu(X) = \infty \geq L(h)$.

Case III. Suppose that $\gamma_m = \infty$ and $\mu(X)$ is arbitrary. Suppose that $\mu(E_m) > 0$. Let γ be any positive number exceeding γ_{m-1}. Let $h_\gamma = \sum_{k=1}^{m-1} \gamma_k \chi_{E_k} + \gamma\chi_{E_m}$. Then clearly we have $h_\gamma \leq h \leq \lim_{n\to\infty} g_n$. Hence $\lim_{n\to\infty} L(g_n) \geq L(h_\gamma) \geq \gamma\mu(E_m)$. Since γ is arbitrary, we see that $\lim_{n\to\infty} L(g_n) = \infty \geq L(h)$.

Suppose finally that $\mu(E_m) = 0$. Let $B = E_1 \cup \ldots \cup E_{m-1}$. Applying case I or case II to $\{g_n \cdot \chi_B\}_{n=1}^{\infty}$, $h \cdot \chi_B$, and B we see that $\lim_{n\to\infty} L(g_n \cdot \chi_B) \geq L(h \cdot \chi_B)$. Now $L(h\cdot\chi_{B'}) = L(h\cdot\chi_{E_m}) = L(\gamma_m \cdot \chi_{E_m}) = \infty \cdot \mu(E_m) = \infty \cdot 0 = 0$. Consequently, applying 3.4.1, we have $L(h) = L(h \cdot \chi_B) + L(h\cdot \chi_{B'}) = L(h \cdot \chi_B) \leq \lim_{n\to\infty} L(g_n \cdot \chi_B) \leq \lim_{n\to\infty} L(g_n)$.

3.4.21 <u>Theorem</u>. Let $\{g_n\}_{n=1}^{\infty}$ be as in 3.4.2 and write $\lim_{n\to\infty} g_n = g$. Then $L(g) = \lim_{n\to\infty} L(g_n)$.

<u>Proof</u>. Let $\{E_k\}_{k=1}^{m}$ be an arbitrary measurable dissection of X, and write $\gamma_k = \inf\{g(x): x \in E_k\}$. Then we have $g \geq \sum_{k=1}^{m} \gamma_k\chi_{E_k}$. By 3.4.2 and 3.3.31, we have $\lim_{n\to\infty} L(g_n) \geq L(\sum_{k=1}^{m} \gamma_k\chi_{E_k}) = \sum_{k=1}^{m} \gamma_k \mu(E_k)$. By 3.3.2, we see that $L(g) = \sup\left\{\sum_{k=1}^{m} \gamma_k\mu(E_k): \{E_k\}_{k=1}^{m}\right.$ is a measurable dissection of $\left. X\right\}$, and thus $L(g) \leq \lim_{n\to\infty} L(g_n)$. Since $g_n \leq g$

for all positive integers n, we have $L(g_n) \leq L(g)$ for all n. Consequently $\lim_{n\to\infty} L(g_n) \leq L(g)$. Hence $L(g) = \lim_{n\to\infty} L(g_n)$.

3.4.3 __Theorem.__ Let f and g be non-negative measurable functions. Then $L(f + g) = L(f) + L(g)$.

__Proof.__ Let $\{f_n\}_{n=1}^{\infty}$ and $\{g_n\}_{n=1}^{\infty}$ be, respectively, increasing sequences of simple, measurable, non-negative functions such that $\lim_{n\to\infty} f_n = f$ and $\lim_{n\to\infty} g_n = g$ (see 3.2.12). We have $f_n + g_n \to f + g$ and $L(f_n + g_n) = L(f_n) + L(g_n)$ for all n. Consequently, $L(f_n + g_n) \to L(f + g)$ and by 3.4.21 we have $L(f_n) \to L(f)$ and $L(g_n) \to L(g)$. Hence $L(f + g) = L(f) + L(g)$.

3.4.4 __Theorem.__ Let f be a non-negative measurable function and let $\alpha \in R$, $\alpha \geq 0$. Then $L(\alpha f) = \alpha L(f)$.

We omit the proof.

3.4.5 __Definition.__ Let $(X, \mathcal{L}, \mu)$ (often written $\mathcal{L}$) be the set of all measurable functions f on X such that $-\infty < L(f) < +\infty$.

3.4.6 __Theorem.__ Let $f \in \mathcal{L}$ and let $f = f_1 - f_2$ where f_1 and f_2 are non-negative functions in $\mathcal{L}$. Then $L(f) = L(f_1) - L(f_2)$.

__Proof.__ Clearly $f = f_1 - f_2 = f^+ - f^-$. Thus $f^+ + f_2 = f_1 + f^-$, and hence $L(f^+ + f_2) = L(f_1 + f^-)$. By 3.4.3, we have $L(f^+) + L(f_2) = L(f_1) + L(f^-)$ and consequently $L(f) = L(f^+) - L(f^-) = L(f_1) - L(f_2)$.

3.4.61 Theorem. The Lebesgue integral L is a linear functional on $\mathcal{L}$. That is, if $f,g \in \mathcal{L}$ and $\alpha,\beta \in R$, then $\alpha f + \beta g \in \mathcal{L}$ and $L(\alpha f + \beta g) = \alpha L(f) + \beta L(g)$.

Proof. We first prove that $L(f + g) = L(f) + L(g)$ for $f,g \in \mathcal{L}$. Clearly $f + g = f^+ + g^+ - (f^- + g^-)$. By 3.4.6 and 3.4.3, we have $L(f + g) = L(f^+ + g^+) - L(f^- + g^-)$ $= L(f^+) + L(g^+) - L(f^-) - L(g^-) = L(f^+) - L(f^-) + L(g^+) -$ $L(g^-) = L(f) + L(g)$.

We now prove that $L(\alpha f) = \alpha L(f)$ for $f \in \mathcal{L}$ and $\alpha \in R$. We first note that $L(-f) = -L(f)$ since from above $L(-f) + L(f) = L(-f + f) = L(0) = 0$. For $\alpha = 0$, $L(\alpha f) = L(0) = 0 = 0 \cdot L(f)$. For $\alpha > 0$, $\alpha f = \alpha f^+ - \alpha f^-$ and hence $L(\alpha f) = L(\alpha f^+) - L(\alpha f^-) = \alpha L(f^+) - \alpha L(f^-)$ by 3.4.6 and 3.4.4. For $\alpha < 0$, we write $\alpha f = -[(-\alpha)f^+ - (-\alpha)f^-]$ and proceed as above.

3.4.7 Exercises.

3.4.71 Exercise. Let f be a measurable function. Prove that $f \in \mathcal{L}$ if and only if $|f| \in \mathcal{L}$.

3.4.72 Exercise. Let f be a measurable function and suppose that $|f| \leq g$ where $g \in \mathcal{L}$. Prove that $f \in \mathcal{L}$.

3.4.73 Exercise. Let f and g be measurable functions and suppose that $f = g$ a.e. on X. Prove that $L(f) = L(g)$ if $L(f)$ or $L(g)$ exists.

3.4.74 Exercise. Let $A \in \mathcal{M}$. Let $L_A(f)$ be the integral of

f using only measurable subsets of A and regarding f as defined only on A. Prove that $L_A(f) = L(f \cdot \chi_A)$ for all functions f on X for which $L(f)$ is defined.

3.4.75 Exercise. Prove that $L_{A\cup B}(f) = L_A(f) + L_B(f)$ if $A, B \in \mathfrak{M}$ and $A \cap B = 0$.

3.5 Countable additivity of the Lebesgue integral.

3.5.1 Theorem. (Lebesgue) Let $\{f_n\}_{n=1}^{\infty}$ be a sequence of non-negative measurable functions on X. We define

$$\sum_{n=1}^{\infty} f_n(x) = \begin{cases} +\infty, & \text{if } \sum_{n=1}^{\infty} f_n(x) \text{ diverges} \\ \sum_{n=1}^{\infty} f_n(x), & \text{if } \sum_{n=1}^{\infty} f_n(x) \text{ converges} \end{cases}.$$

Then $L(\sum_{n=1}^{\infty} f_n) = \sum_{n=1}^{\infty} L(f_n)$.

Proof. Write $h(x) = \sum_{n=1}^{\infty} f_n(x)$. For all $x \in X$, $h(x) \geq \sum_{n=1}^{m} f_n(x)$ so that $L(h) \geq L(\sum_{n=1}^{m} f_n) = \sum_{n=1}^{m} L(f_n)$. Therefore $L(h) \geq \lim_{m\to\infty} \sum_{n=1}^{m} L(f_n) = \sum_{n=1}^{\infty} L(f_n)$.

For each positive integer n, let $\{s_n^{(k)}\}_{k=1}^{\infty}$ be an increasing sequence of non-negative, simple, measurable functions such that $\lim_{k\to\infty} s_n^{(k)}(x) = f_n(x)$ for all $x \in X$ (see 3.2.12). Let $g_k(x) = \sum_{j=1}^{k} s_j^{(k)}(x)$. Evidently we have $g_1 \leq g_2 \leq \cdots \leq g_k \leq \cdots$. Consider an arbitrary positive integer m. For $k \geq m$, we have

$$\sum_{j=1}^{m} s_j^{(k)}(x) \leq g_k(x) = \sum_{j=1}^{k} s_j^{(k)}(x) \leq \sum_{j=1}^{k} f_j(x) \leq h(x).$$

Taking the limit as $k \to \infty$ in this inequality, we have

$$\sum_{j=1}^{m} f_j(x) \leq \lim_{k\to\infty} g_k(x) \leq h(x).$$

Taking next the limit as $m \to \infty$, we find that

$$\lim_{k\to\infty} g_k(x) = h(x).$$

Applying 3.4.21, we have

$$\lim_{k\to\infty} L(g_k) = L(h).$$

Since $g_k(x) \leq \sum_{j=1}^{k} f_j(x)$, we apply 3.3.4 to infer that

$$\sum_{j=1}^{\infty} L(f_j) \geq L(h).$$

This completes the proof.

3.5.11 <u>Theorem</u>. (Lebesgue, B. Levi) Let $\{f_n\}_{n=1}^{\infty}$ be an increasing sequence of non-negative measurable functions. Then

$$\lim_{n\to\infty} L(f_n) = L(\lim_{n\to\infty} f_n).$$

<u>Proof</u>. If $L(f_m) = \infty$ for some m, then $L(\lim_{n\to\infty} f_n) \geq L(f_m) = \infty$ and thus $\lim_{n\to\infty} L(f_n) = \infty = L(\lim_{n\to\infty} f_n)$.

Suppose that $L(f_n) < \infty$ for all n. Let

$$g_n(x) = \begin{cases} f_{n+1}(x) - f_n(x) & \text{if } f_{n+1}(x) \text{ is finite} \\ +\infty & \text{if } f_{n+1}(x) \text{ is infinite} \end{cases}.$$

Then $f_1 + \sum_{n=1}^{\infty} g_n = \lim_{n\to\infty} f_n$. By 3.5.1, we have

$$L(\lim_{n\to\infty} f_n) = L(f_1) + \sum_{n=1}^{\infty} L(f_{n+1} - f_n) = L(f_1) + \lim_{m\to\infty} \Big(L(f_2) -$$

$L(f_1) + L(f_3) - L(f_2) + \ldots + L(f_{m+1}) - L(f_m)\Big) =$

$L(f_1) + \lim\limits_{m\to\infty} (L(f_{m+1}) - L(f_1)) = \lim\limits_{m\to\infty} L(f_{m+1})$.

3.5.2 Theorem. (Fatou's Lemma) Let $\{f_n\}_{n=1}^{\infty}$ be any sequence of non-negative measurable functions. Then

$L(\underline{\lim}_{n\to\infty} f_n) \leq \underline{\lim}_{n\to\infty} L(f_n)$.

Proof. Let $g_k = \inf(f_k, f_{k+1}, \ldots)$ for $k = 1, 2, \ldots$. Evidently each g_k is a non-negative measurable function, $g_1 \leq g_2 \leq \ldots \leq g_k \leq \ldots$, and $g_k \leq f_k$ for all k. By 3.5.11 we have $L(\underline{\lim}_{n\to\infty} f_n) = L(\lim\limits_{k\to\infty} g_k) = \lim\limits_{k\to\infty} L(g_k)$. Since $L(g_k) \leq L(f_k)$ for all k, we conclude that

$L(\underline{\lim}_{n\to\infty} f_n) = \lim\limits_{k\to\infty} L(g_k) \leq \underline{\lim}_{k\to\infty} L(f_k)$.

3.5.21 Theorem. (Lebesgue's theorem on dominated convergence) Let $\{f_n\}_{n=1}^{\infty}$ be a sequence of measurable functions such that $|f_n(x)| \leq s(x)$ for $n = 1, 2, \ldots$ and almost all $x \in X$, where s is a measurable function and $L(s) < +\infty$. Then $L(\underline{\lim}_{n\to\infty} f_n) \leq \underline{\lim}_{n\to\infty} L(f_n)$ and $L(\overline{\lim}_{n\to\infty} f_n) \geq \overline{\lim}_{n\to\infty} L(f_n)$. Furthermore, if $\lim\limits_{n\to\infty} f_n(x)$ exists for almost all $x \in X$, then $\lim\limits_{n\to\infty} L(f_n) = L(\lim\limits_{n\to\infty} f_n)$.

Proof. Since $L(s) < \infty$, $s(x)$ is finite a.e. on X. Hence if we redefine s and each f_n to be zero where $s(x)$ is infinite, the values of the integrals will be unaltered. Clearly $\{s + f_n\}_{n=1}^{\infty}$ is a sequence of non-negative functions. Using 3.5.2, we have

$L(s) + L(\underline{\lim}_{n\to\infty} f_n) = L(s + \underline{\lim}_{n\to\infty} f_n) = L(\underline{\lim}_{n\to\infty} (s + f_n)) \leq$

$\underline{\lim}_{n\to\infty} L(s + f_n) = \underline{\lim}_{n\to\infty} (L(s) + L(f_n)) = L(s) + \underline{\lim}_{n\to\infty} L(f_n)$.

Consequently, $L(\underline{\lim}_{n\to\infty} f_n) \leq \underline{\lim}_{n\to\infty} L(f_n)$.

In like manner we use the sequence $\{s - f_n\}_{n=1}^{\infty}$ to obtain $L(\underline{\lim}_{n\to\infty} (-f_n)) \leq \underline{\lim}_{n\to\infty} L(-f_n)$. Hence

$-L(\underline{\lim}_{n\to\infty} (-f_n)) \geq - \underline{\lim}_{n\to\infty} L(-f_n)$ or $L(-\underline{\lim}_{n\to\infty} (-f_n)) \geq -\underline{\lim}_{n\to\infty} (-L(f_n))$. This is equivalent to the inequality

$L(\overline{\lim}_{n\to\infty} f_n) \geq \overline{\lim}_{n\to\infty} L(f_n)$.

We now prove the last assertion. Since $\lim_{n\to\infty} f_n(x)$ exists a.e. on X we may, as above, assume that $\lim_{n\to\infty} f_n(x)$ exists everywhere. Let $f(x) = \lim_{n\to\infty} f_n(x)$.

We have $L(f) = L(\underline{\lim}_{n\to\infty} f_n) \leq \underline{\lim}_{n\to\infty} L(f_n) \leq \overline{\lim}_{n\to\infty} L(f_n) \leq$

$L(\overline{\lim}_{n\to\infty} f_n) = L(f)$. Thus $\lim_{n\to\infty} L(f_n) = L(f) = L(\lim_{n\to\infty} f_n)$.

3.5.22 <u>Theorem</u>. Let $f \in \mathcal{L}$ and let $\{A_n\}_{n=1}^{\infty}$ be a sequence of pairwise disjoint measurable subsets of X. Then

$$L(f \cdot \chi_{\bigcup_{n=1}^{\infty} A_n}) = \sum_{n=1}^{\infty} L(f \cdot \chi_{A_n}).$$

3.5.23 <u>Theorem</u>. Let $\{f_n\}_{n=1}^{\infty}$ be a sequence of measurable functions such that $\sum_{n=1}^{\infty} |f_n(x)| < \infty$ for almost all $x \in X$ and $\sum_{n=1}^{\infty} |f_n| \in \mathcal{L}$. Then $L(\sum_{n=1}^{\infty} f_n) = \sum_{n=1}^{\infty} L(f_n)$.

3.5.24 Theorem. Let $\mu(X)$ be finite. If $\{f_n\}_{n=1}^{\infty}$ is a sequence of measurable functions on X such that $\lim_{n\to\infty} f_n(x)$ exists for almost all $x \in X$ and if $|f_n(x)| \leq \alpha$ for all $n = 1, 2, 3, \ldots$ and almost all $x \in X$, where $\alpha \geq 0$, then $\lim_{n\to\infty} L(f_n) = L(\lim_{n\to\infty} f_n)$.

We omit the proofs of 3.5.22 - 3.5.24.

3.5.3 Notation. For a function f on a measure space $(X, \mathcal{M}, \mu)$, we now write $L(f)$ as $\int_X f(x)d\mu(x)$. We also write $\int_A f(x)d\mu(x)$ for $\int_X f(x)\chi_A(x)d\mu(x)$ for $A \in \mathcal{M}$. If $X = R$ we write $\int_{-\infty}^{\infty} f(x)d\mu(x)$ for $\int_R f(x)d\mu(x)$. If $X = R$ and $\mu = \lambda$ (λ is Lebesgue measure), we write $\int_a^b f(x)d\lambda(x)$ for $\int_{[a,b]} f(x)d\lambda(x)$.

3.5.4 Theorem. Let $f \in \mathcal{L}$. Then for every $\varepsilon > 0$, there exists a δ (depending upon ε) such that $A \in \mathcal{M}$ and $\mu(A) < \delta$ implies $|\int_A f(x)d\mu(x)| < \varepsilon$.

Proof. Case I. Suppose that f is bounded, i.e., $|f(x)| \leq M$ for all $x \in X$. If $M = 0$, the assertion is trivial. Otherwise for $\varepsilon > 0$, let $\delta = \frac{\varepsilon}{M}$. Then if $A \in \mathcal{M}$ and $\mu(A) < \delta$, we have

$$|\int_A f(x)d\mu(x)| = |\int_X f(x)\chi_A(x)d\mu(x)| \leq \int_X |f(x)|\chi_A(x)d\mu(x) \leq$$

$$\int_X M\chi_A(x)d\mu(x) = M\mu(A) < M\delta = \varepsilon.$$

Case II. Suppose that f is unbounded. Let

$\psi_n(x) = \begin{cases} |f(x)| & \text{if } |f(x)| \leq n \\ 0 & \text{if } |f(x)| > n \end{cases}$. The sequence $\{\psi_n\}_{n=1}^{\infty}$ converges pointwise to $|f|$. Furthermore $0 \leq \psi_n(x) \leq |f(x)|$ for all n and all $x \in X$. Theorem 3.5.21 implies that $\lim_{n\to\infty} \int_X \psi_n(x)d\mu(x) = \int_X |f(x)|d\mu(x)$. We have

$$\int_X [|f(x)| - \psi_n(x)]\chi_A(x)d\mu(x) \leq \int_X |f(x)|d\mu(x) - \int_X \psi_n(x)d\mu(x)$$

and consequently the first integral tends to 0 as $n \to \infty$, independently of A. Choose n so large that

$\int_X |f(x)|d\mu(x) - \int_X \psi_n(x)d\mu(x) < \frac{\varepsilon}{2}$. Let $\delta = \frac{\varepsilon}{2n}$.

If $A \in \mathfrak{M}$ and $\mu(A) < \delta$, then

$$|\int_A f(x)d\mu(x)| \leq \int_X |f(x)|\chi_A(x)d\mu(x) =$$

$$\int_X [|f(x)| - \psi_n(x)]\chi_A(x)d\mu(x) + \int_X \psi_n(x)\chi_A(x)d\mu(x) <$$

$$\frac{\varepsilon}{2} + n\mu(A) \leq \frac{\varepsilon}{2} + n\frac{\varepsilon}{2n} = \varepsilon.$$

3.5.5 Theorem. (Vitali) Suppose that $\mu(X) < +\infty$. Let $\{f_n\}_{n=1}^{\infty}$ be a sequence of functions in $\mathcal{L}$ converging in measure to a measurable function f. Suppose also that for every $\varepsilon > 0$, there exists a $\delta > 0$ such that $|\int_A f_n(x)d\mu(x)| < \varepsilon$ for all $n = 1, 2, \ldots$ whenever $\mu(A) < \delta$. Then $f \in \mathcal{L}$ and $\lim_{n\to\infty} \int_X f_n(x)d\mu(x) = \int_X f(x)d\mu(x)$.

Proof. See Theorem 2, page 152, Natanson.

3.5.6 Exercises.

3.5.61 Final Exercise # 11. Let $(X, \mathcal{M}, \mu)$ be a measure space with total measure finite. For every pair f,g of finite valued measurable functions on X, let

$$\rho(f,g) = \int_X \frac{|f(x) - g(x)|}{1 + |f(x) - g(x)|} \, d\mu(x).$$

Prove the following properties of ρ:

i) $\rho(f,g) \geq 0$ and $\rho(f,g) = 0$ if and only if $f(x) = g(x)$ a.e. on X;

ii) $\rho(f,g) = \rho(g,f)$;

iii) $\rho(f,h) \leq \rho(f,g) + \rho(g,h)$;

iv) $\lim_{n\to\infty} \rho(f_n,f) = 0$ if and only if $f_n \to f$ (measure).

3.5.62 Exercise. Let $(X, \mathcal{M}, \mu)$ be any σ-finite measure space. Suppose that ϕ is a measurable function and that $f\phi \in \mathcal{L}$ for all $f \in \mathcal{L}$. Prove that ϕ is bounded a.e. That is, there is a number α such that $\mu\{x\colon\ x \in X, |\phi(x)| > \alpha\} = 0$.

3.5.63 Exercise. Let $(X, \mathcal{M}, \mu)$ be any measure space. Let f be a measurable, non-negative, bounded function on X. Let $\alpha = \inf\{f(x)\colon\ x \in X\}$ and $\beta = \sup\{f(x)\colon\ x \in X\}$. For $i = 1, 2, \ldots, n-1$, let $A_i = \{x\colon\ x \in X,\ \alpha + \frac{(i-1)(\beta-\alpha)}{n} \leq f(x) < \alpha + \frac{i(\beta-\alpha)}{n}\}$ and let $A_n = \{x\colon\ x \in X,\ \alpha + \frac{(n-1)(\beta-\alpha)}{n} \leq f(x) \leq \beta\}$. The Lebesgue sums for f are defined as the numbers $s_n = \sum_{i=1}^{n} (\alpha + \frac{(i-1)(\beta-\alpha)}{n}) \cdot \mu(A_i)$. Prove that $\lim_{n\to\infty} s_n = \int_X f(x) d$

Suppose next that $\mu(X) < \infty$. Let f be any bounded measurable function on X. Define s_n as above. Prove that $\lim_{n\to\infty} s_n = \int_X f(x)d\mu(x)$.

3.6 <u>Riemann and Lebesgue integrals on a closed interval</u>. In this section X will be $[a,b]$, $-\infty < a < b < +\infty$, $\mathcal{M}$ will be the family of all Lebesgue measurable subsets of $[a,b]$, and λ will be, as usual, Lebesgue measure.

3.6.1 <u>Definition</u>. Let f be any function on $[a,b]$. For $\delta > 0$ and $x \in [a,b]$, let $m_\delta(x) = \inf \{f(y): y \in [a,b] \cap]x - \delta, x + \delta[\}$ and $M_\delta(x) = \sup \{f(y): y \in [a,b] \cap]x - \delta, x + \delta[\}$.

For a fixed x it is evident that $m_\delta(x)$ increases as δ decreases and $M_\delta(x)$ decreases as δ decreases. Hence we may define $m(x) = \lim_{\delta\to 0} m_\delta(x)$ and $M(x) = \lim_{\delta\to 0} M_\delta(x)$.

3.6.11 <u>Theorem</u>. A bounded function f is continuous at $x \in [a,b]$ if and only if $m(x) = M(x)$.

The proof is omitted.

3.6.2 <u>Theorem</u>. Let f be a bounded function. Consider a sequence of subdivisions of $[a,b]$:

$$a = x_0^{(1)} < x_1^{(1)} < \ldots < x_{n_1}^{(1)} = b$$

$$\ldots$$

$$a = x_0^{(j)} < x_1^{(j)} < \ldots < x_{n_j}^{(j)} = b$$

$$\ldots$$

such that $\lim_{j\to\infty} [\max \{x_{k+1}^{(j)} - x_k^{(j)}\}: k = 0, 1, \ldots, n_j - 1] = 0$.

Let $m_k^{(j)} = \inf \{f(x): x_k^{(j)} \leq x \leq x_{k+1}^{(j)}\}$, $k = 0, 1, \ldots, n_j - 1$.

Let ϕ_j be the function on $[a,b]$ defined by

$$\phi_j(x) = \begin{cases} 0 & \text{if } x = x_0^{(j)}, \ldots, x_{n_j}^{(j)}, \\ m_k^{(j)} & \text{if } x_k^{(j)} < x < x_{k+1}^{(j)}. \end{cases}$$

If $y \varepsilon [a,b]$ and y is distinct from all $x_k^{(j)}$, then $\lim_{j\to\infty} \phi_j(y) = m(y)$.

Proof. Let j be an arbitrary fixed positive integer. Then $x_k^{(j)} < y < x_{k+1}^{(j)}$ for just one value of k. For sufficiently small δ, $m_\delta(y) \geq m_k^{(j)} = \phi_j(y)$. Consequently $m(y) \geq \phi_j(y)$ for all j. Hence $\overline{\lim}_{j\to\infty} \phi_j(y) \leq m(y)$. $m(y)$ is clearly finite. Choose any number $h < m(y)$. Choose $\delta > 0$ so small that $h < m_\delta(y) \leq m(y)$. Choose j_0 so large that for $j > j_0$, the interval $[x_k^{(j)}, x_{k+1}^{(j)}]$ containing y is a subset of $]y - \delta, y + \delta[$. Then $\phi_j(y) = m_k^{(j)} \geq m_\delta(y) > h$ for $j > j_0$. Hence $\underline{\lim}_{j\to\infty} \phi_j(y) \geq h$. Since h is arbitrary, we have $\underline{\lim}_{j\to\infty} \phi_j(y) \geq m(y)$. Finally, we have $\underline{\lim}_{j\to\infty} \phi_j(y) \geq m(y) \geq \overline{\lim}_{j\to\infty} \phi_j(y) \geq \underline{\lim}_{j\to\infty} \phi_j(y)$ and so $\lim_{j\to\infty} \phi_j(y) = m(y)$.

3.6.21 Theorem. The functions m and M are measurable.

Proof. Each ϕ_j is simple and measurable and $\phi_j(y) \to m(y)$ a.e. on $[a,b]$. Therefore, by 3.1.31, m is measurable.

In like manner, M is shown to be measurable.

3.6.22 Theorem. Let s_j be the jth lower Darboux sum for the function f defined by the subdivision $\{x_k^{(j)}\}_{k=o}^{n_j}$. Then

$$\lim_{j\to\infty} s_j = \int_a^b m(x)d\lambda(x).$$

Proof. By definition, $s_j = \sum_{k=o}^{n_j-1} \inf [f(x): x_k^{(j)} \leq x \leq x_{k+1}^{(j)}]$. $(x_{k+1}^{(j)} - x_k^{(j)}) = \int_a^b \phi_j(x)d\lambda(x)$. We have $\phi_j(x) \to m(x)$ a.e. on $[a,b]$ and all ϕ_j and m are bounded functions. By 3.5.21, we have $\lim_{j\to\infty} s_j = \lim_{j\to\infty} \int_a^b \phi_j(x)d\lambda(x) = \int_a^b m(x)d\lambda(x)$.

3.6.221 Theorem. The upper Darboux sums S_j for the function f defined by the subdivisions $\{x_k^{(j)}\}_{k=o}^{n_j}$ converge to $\int_a^b M(x)d\lambda(x)$.

The proof is similar to the proof of 3.6.22.

3.6.23 Theorem. A bounded function f on $[a,b]$ is Riemann integrable on $[a,b]$ if and only if f is continuous except for a set of Lebesgue measure zero.

Proof. Let s_j and S_j be, as above, the lower and upper Darboux sums defined by the subdivision $\{x_k^{(j)}\}_{k=o}^{n_j}$.

The function f is Riemann integrable if and only if $\lim_{j\to\infty} (S_j - s_j) = 0$. This is equivalent to the equality $\lim_{j\to\infty} S_j - \lim_{j\to\infty} s_j = 0$ and hence equivalent to $\int_a^b M(x)d\lambda(x) -$

$\int_a^b m(x)d\lambda(x) = 0$. Now $\int_a^b M(x)d\lambda(x) - \int_a^b m(x)d\lambda(x) = 0$ if and only if $\int_a^b [M(x) - m(x)]d\lambda(x) = 0$ and since $M(x) - m(x) \geq 0$ for all $x \in [a,b]$, 3.3.5 implies that this is equivalent to the relation $M(x) = m(x)$ a.e. on $[a,b]$. By 3.6.11, $M(x) = m(x)$ a.e. on $[a,b]$ if and only if $f(x)$ is continuous a.e. on $[a,b]$. Therefore f is Riemann integrable on $[a,b]$ if and only if it is continuous a.e. on $[a,b]$.

3.6.24 Theorem. Let f be a bounded function on $[a,b]$ and suppose that f is Riemann integrable. Then f is Lebesgue integrable on $[a,b]$ and $(R) \int_a^b f(x)dx = \int_a^b f(x)d\lambda(x)$, where $(R) \int_a^b$ denotes the Riemann integral on $[a,b]$.

Proof. Since f is Riemann integrable, $m(x) = M(x)$ a.e. on $[a,b]$. Clearly $m(x) \leq f(x) \leq M(x)$ everywhere on $[a,b]$, so that $m(x) = f(x)$ a.e. on $[a,b]$. Hence $f(x) = \lim_{j\to\infty} \phi_j(x)$ a.e. Therefore f is λ-measurable. By 3.3.5 and 3.6.22,

$$\int_a^b f(x)d\lambda(x) = \int_a^b m(x)d\lambda(x) = \lim_{j\to\infty} s_j = (R) \int_a^b f(x)dx.$$

3.6.25 Example. Let D be the function on $[0,1]$ defined by $D(x) = \begin{Bmatrix} 0 & \text{if} & x & \text{rational} \\ 1 & \text{if} & x & \text{irrational} \end{Bmatrix}$. We have $\int_0^1 D(x)d\lambda(x) = 1$ since $D(x) = 1$ a.e. However, $(R) \int_0^1 D(x)dx$ does not exist since D is discontinuous everywhere on $[0,1]$ (see 3.6.23).

A result analogous to 3.5.21 does not exist for Riemann integrable functions. For example, it is easy to show that $D = \lim_{n\to\infty} D_n$ where each D_n is Riemann integrable. However, if $f_n \to f$ pointwise and dominatedly on $[a,b]$, and if all f_n and f are Riemann integrable, then $\lim_{n\to\infty} (R) \int_a^b f_n(x)dx = (R) \int_a^b f(x)dx$. This follows from 3.5.21 and 3.6.24. The whole situation is somewhat artificial, and points up the virtues of Lebesgue's integral.

3.6.26 <u>Theorem</u>. Let f be a measurable, non-negative (possibly infinite) function defined on R. Then $\lim_{n\to\infty} \int_{-n}^{n} f(x)d\lambda(x) = \int_{-\infty}^{\infty} f(x)d\lambda(x)$. If f is any function in $\mathcal{L}(R, \mathfrak{M}, \lambda)$, then we obtain the same conclusion.

<u>Proof</u>. Clearly $\int_{-n}^{n} f(x)d\lambda(x) = \int_{-\infty}^{\infty} f(x)\chi_{[-n,n]}(x)d\lambda(x)$. The first statement now follows by 3.5.11 and the second statement follows by 3.5.21.

3.6.3 <u>Theorem</u>. For any function f defined on R, and any $h \in R$, let f_h denote the function such that $f_h(x) = f(x + h)$. Let $\check{f}$ be the function such that $\check{f}(x) = f(-x)$. If f is measurable and $\int_{-\infty}^{\infty} f(x)d\lambda(x)$ exists, then

$$\int_{-\infty}^{\infty} f(x)d\lambda(x) = \int_{-\infty}^{\infty} f_h(x)d\lambda(x) = \int_{-\infty}^{\infty} \check{f}(x)d\lambda(x).$$

Proof. Suppose that $A \in \mathfrak{M}$. As in 2.6.5, we have $(\chi_A)_h = \chi_{A-h}$. Thus, using 2.3.48, we have $\int_{-\infty}^{\infty} \chi_A(x)d\lambda(x) = \lambda(A) = \lambda(A-h) = \int_{-\infty}^{\infty} \chi_{A-h}(x)d\lambda(x) = \int_{-\infty}^{\infty} (\chi_A)_h(x)d\lambda(x)$.

Suppose $f = \sum_{k=1}^{n} \alpha_k \chi_{A_k}$ is a simple measurable function. We have $(\sum_{k=1}^{n} \alpha_k \chi_{A_k})_h = \sum_{k=1}^{n} \alpha_k (\chi_{A_k})_h$. Thus by 3.3.31 and the above we see that $\int_{-\infty}^{\infty} f(x)d\lambda(x) = \int_{-\infty}^{\infty} f_h(x)d\lambda(x)$ if f is a simple measurable function.

Suppose f is any measurable non-negative function. Then $f = \lim_{n\to\infty} s_n$ where $\{s_n\}_{n=1}^{\infty}$ is an increasing sequence of simple functions (3.2.12). Evidently $f_h = \lim_{n\to\infty} (s_n)_h$. By 3.4.21, $\lim_{n\to\infty} \int_{-\infty}^{\infty} s_n(x)d\lambda(x) = \int_{-\infty}^{\infty} f(x)d\lambda(x)$ and $\lim_{n\to\infty} \int_{-\infty}^{\infty} (s_n)_h(x)d\lambda(x) = \int_{-\infty}^{\infty} f_h(x)d\lambda(x)$. From the above, we infer that $\int_{-\infty}^{\infty} (s_n)_h(x)d\lambda(x) = \int_{-\infty}^{\infty} s_n(x)d\lambda(x)$. Consequently, $\int_{-\infty}^{\infty} f(x)d\lambda(x) = \int_{-\infty}^{\infty} f_h(x)d\lambda(x)$.

Suppose now that f is any measurable function for which $\int_{-\infty}^{\infty} f(x)d\lambda(x)$ exists. We have $f = f^+ - f^-$ and $f_h = f_h^+ - f_h^-$. Therefore, $\int_{-\infty}^{\infty} f(x)d\lambda(x) = \int_{-\infty}^{\infty} f^+(x)d\lambda(x) - \int_{-\infty}^{\infty} f^-(x)d\lambda(x) = \int_{-\infty}^{\infty} f_h^+(x)d\lambda(x) - \int_{-\infty}^{\infty} f_h^-(x)d\lambda(x) = \int_{-\infty}^{\infty} f_h(x)d\lambda(x$

In a similar way we prove that $\int_{-\infty}^{\infty} f(x)d\lambda(x) = \int_{-\infty}^{\infty} \check{f}(x)d\lambda(x)$.

3.6.31 __Theorem.__ Let f be a function in $\mathcal{L}$ on $[a,b]$ where $-\infty < a < b < \infty$. For every positive number ε, there is a continuous function ϕ such that

$$\int_a^b |f(x) - \phi(x)|d\lambda(x) < \varepsilon.$$

__Proof.__ Let f be the characteristic function of a measurable subset A of $[a,b]$. By 2.3.492 there exists an open set G and a closed set F such that $F \subset A \subset G$ and $\lambda(G \cap F') < \varepsilon$. Define $\psi(x) = \inf\{|x-y|: y \varepsilon G'\}$ for each $x \varepsilon [a,b]$. Clearly $\psi(x) = 0$ if and only if $x \varepsilon G'$. We see that ψ is a continuous function as follows. It suffices to prove that $|\psi(x) - \psi(y)| \leq |x - y|$ for all $x,y \varepsilon [a,b]$. For $\eta > 0$, let $z \varepsilon G'$ be such that $|y - z| \leq \psi(y) + \eta$. Then $\psi(x) \leq |x - z| \leq |x - y| + |y - z| \leq |x - y| + \psi(y) + \eta$. Consequently, $\psi(x) - \psi(y) \leq |x - y| + \eta$. Since η is arbitrary, $\psi(x) - \psi(y) \leq |x - y|$. Similarly, $\psi(y) - \psi(x) \leq |x - y|$ and thus $|\psi(x) - \psi(y)| \leq |x - y|$.

The minimum value α of the function ψ on F is positive, since F is compact. Let ϕ be the function such that $\phi(x) = \frac{1}{\alpha}\min(\psi(x),\alpha)$. ϕ is a continuous function, $\phi(x) = \begin{cases} 1 & \text{if } x \varepsilon F \\ 0 & \text{if } x \varepsilon G' \end{cases}$, and $0 \leq \phi(x) \leq 1$ for all $x \varepsilon [a,b]$. Since $\phi(x) - \chi_A(x) = 0$ for $x \varepsilon F \cup G'$, we have $\int_a^b |\phi(x) - \chi_A(x)|d\lambda(x) = \int_{G\cap F'} |\phi(x) - \chi_A(x)|d\lambda(x) \leq \int_a^b \chi_{G\cap F'}(x)d\lambda(x) = \lambda(G \cap F') < \varepsilon.$

Suppose now that $f = \sum_{j=1}^{m} \beta_j \chi_{B_j}$, $\beta_j \neq 0$, is a finite-valued simple measurable function. For $j = 1, 2, \ldots, m$, there exist continuous functions ϕ_j such that $\int_a^b |\phi_j(x) - \chi_{B_j}(x)| d\lambda(x) < \frac{\varepsilon}{|\beta_j| m}$. Then

$$\int_a^b \left| \sum_{j=1}^{m} \beta_j \phi_j(x) - f(x) \right| d\lambda(x) = \int_a^b \left| \sum_{j=1}^{m} \beta_j \phi_j(x) - \sum_{j=1}^{m} \beta_j \chi_{B_j}(x) \right| d\lambda$$

$$\leq \int_a^b \sum_{j=1}^{m} |\beta_j \phi_j(x) - \beta_j \chi_{B_j}(x)| d\lambda(x) \leq \sum_{j=1}^{m} |\beta_j| \int_a^b |\phi_j(x) - \chi_{B_j}(x)| d\lambda(x) < \sum_{j=1}^{m} |\beta_j| \frac{\varepsilon}{|\beta_j| m} = \varepsilon.$$

Finally, suppose f is an arbitrary function in $\mathcal{L}$ on $[a,b]$. By 3.2.12, 3.3.3, and 3.4.21, there exists a simple function s such that $\int_a^b |f(x) - s(x)| d\lambda(x) < \frac{\varepsilon}{2}$. From the above, we have a continuous function ϕ such that $\int_a^b |s(x) - \phi(x)| d\lambda(x) < \frac{\varepsilon}{2}$. Therefore $\int_a^b |f(x) - \phi(x)| d\lambda(x) < \varepsilon$.

3.6.311 <u>Corollary</u>. Theorem 3.6.31 holds for integrals over the intervals $]-\infty, a]$, $[a, +\infty[$, where $a \in R$, and for $]-\infty, +\infty[$.

The proof is omitted.

3.6.32 <u>Exercise</u>. Let f be a function in $\mathcal{L}$ on $]a,b[$, $-\infty \leq a < b \leq +\infty$. If $\int_a^x f(t) d\lambda(t) = 0$ for all $x \in]a,b[$, then $f(t) = 0$ a.e. on $]a,b[$.

3.6.33 Exercise. Suppose that ϕ is a continuous, monotone increasing function on $[a,b]$, $-\infty < a < b < +\infty$. Then ϕ' exists a.e. on $[a,b]$; define ϕ' to be anything you like where it does not a priori exist. Prove that $\phi' \varepsilon \mathcal{L}$ on $[a,b]$ and that $\int_a^b \phi'(x)d\lambda(x) \leq \phi(b) - \phi(a)$.

3.6.34 Theorem. Let $f \varepsilon \mathcal{L}$ on $[a,b]$, $-\infty < a < b < +\infty$. Let F be the function on $[a,b]$ such that $F(x) = \int_a^x f(t)d\lambda(t)$ for $x \varepsilon [a,b]$. Then F is finite-valued, continuous, and differentiable a.e. on $[a,b]$. Furthermore, the equality $F'(x) = f(x)$ holds a.e. on $[a,b]$.

Proof. We have

$$|F(x)| = |\int_a^b f(t)\chi_{[a,x]}(t)d\lambda(t)| \leq \int_a^b |f(t)|\chi_{[a,x]}(t)d\lambda(t) \leq$$

$\int_a^b |f(t)|d\lambda(t) < \infty$; the last inequality follows from 3.4.71. Therefore, F is finite-valued. We infer from 3.5.4 that for every $\varepsilon > 0$, there exists a $\delta > 0$ such that $|x_1 - x_2| < \delta$ implies $|F(x_1) - F(x_2)| =$

$|\int_{\min(x_1,x_2)}^{\max(x_1,x_2)} f(t)d\lambda(t)| < \varepsilon$. Hence F is a continuous function on $[a,b]$.

Since $f = f^+ - f^-$, we have

$F(x) = \int_a^x f^+(t)d\lambda(t) - \int_a^x f^-(t)d\lambda(t)$; that is, F is the difference of two monotonic functions. By 2.5.6, each of the monotonic functions is differentiable a.e. and hence F is differentiable a.e.

To prove that $F'(x) = f(x)$ a.e. on $[a,b]$ it is convenient to extend the definition of F to $[a,b+1]$ by the relation $F(x) = F(b)$ for $b < x \leq b+1$. Now let $\phi_n(x) = n[F(x+\frac{1}{n}) - F(x)]$ for $n = 1, 2, \ldots$ and $x \in [a,b]$. It is obvious that

$$\lim_{n\to\infty} \phi_n(x) = F'(x) \quad \text{a.e. on } [a,b].$$

Since the functions ϕ_n are continuous, it follows that F' is measurable.

Case I. Suppose that $f \in \mathcal{L}$ on $[a,b]$ and that f is bounded. That is, for some real number M, we have $|f(x)| \leq M$ for all $x \in [a,b]$. We have for each $x \in [a,b]$ and each n, $|\phi_n(x)| = |n[F(x+\frac{1}{n}) - F(x)]| =$

$n|\int_x^{x+\frac{1}{n}} f(t)d\lambda(t)| \leq M \cdot n\frac{1}{n} = M$. By 3.5.24, we see that

$$\lim_{n\to\infty} \int_a^x \phi_n(t)d\lambda(t) = \int_a^x F'(t)d\lambda(t) \quad \text{for all } x \in [a,b].$$

Also we see, using 3.4.61 and 3.6.3, that $\int_a^x \phi_n(t)d\lambda(t) =$

$n\int_a^x [F(t+\frac{1}{n}) - F(t)]d\lambda(t) = n\int_a^x F(t+\frac{1}{n})d\lambda(t) -$

$n\int_a^x F(t)d\lambda(t) = n\int_{a+\frac{1}{n}}^{x+\frac{1}{n}} F(t)d\lambda(t) - n\int_a^x F(t)d\lambda(t) =$

$n\int_x^{x+\frac{1}{n}} F(t)d\lambda(t) - n\int_a^{a+\frac{1}{n}} F(t)d\lambda(t)$. For a continuous function g defined on $[a,b]$ and $u \in [a,b]$, we have from elementary analysis that $\lim_{\substack{h\to 0 \\ u+h\in[a,b]}} \frac{1}{h}\int_u^{u+h} g(t)dt = g(u)$.

Consequently, $\int_a^x F'(t)d\lambda(t) = \lim_{n\to\infty} \int_a^x \phi_n(t)d\lambda(t) =$ $F(x) - F(a) = F(x)$ (recall that $F(a) = 0$). Since $F(x) = \int_a^x f(t)d\lambda(t)$ for all $x \in [a,b]$ and $F(x) = \int_a^x F'(t)d\lambda(t)$ for all $x \in [a,b]$ we see that $\int_a^x [f(t) - F'(t)]d\lambda(t) = 0$ for all $x \in [a,b]$. By 3.6.32, we infer that $f(x) = F'(x)$ a.e. on $[a,b]$.

Case II. Suppose that f is an arbitrary function in $\mathcal{L}$ on $[a,b]$. Since $f = f^+ - f^-$, we may without loss of generality suppose that $f \geq 0$. Define, for each positive integer n, $f_n = \min [f,n]$. Evidently $\{f_n\}_{n=1}^{\infty}$ is an increasing sequence of functions converging to f. For each n, let $\psi_n(x) = \int_a^x [f(t) - f_n(t)]d\lambda(t)$. Since for each n, $f(x) - f_n(x) \geq 0$ for all $x \in [a,b]$, $\psi_n(x)$ is a monotone increasing function in x. Hence $\psi_n'(x) \geq 0$ wherever it exists and $F'(x) = \frac{d}{dx} \int_a^x f(t)d\lambda(t) \geq$ $\frac{d}{dx} \int_a^x f_n(t)d\lambda(t) = f_n(x)$ a.e. on $[a,b]$; the last equality follows by Case I above. Therefore, $f(x) \leq F'(x)$ a.e. on $[a,b]$. Using 3.6.33, we have $F(b) = \int_a^b f(t)d\lambda(t) \leq$ $\int_a^b F'(t)d\lambda(t) \leq F(b) - F(a) = F(b)$. Hence $\int_a^b f(t)d\lambda(t) =$ $\int_a^b F'(t)d\lambda(t)$ or $\int_a^b [F'(t) - f(t)]d\lambda(t) = 0$. Since $f(x) \leq F'(x)$ a.e. on $[a,b]$ we apply 3.3.6 to conclude that $F'(t) = f(t)$ a.e. on $[a,b]$.

3.6.341 Exercise. Extend Theorem 3.6.34 to intervals $]-\infty,a]$, $[a,\infty[$ for $a \in R$ and to $]-\infty, \infty[$.

3.6.35 Theorem (Lebesgue). Let $f \in \mathcal{L}$ on $[a,b]$, where $-\infty < a < b < \infty$. Then there is a set N such that $\lambda(N) = 0$ and for every real number α,

$$\lim_{h\to 0} \frac{1}{h} \int_x^{x+h} |f(t) - \alpha| d\lambda(t) = |f(x) - \alpha| \quad \text{whenever}$$

$x \in [a,b] \cap N'$.

Proof. Let $\{\alpha_n\}_{n=1}^{\infty}$ be any well-ordering as a sequence of the set of rational numbers Q. For each positive integer n, let g_n be defined by the relation $g_n(x) = |f(x) - \alpha_n|$ for all $x \in [a,b]$. For each n, let $G_n(x) = \int_a^x g_n(t)d\lambda(t)$. By 3.6.34, there exists a set N_n such that $\lambda(N_n) = 0$ and $G_n'(x) = g_n(x)$ for all $x \in [a,b] \cap N_n'$. This means that $G_n'(x) = \lim_{h\to 0} \frac{1}{h} \int_x^{x+\frac{1}{h}} |f(t) - \alpha_n| d\lambda(t) = |f(x) - \alpha_n|$ for all $x \in [a,b] \cap N_n'$. Let $N = \bigcup_{n=1}^{\infty} N_n$; clearly $\lambda(N) = 0$.

Let β be any real number. Let ε be any positive real number. Then there exists an n such that $|\beta - \alpha_n| < \frac{\varepsilon}{3}$. For all $t \in [a,b]$, $\big||f(t) - \alpha_n| - |f(t) - \beta|\big| \leq |\alpha_n - \beta|$. Therefore, if h is positive, we have $\frac{1}{h} \left|\int_x^{x+h} |f(t) - \alpha_n| d\lambda(t) - \int_x^{x+h} |f(t) - \beta| d\lambda(t)\right| \leq \frac{1}{h} \int_x^{x+h} |\alpha_n - \beta| d\lambda(t) = \frac{1}{h}|\alpha_n - \beta| \cdot h = |\alpha_n - \beta| < \frac{\varepsilon}{3}$ for all

$x \in [a,b]$. We also have $\lim_{h\to 0} \frac{1}{h} \int_x^{x+h} |f(t) - \alpha_n| d\lambda(t) = |f(x) - \alpha_n|$ for all $x \in [a,b] \cap N'$. For h sufficiently small (depending on x) we have $\left| \frac{1}{h} \int_x^{x+h} |f(t) - \alpha_n| d\lambda(t) - |f(x) - \alpha_n| \right| < \frac{\varepsilon}{3}$ for all $x \in [a,b] \cap N'$. Thus we have, for sufficiently small h (depending on x), $\left| \frac{1}{h} \int_x^{x+h} |f(t) - \beta| d\lambda(t) - |f(x) - \beta| \right| \leq \left| \frac{1}{h} \int_x^{x+h} |f(t) - \beta| d\lambda(t) - \frac{1}{h} \int_x^{x+h} |f(t) - \alpha_n| d\lambda(t) \right| + \left| \frac{1}{h} \int_x^{x+h} |f(t) - \alpha_n| d\lambda(t) - |f(x) - \alpha_n| \right| + \left| |f(x) - \alpha_n| - |f(x) - \beta| \right| < \varepsilon$. Hence for $x \in [a,b] \cap N'$, $\lim_{h\to 0} \left| \frac{1}{h} \int_x^{x+h} |f(t) - \beta| d\lambda(t) - |f(x) - \beta| \right| < \varepsilon$. Since ε is arbitrary, $\lim_{h\to 0} \frac{1}{h} \int_x^{x+h} |f(t) - \beta| d\lambda(t) = |f(x) - \beta|$ for $x \in [a,b] \cap N'$. This completes the proof.

3.6.36 __Note.__ In 3.6.35, we may take α to be $f(x)$, wherever $f(x)$ is finite. Then for almost all $x \in [a,b]$ we have $\lim_{h\downarrow 0} \frac{1}{h} \int_x^{x+h} |f(t) - f(x)| d\lambda(t) = 0$ or, equivalently, $\lim_{h\downarrow 0} \frac{1}{h} \int_0^{h} |f(x+t) - f(x)| d\lambda(t) = 0$. The set of points $x \in [a,b]$ for which $\lim_{h\downarrow 0} \frac{1}{h} \int_0^{h} |f(x+t) - f(x)| d\lambda(t) = 0$ is called the Lebesgue set of f.

3.6.4 __Exercises.__

3.6.41 __Exercise.__ Let f be a real-valued continuous function on $[a,b]$, and suppose that f' exists everywhere on $[a,b]$ and that f' is bounded. Then $\int_a^x f'(t) d\lambda(t) = f(x) - f(a)$ for all $x \in [a,b]$.

Hint: Use the mean-value theorem for derivatives and

imitate the proof of 3.6.34.

3.6.42 Final Exercise # 12. Let f be a finite-valued function in $\mathcal{L}$ on $[a,b+1]$. Suppose that $\lim_{h\downarrow 0} \frac{1}{h} \int_a^b |f(x+h) - f(x)| d\lambda(x) = 0$. Prove that f is constant a.e. on $[a,b]$.

3.6.5 An application to Fourier series. We recall the following facts that will be used in this section. By definition, $e^{i\theta} = \cos\theta + i\sin\theta$ for θ any real number. We have $|e^{i\theta_1}| = 1$ and $e^{i\theta_1} e^{i\theta_2} = e^{i(\theta_1+\theta_2)}$ for all θ_1, $\theta_2 \in R$. In addition, we have the identities: $e^{i\theta} + e^{-i\theta} = 2\cos\theta$ and $e^{i\theta} - e^{-i\theta} = 2i\sin\theta$.

We shall discuss the convergence and integrability of the series $\sum_{n=1}^{\infty} \frac{1}{n} \sin n\theta$.

3.6.51 Theorem. Let p and q be positive integers, such that $p < q$. Let $\lambda_p \geq \lambda_{p+1} \geq \ldots \geq \lambda_{q-1} \geq \lambda_q \geq 0$ be given non-negative real numbers. Then for $\theta \neq 2k\pi$, $k = 0, \pm 1, \pm 2, \ldots$, we have $|\sum_{k=p}^{q} \lambda_k e^{ik\theta}| \leq \frac{\lambda_p}{|\sin\frac{\theta}{2}|}$.

Proof. We first observe that for $m \geq p$,

$$|\sum_{k=p}^{m} e^{ik\theta}| = |e^{ip\theta}(1 + e^{i\theta} + \ldots + e^{i(m-p)\theta})| =$$

$$|e^{ip\theta}| \cdot \left| \frac{1 - e^{(m-p+1)i\theta}}{1 - e^{i\theta}} \right| = \left| \frac{e^{\frac{-i\theta}{2}} - e^{(m-p+\frac{1}{2})i\theta}}{e^{-\frac{i\theta}{2}} - e^{\frac{i\theta}{2}}} \right| \leq$$

$$\frac{2}{|2i\sin\frac{\theta}{2}|} = \frac{1}{|\sin\frac{\theta}{2}|}$$ unless $\theta = 2k\pi$ for some

integer k.

We will also need Abel's transformation of a sum, namely the identity $\sum_{k=p}^{q} a_k\lambda_k = \sum_{k=p}^{q} (s_k - s_{k-1})\lambda_k =$

$\sum_{k=p}^{q-1} s_k(\lambda_k - \lambda_{k+1}) + s_q\lambda_q$ where $s_k = \sum_{j=p}^{k} a_j$ for $k = p$, $p + 1, \ldots, q$ and $s_{p-1} = 0$.

Using Abel's transformation with $a_k = e^{ik\theta}$ and applying the first paragraph, we obtain the inequality,

$$\left| \sum_{k=p}^{q} \lambda_k e^{ik\theta} \right| = \left| \sum_{k=p}^{q-1} \left(\sum_{j=p}^{k} e^{ij\theta} \right)(\lambda_k - \lambda_{k+1}) + \left(\sum_{j=p}^{q} e^{ij\theta} \right)\lambda_q \right| \leq$$

$$\sum_{k=p}^{q-1} \left| \sum_{j=p}^{k} e^{ij\theta} \right| (\lambda_k - \lambda_{k+1}) + \left| \sum_{j=p}^{q} e^{ij\theta} \right| \lambda_q \leq$$

$$\sum_{k=p}^{q-1} \frac{1}{|\sin \frac{\theta}{2}|}(\lambda_k - \lambda_{k+1}) + \frac{1}{|\sin \frac{\theta}{2}|}\lambda_q =$$

$$\frac{1}{|\sin \frac{\theta}{2}|} [\lambda_p - \lambda_{p+1} + \lambda_{p+1} - \lambda_{p+2} + \cdots + \lambda_{q-1} - \lambda_q + \lambda_q] =$$

$$\frac{\lambda_p}{|\sin \frac{\theta}{2}|} .$$

3.6.52 Theorem. Let $\{\lambda_n\}_{n=1}^{\infty}$ be a sequence of positive real numbers such that $\lambda_1 \geq \lambda_2 \geq \cdots \geq \lambda_n \geq \cdots$. Suppose further that for some positive real number H, we have $\lambda_n < \frac{H}{n}$ for all n. Then the series $S(\theta) = \sum_{n=1}^{\infty} \lambda_n \sin n\theta$ converges boundedly for all θ; that is, there exists a positive number M such that $\left| \sum_{n=1}^{p} \lambda_n \sin n\theta \right| \leq M$ for all positive integers p and all $\theta \in R$, and $\lim_{p\to\infty} \sum_{n=1}^{p} \lambda_n \sin n\theta$ exists for all $\theta \in R$.

Proof. If $S(\theta)$ converges boundedly for all $\theta \in [-\pi,\pi]$, then it converges boundedly everywhere since $\sin n\theta$ has period 2π for all n. Noting that $S(0) = S(\pi) = 0$ and that $\sin (n(-\theta)) = -\sin n\theta$ we see that if $S(\theta)$ converges boundedly for all $\theta \in]0,\pi[$, then it converges boundedly everywhere.

Let $\theta \in]0,\pi[$ be fixed and let p be a fixed positive integer. Let $\nu = [\min(p,\frac{1}{\theta})]$ where $[x]$ is defined as the greatest integer less than or equal to x. We will exhibit a bound for $\sum_{n=1}^{p} \lambda_n \sin n\theta$ (independent of p and θ) using the inequality $|\sum_{n=1}^{p} \lambda_n \sin n\theta| \leq |\sum_{n=1}^{\nu} \lambda_n \sin n\theta| + |\sum_{n=\nu+1}^{p} \lambda_n \sin n\theta|$.

Since $|\sin t| \leq |t|$ for all $t \in R$, we have

$$|\sum_{n=1}^{\nu} \lambda_n \sin n\theta| \leq \sum_{n=1}^{\nu} \lambda_n |\sin n\theta| \leq \sum_{n=1}^{\nu} \lambda_n \cdot n\theta < \nu H\theta \leq \frac{1}{\theta} H\theta = H.$$

Note that for $\phi \in [0,\frac{\pi}{2}]$, $\sin \phi \geq \frac{2}{\pi} \phi$. Using this and 3.6.51, we obtain the inequality $|\sum_{n=\nu+1}^{p} \lambda_n \sin n\theta| \leq$

$$|\sum_{n=\nu+1}^{p} \lambda_n e^{in\theta}| \leq \frac{\lambda_{\nu+1}}{\sin \frac{\theta}{2}} \leq \frac{\pi}{2} \cdot \frac{\lambda_{\nu+1}}{\frac{\theta}{2}} = \frac{\pi\lambda_{\nu+1}}{\theta} < \frac{\pi H}{(\nu+1)\theta}.$$

If $\frac{1}{\theta} \geq p$, $\nu = p$ and the summand $\sum_{n=\nu+1}^{p} \lambda_n \sin n\theta$ does not appear. If $\frac{1}{\theta} < p$, then $\nu = [\frac{1}{\theta}]$ and thus $\nu \leq \frac{1}{\theta} < \nu + 1$

Therefore $\frac{1}{\theta(\nu+1)} < 1$. Hence $|\sum_{n=\nu+1}^{p} \lambda_n \sin n\theta| < \frac{H\pi}{(\nu+1)\theta} <$ $H\pi$ and so $|\sum_{n=1}^{p} \lambda_n \sin n\theta| < (\pi + 1)H$ for $p = 1, 2, \ldots$ and all $\theta \in]0,\pi[$.

We now show convergence of $\sum_{n=1}^{\infty} \lambda_n \sin n\theta$ using the Cauchy criterion on partial sums. Fix θ, $0 < \theta < \pi$. Pick $\varepsilon > 0$ and let N (depending on ε) be such that $\frac{H}{(N+1)\sin\frac{\theta}{2}} \leq \varepsilon$. Then for $q > p \geq N$ we have

$$|\sum_{n=1}^{q} \lambda_n \sin n\theta - \sum_{n=1}^{p} \lambda_n \sin n\theta| = |\sum_{n=p+1}^{q} \lambda_n \sin n\theta| \leq$$

$$\frac{\lambda_{p+1}}{\sin\frac{\theta}{2}} < \frac{H}{(p+1)\sin\frac{\theta}{2}} \leq \frac{H}{(N+1)\sin\frac{\theta}{2}} \leq \varepsilon.$$ We have thus shown that $S(\theta)$ converges boundedly on $[0,\pi]$.

3.6.521 <u>Remarks</u>. The Fourier series of a function $f \in \mathcal{L}$ on $[-\pi,\pi]$ is the series $\frac{a_0}{2} + \sum_{n=1}^{\infty} [a_n \cos n\theta + b_n \sin n\theta]$ where $a_n = \frac{1}{\pi}\int_{-\pi}^{\pi} f(\theta) \cos n\theta \, d\lambda(\theta)$ and $b_n = \frac{1}{\pi}\int_{-\pi}^{\pi} f(\theta) \sin n\theta \, d\lambda(\theta)$. We will see later that two functions having the same Fourier series can differ only on a set of measure zero.

The following identities will be found useful:

$\frac{1}{\pi}\int_{-\pi}^{\pi} \cos n\theta \sin m\theta d\theta = 0$ for $m = 0, 1, 2, \ldots$ and $n = 0, 1, 2, \ldots$;

$\frac{1}{\pi}\int_{-\pi}^{\pi} \cos m\theta \cos n\theta \, d\theta = \delta_{mn}$ for $m = 1, 2, \ldots$ and $n = 1, 2, \ldots$;

$\frac{1}{\pi}\int_{-\pi}^{\pi} \sin m\theta \sin n\theta \, d\theta = \delta_{mn}$ for $m = 1, 2, \ldots$ and $n = 1, 2, \ldots$;

$\frac{1}{2\pi}\int_{-\pi}^{\pi} \cos n\theta \, d\theta = 1$ for $n = 0$.

δ_{mn} is the Kronecker delta-function; see page 53.

3.6.53 <u>Theorem</u>. The Fourier series of S is the series $\sum_{n=1}^{\infty} \lambda_n \sin n\theta$.

<u>Proof</u>. Using 3.5.24 we have for $m = 0, 1, 2, \ldots,$

$$a_m = \frac{1}{\pi}\int_{-\pi}^{\pi} S(\theta) \cos m\theta \, d\lambda(\theta) = \frac{1}{\pi}\int_{-\pi}^{\pi} \left(\sum_{n=1}^{\infty} \lambda_n \sin n\theta\right)\cdot$$
$$\cos m\theta \, d\lambda(\theta) = \frac{1}{\pi}\sum_{n=1}^{\infty} \lambda_n \int_{-\pi}^{\pi} \sin n\theta \cos m\theta \, d\lambda(\theta) = 0.$$

For $m = 1, 2, \ldots,$ we obtain, in a similar manner,

$$b_m = \frac{1}{\pi}\sum_{n=1}^{\infty} \lambda_n \int_{-\pi}^{\pi} \sin n\theta \sin m\theta \, d\lambda(\theta) = \frac{1}{\pi}\sum_{n=1}^{\infty} \lambda_n \cdot \pi\delta_{mn} = \lambda_m.$$

3.6.54 <u>Example</u>. Suppose that $\lambda_n = \frac{1}{n}$. Then $\sum_{n=1}^{\infty} \frac{1}{n} \sin n\theta$ converges everywhere and boundedly to $S(\theta)$. It turns out that the function $F(\theta)$ defined to be $\frac{1}{2}(\pi - \theta)$ for $\theta \in \,]0, 2\pi[$, zero at $\theta = 0$, and having period 2π (see figure) has $\sum_{n=1}^{\infty} \frac{1}{n} \sin n\theta$ as its Fourier series.

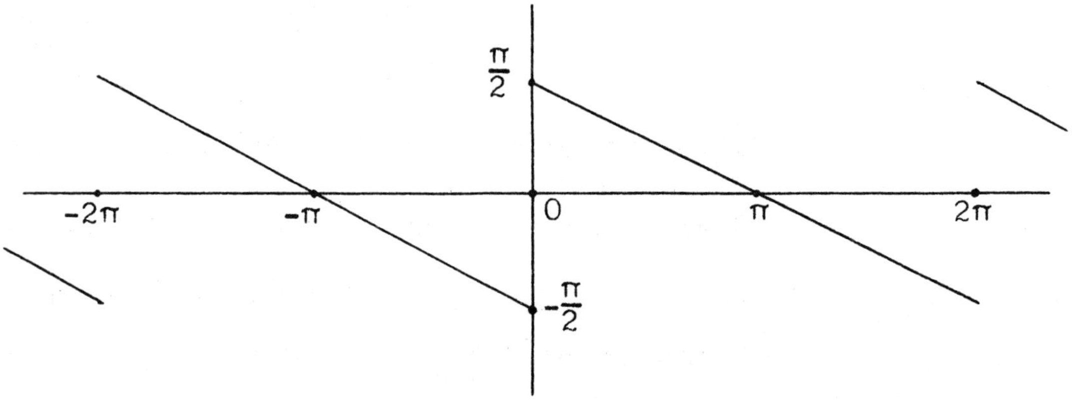

F(θ)

Consequently, $F(\Theta) = \sum_{n=1}^{\infty} \frac{1}{n} \sin n\Theta$. Evidently, the convergence of this series cannot be uniform. However, if $\sum_{n=1}^{\infty} \lambda_n < \infty$ then $\sum_{n=1}^{\infty} \lambda_n \sin n\Theta$ converges absolutely and uniformly for all Θ.

3.7 The real linear space $\mathcal{L}_1(X, \mathcal{M}, \mu)$. In this section, unless otherwise specified, $(X, \mathcal{M}, \mu)$ will be an arbitrary measure space.

3.7.1 Discussion. We are interested in obtaining a way of measuring the size of functions of various sorts. One way this can be done for continuous functions ϕ on $[0,1]$ is to define the uniform norm as $\|\phi\|_u = \max\{|\phi(x)| : 0 \le x \le 1\}$. This norm enjoys the following properties:

i) $\phi_n \to \phi$ (uniformly) if and only if $\lim_{n\to\infty} \|\phi_n - \phi\|_u = 0$;

ii) $\|\phi + \psi\|_u \le \|\phi\|_u + \|\psi\|_u$;

iii) $\|\alpha\phi\|_u = |\alpha| \cdot \|\phi\|_u$;

iv) $0 \le \|\phi\|_u < \infty$;

v) $\|\phi\|_u = 0$ if and only if $\phi = 0$.

If we define $\rho(\phi,\psi) = \|\phi - \psi\|_u$ we obtain a metric over the space of continuous real-valued functions on $[0,1]$.

Another way of determining the size of certain functions follows. For $f \in \mathcal{L}$ on $[0,1]$, the number $\int_0^1 |f(x)|d\lambda(x)$ represents, roughly, the "average" value of $|f|$. We know that $\int_0^1 |f(x)|d\lambda(x) = 0$ if and only if $f = 0$ a.e. on $[0,1]$. In order to obtain a metric for $\mathcal{L}([0,1])$ in this fashion it is necessary to identify functions that differ only on a set of measure zero. We will do this precisely and in a general setting.

3.7.2 __Definition__. Let $\mathcal{L} = \mathcal{L}(X, \mathcal{M}, \mu)$. For $f,g \in \mathcal{L}$, we write $f \sim g$ if $f(x) = g(x)$ a.e. on X. We write $\hat{f} = \{g: g \in \mathcal{L}, g \sim f\}$.

3.7.21 __Theorem__. For $f,g,h \in \mathcal{L}$, we have

i) $f \sim f$;

ii) $f \sim g$ implies $g \sim f$;

iii) $f \sim g$ and $g \sim h$ implies $f \sim h$.

3.7.22 __Theorem__. If $f,g \in \mathcal{L}$ then either $\hat{f} = \hat{g}$ or $\hat{f} \cap \hat{g}$ is void.

3.7.23 __Theorem__. If $f_1 \sim f_2$ and $\alpha \in R$, then $\alpha f_1 \sim \alpha f_2$. If $f_1 \sim f_2$ and $g_1 \sim g_2$, then $f_1 + g_1 \sim f_2 + g_2$.

The proofs of 3.7.21-3 are omitted.

3.7.3 __Definition__. For $f,g \in \mathcal{L}$, define $\hat{f} + \hat{g} = \widehat{f + g}$.

3.7.31 __Theorem__. The definition of $\hat{f} + \hat{g}$ in 3.7.3 is unambiguous: if $f_1 \in \hat{f}$ and $g_1 \in \hat{g}$, then $\hat{f}_1 + \hat{g}_1 = \hat{f} + \hat{g}$.

__Proof__. If $f_1 \in \hat{f}$ and $g_1 \in \hat{g}$, then $f_1 \sim f$ and $g_1 \sim g$. Therefore $f_1 + g_1 \sim f + g$ and so $f_1 + g_1 \in \widehat{f + g}$. Hence $\hat{f}_1 + \hat{g}_1 = \widehat{f_1 + g_1} = \widehat{f + g} = \hat{f} + \hat{g}$.

3.7.32 __Definition__. For $f \in \mathcal{L}$ and $\alpha \in R$, let $\alpha(\hat{f}) = \widehat{(\alpha f)}$.

3.7.33 __Theorem__. Definition 3.7.32 defines $\alpha(\hat{f})$ unambiguously: if $f_1 \in \hat{f}$, then $\alpha(\hat{f}_1) = \alpha(\hat{f})$.

The proof is like that of 3.7.31.

3.7.34 Theorem. Let $\mathcal{L}_1(X, \mathcal{M}, \mu)$ be the set of all equivalence classes $\hat{f}$ for $f \in \mathcal{L}(X, \mathcal{M}, \mu)$. With the definitions of $\hat{f} + \hat{g}$ and $\alpha\hat{f}$ given above, $\mathcal{L}_1$ is a linear space over the real number field.

The verification of the axioms for a real linear space is routine: we omit the details.

3.7.4 Definition. For $\hat{f} \in \mathcal{L}_1$, let $\|\hat{f}\|_1 = \int_X |f_1(x)| d\mu(x)$ for any $f_1 \in \hat{f}$. We will occasionally write $\|f\|_1$ for $\|\hat{f}\|_1$.

3.7.41 Theorem. $\|\hat{f}\|_1$ is unambiguously defined, and has the following properties:

i) $\|\hat{f}\|_1 \geq 0$, and $\|\hat{f}\|_1 = 0$ if and only if $\hat{f} = \hat{0}$, for all $\hat{f} \in \mathcal{L}_1$;

ii) $\|\alpha\hat{f}\|_1 = |\alpha| \cdot \|\hat{f}\|_1$ for all $\hat{f} \in \mathcal{L}_1$ and $\alpha \in R$;

iii) $\|\hat{f} + \hat{g}\|_1 \leq \|\hat{f}\|_1 + \|\hat{g}\|_1$ for all $\hat{f}, \hat{g} \in \mathcal{L}_1$.

Proof. As an example, we prove assertion (iii); we have $\|\hat{f} + \hat{g}\|_1 = \int_X |f(x) + g(x)| d\mu(x) \leq \int_X |f(x)| d\mu(x) + \int_X |g(x)| d\mu(x) = \|\hat{f}\|_1 + \|\hat{g}\|_1$.

3.7.42 Remark. A norm in a linear space is any real-valued function defined on the space that satisfies (i) - (iii) of 3.7.41. Thus 3.7.34 and 3.7.41 may be restated as follows.

3.7.43 Theorem. $\mathcal{L}_1(X, \mathcal{M}, \mu)$ is a real normed linear space with the norm of 3.7.4 and the linear operations defined in

3.7.3 and 3.7.32.

3.7.5 Theorem. Let $(X, \mathcal{M}, \mu)$ be a measure space such that all subsets of sets of μ-measure zero are μ-measurable. Let $\{\hat{f}_n\}_{n=1}^{\infty}$ be any sequence of elements of $\mathcal{L}_1$ such that $\lim_{m,n\to\infty} \|\hat{f}_n - \hat{f}_m\|_1 = 0$. Then there exists a $\hat{g} \in \mathcal{L}_1$ such that $\lim_{n\to\infty} \|\hat{g} - \hat{f}_n\|_1 = 0$. (This property of a normed linear space is called completeness.)

Proof. Choose any $f_n \in \hat{f}_n$ $(n = 1, 2, \ldots)$. Choose n_1 so large that for $n \geq n_1$, $\|f_n - f_{n_1}\|_1 < \frac{1}{2}$. Choose $n_2 > n_1$ such that $\|f_n - f_{n_2}\|_1 < \frac{1}{4}$ if $n \geq n_2$. When $n_1, \ldots, n_k$ are chosen, select $n_{k+1} > n_k$ such that $\|f_n - f_{n_{k+1}}\|_1 < \frac{1}{2^{k+1}}$ for all $n \geq n_{k+1}$. We have thus defined by induction a subsequence $\{f_{n_k}\}_{k=1}^{\infty}$ of $\{f_n\}_{n=1}^{\infty}$. Evidently, for each k, $\int_X |f_{n_k}(x) - f_{n_{k+1}}(x)|d\mu(x) < \frac{1}{2^k}$. We thus have, using 3.5.1, $1 = \sum_{k=1}^{\infty} \frac{1}{2^k} > \sum_{k=1}^{\infty} \int_X |f_{n_k}(x) - f_{n_{k+1}}(x)|d\mu(x) = \int_X (\sum_{k=1}^{\infty} |f_{n_k}(x) - f_{n_{k+1}}(x)|)d\mu(x)$. By 3.3.21, $\sum_{k=1}^{\infty} |f_{n_k}(x) - f_{n_{k+1}}(x)|$ is finite a.e. on X. Therefore, $\sum_{k=1}^{\infty} (f_{n_k}(x) - f_{n_{k+1}}(x))$ converges a.e. on X. We note that $\sum_{k=1}^{p} (f_{n_k}(x) - f_{n_{k+1}}(x)) = f_{n_1}(x) - f_{n_2}(x) + \ldots + f_{n_p}(x) - f_{n_{p+1}}(x) = f_{n_1}(x) - f_{n_{p+1}}(x)$. Since the partial sums have a finite limit a.e., we infer that $\lim_{p\to\infty} f_{n_p}(x) = g(x)$ exists and is finite a.e. on X. Let $g(x) = 0$ where g is not already defined.

The function g is measurable (3.1.31). Choose $\varepsilon > 0$. There exists a positive integer $N(\varepsilon)$ such that whenever $m,n \geq N(\varepsilon)$ we have $\int_X |f_n(x) - f_m(x)|d\mu(x) < \varepsilon$. If $n_p \geq N(\varepsilon)$, then $\int_X |f_{n_p}(x) - f_m(x)|d\mu(x) < \varepsilon$. By Fatou's lemma (3.5.2), for $m \geq N(\varepsilon)$, we have $\int_X |g(x) - f_m(x)|d\mu(x) = \int_X \underline{\lim}_{p\to\infty} |f_{n_p}(x) - f_m(x)|d\mu(x) \leq \underline{\lim}_{p\to\infty} \int_X |f_{n_p}(x) - f_m(x)|d\mu(x) \leq \varepsilon$. In particular, $g - f_{N(\varepsilon)} \in \mathcal{L}$ and consequently, $g = g - f_{N(\varepsilon)} + f_{N(\varepsilon)} \in \mathcal{L}$; that is, $\hat{g} \in \mathcal{L}_1$. We also infer that $\lim_{m\to\infty} \int_X |g(x) - f_m(x)|d\mu(x) = 0$. Hence $\lim_{n\to\infty} \|\hat{g} - \hat{f}_n\| = 0$.

3.7.6 Remark. A real linear space with a norm that is complete under this norm is often called a (real) Banach space, after the Polish mathematician Stefan Banach, who contributed greatly to the theory of these spaces. Thus we may summarize the results of the present section as follows. The space $\mathcal{L}_1(X, \mathfrak{M}, \mu)$ is a real Banach space if all subsets of sets of μ-measure 0 are measurable. Henceforth, given $(X, \mathfrak{M}, \mu)$, we will suppose that all subsets of sets of μ-measure 0 are measurable.

3.7.7 Definition. Let f be a complex-valued function defined on a measure space $(X, \mathfrak{M}, \mu)$ such that $\mathfrak{R}f$ and $\mathfrak{I}f$ are measurable and in $\mathcal{L}_1(X, \mathfrak{M}, \mu)$. Then we define

$\int_X f(x)d\mu(x) = \int_X \Re f(x)d\mu(x) + i \int_X \Im f(x)d\mu(x)$.

Recall that K denotes the field of complex numbers.

3.7.71 Theorem. For f and g complex-valued functions and $\alpha \in K$, we have $\int_X (f + g)(x)\, d\mu(x) = \int_X f(x)d\mu(x) + \int_X g(x)d\mu(x)$ and $\int_X \alpha f(x)d\mu(x) = \alpha \int_X f(x)d\mu(x)$.

The proofs are obvious.

3.7.72 Theorem. If $\Re f$ and $\Im f$ are in $\mathcal{L}_1(X, \mathfrak{m}, \mu)$, then $|\int_X f(x)d\mu(x)| \leq \int_X |f(x)|d\mu(x)$.

Proof. We need to show that

$[(\int_X \Re f(x)d\mu(x))^2 + (\int_X \Im f(x)d\mu(x))^2]^{1/2} \leq$

$\int_X [\Re f(x)^2 + \Im f(x)^2]^{1/2}d\mu(x)$, which is less obvious than the corresponding inequality for real-valued functions. Let $\int_X f(x)d\mu(x) = \rho e^{i\theta}$. Writing $g(x) = e^{-i\theta}f(x)$, we have $|\int_X f(x)d\mu(x)| = \rho = e^{-i\theta} \int_X f(x)d\mu(x) =$ $\int_X e^{-i\theta}f(x)d\mu(x) = \int_X g(x)d\mu(x) = \int_X \Re g(x)d\mu(x) +$ $i \int_X \Im g(x)d\mu(x)$. Equating imaginary parts, we see that $\int_X \Im g(x)d\mu(x) = 0$. Hence $|\int_X f(x)d\mu(x)| = \int_X \Re g(x)d\mu(x) =$ $\int_X \Re(e^{-i\theta}f(x))d\mu(x) \leq \int_X |e^{-i\theta}f(x)|d\mu(x) = \int_X |f(x)|d\mu(x)$.

3.7.73 Definition. $\mathcal{L}_{1,K}(X, \mathfrak{m}, \mu)$ is the normed linear space of all complex-valued functions f on X such that $\Re f$ and $\Im f$ are in $\mathcal{L}_1(X, \mathfrak{m}, \mu)$. Sums and complex scalar multiples are defined pointwise. Two functions will be regarded as identical if they are equal a.e. The norm is defined by $\|f\|_1 = \int_X |f(x)|d\mu(x)$.

3.7.74 Theorem. Let $\{f_n\}_{n=1}^{\infty}$ be a sequence of functions in $\mathcal{L}_{1,K}$ such that $f_n \to g$ a.e. on X. Suppose further that $|f_n(x)| \leq s(x)$ a.e. for all n, where s is a real-valued, non-negative function in $\mathcal{L}_1$. Then

$$\lim_{n\to\infty} \int_X f_n(x)d\mu(x) = \int_X g(x)d\mu(x).$$

Proof. Note that $|\mathfrak{R}f_n(x)| \leq |f_n(x)| \leq s(x)$, $|\mathfrak{I}f_n(x)| \leq |f_n(x)| \leq s(x)$, $\mathfrak{R}f_n \to \mathfrak{R}g$ a.e., and $\mathfrak{I}f_n \to \mathfrak{I}g$ a.e. By Lebesgue's theorem on dominated convergence (3.5.21), we have $\lim_{n\to\infty} \int_X \mathfrak{R}f_n(x)d\mu(x) = \int_X \mathfrak{R}g(x)d\mu(x)$ and $\lim_{n\to\infty} \int_X \mathfrak{I}f_n(x)d\mu(x) = \int_X \mathfrak{I}g(x)d\mu(x)$. It follows that $\lim_{n\to\infty} \int_X f_n(x)d\mu(x) = \int_X g(x)d\mu(x)$.

3.7.75 Theorem. $\mathcal{L}_{1,K}$ is complete: if $\{f_n\}_{n=1}^{\infty}$ is a sequence of functions in $\mathcal{L}_{1,K}$ such that $\lim_{m,n\to\infty} \int_X |f_m(x) - f_n(x)|d\mu(x) = 0$, then there exists a function $g \in \mathcal{L}_{1,K}$ such that $\lim_{n\to\infty} \int_X |f_n(x) - g(x)|d\mu(x) = 0$.

The proof is immediate from 3.7.5.

3.8 The complex function space $\mathcal{L}_{p,K}$ $(X, \mathcal{M}, \mu)$, $(1 < p < \infty)$.

3.8.1 Definition. Let p be a real number, $1 < p < \infty$. A complex function f on X is said to be in $\mathcal{L}_{p,K}(X, \mathcal{M}, \mu)$ if the functions $\mathfrak{R}f$ and $\mathfrak{I}f$ are measurable and $|f|^p \in \mathcal{L}_1$. $\mathcal{L}_p$ will denote all the real-valued functions in $\mathcal{L}_{p,K}$.

3.8.11 Examples. i) Suppose that $X = \{1, 2, 3, \ldots\}$, $\mathcal{M}$ is all subsets of X, and μ is such that $\mu(A) = \begin{cases} \bar{\bar{A}} & \text{if } A \text{ is finite} \\ \infty & \text{if } A \text{ is infinite} \end{cases}$. A function $f(n)$ is in $\mathcal{L}_p$ if and only if $\sum_{n=1}^{\infty} |f(n)|^p < \infty$.

Therefore, the function $f(n) = \frac{1}{n}$ is not in $\mathcal{L}_1$ but is in $\mathcal{L}_p$ for $p > 1$.

ii) Suppose that $X = [1, \infty[$, $\mathcal{M}$ is the Lebesgue measurable subsets of X, and $\mu = \lambda$. Then the function $f(x) = \frac{1}{x}$ is not in $\mathcal{L}_1$ but is in $\mathcal{L}_p$ for $p > 1$.

iii) Suppose that $X = [0,1]$, $\mathcal{M}$ is the Lebesgue measurable subsets, and $\mu = \lambda$. The function $f(x) = x^{-1/2}$ is in $\mathcal{L}_1$; however, $f \notin \mathcal{L}_2$.

iv) For $X = [0, \infty[$, $\mathcal{M}$ = Lebesgue measurable sets, and $\mu = \lambda$, we have $x^{-1/2}(1 + |\log x|)^{-1} \in \mathcal{L}_2$ and in no other $\mathcal{L}_p$.

3.8.12 Definition. For $f \in \mathcal{L}_{p,K}$, the norm $\|f\|_p$ of f is the number, $\{\int_X |f(x)|^p d\mu(x)\}^{1/p}$.

3.8.2 Definition. Let $\{a_1, \ldots, a_n\} = a$ be any finite sequence of non-negative real numbers. Let $\{q_1, \ldots, q_n\}$ be a fixed sequence of positive real numbers such that $\sum_{j=1}^{n} q_j = 1$. For a real number $r > 0$, let $M_r(a) = (\sum_{j=1}^{n} q_j a_j^r)^{1/r}$. The geometric mean of a is $G(a) = \prod_{j=1}^{n} a_j^{q_j}$.

3.8.21 Theorem. $\lim_{r\downarrow 0} M_r(a) = G(a)$.

Proof. We will need the following estimate. For a fixed $t > 0$ and $0 < r \leq 1$, we have $t^r = e^{r \log t} = 1 + r \log t + \frac{r^2(\log t)^2}{2!} + \ldots = 1 + r \log t + r^2 B_t(r)$ where $B_t(r)$ is bounded for $r \in]0,1]$.

Case I. Suppose that each $a_j > 0$. Then $M_r(a) = (\sum_{j=1}^{n} q_j a_j^r)^{1/r} = e^{1/r \log(\sum_{j=1}^{n} q_j a_j^r)} =$

$$e^{1/r \log(\sum_{j=1}^{n} q_j(1 + r \log a_j) + r^2 B(r))} =$$

$$e^{1/r \log(1 + r \sum_{j=1}^{n} \log(a_j^{q_j}) + r^2 B(r))}$$ where $B(r)$ and $B'(r)$ are bounded on $]0,1]$. Let $A = \sum_{j=1}^{n} \log(a_j^{q_j})$.

Using the mean value theorem for derivatives, we have

$$\frac{1}{r} \log(1 + Ar + r^2 B(r)) = \frac{A + 2r\theta B(r\theta) + (r\theta)^2 B'(r\theta)}{1 + Ar\theta + (r\theta)^2 B(r\theta)}$$

for some θ, $0 < \theta < 1$. Consequently, $\lim_{r\downarrow 0} \frac{1}{r} \log(1 + Ar + r^2 B(r)) = A$. Now we obtain $\lim_{r\downarrow 0} M_r(a) = e^A =$

$$e^{\sum_{j=1}^{n} \log(a_j^{q_j})} = \prod_{j=1}^{n} e^{\log(a_j^{q_j})} = \prod_{j=1}^{n} (a_j^{q_j}) = G(a).$$

Case II. Suppose that some of the a_j are zero. If all are zero, the theorem is obvious. It is merely a notational matter to suppose that $a_1, \ldots, a_k > 0$ and $a_{k+1} = \ldots = a_n = 0, 1 \leq k < n$. Letting $p_j = \frac{q_j}{\sum_{m=1}^{k} q_m}$

and applying Case I, we obtain

$\lim_{r\downarrow 0} (\sum_{j=1}^{k} p_j a_j^r)^{1/r} = \prod_{j=1}^{k} a_j^{p_j}$. We have $(\sum_{j=1}^{k} p_j a_j^r)^{1/r} =$

$(\sum_{j=1}^{k} \frac{q_j}{\sum_{m=1}^{k} q_m} a_j^r)^{1/r} = (\sum_{m=1}^{k} q_m)^{-1/r} (\sum_{j=1}^{k} q_j a_j^r)^{1/r}$, or

$(\sum_{j=1}^{k} q_j a_j^r)^{1/r} = (\sum_{m=1}^{k} q_m)^{1/r} (\sum_{j=1}^{k} p_j a_j^r)^{1/r}$. Since $\sum_{m=1}^{k} q_m < 1$,

we have $\lim_{r\downarrow 0} (\sum_{j=1}^{k} q_j a_j^r)^{1/r} = \lim_{r\downarrow 0} (\sum_{m=1}^{k} q_m)^{1/r} \prod_{j=1}^{k} a_j^{p_j} = 0 = G(a)$

the last equality is clear since some $a_j = 0$.

3.8.22 Theorem (Cauchy's inequality). Let $\{a_1, \ldots, a_n\}$ and $\{b_1, \ldots, b_n\}$ be any sequence of non-negative numbers. Then $(\sum_{j=1}^{n} a_j b_j)^2 < (\sum_{j=1}^{n} a_j^2)(\sum_{j=1}^{n} b_j^2)$ unless there exist numbers A and B, not both zero, such that $Aa_j = Bb_j$ for $j = 1, 2, \ldots, n$. In this case, equality occurs.

Proof. The inequality follows from the algebraic identity,

$$(\sum_{j=1}^{n} a_j^2)(\sum_{j=1}^{n} b_j^2) - (\sum_{k=1}^{n} a_k b_k)^2 = \frac{1}{2}\left(\sum_{j=1}^{n}\sum_{k=1}^{n}(a_j b_k - a_k b_j)^2\right) \geq 0.$$

If all of the a_j are zero, the equality clearly holds and $1 \cdot a_j = 0 \cdot b_j$ for all j. Otherwise, let $B = a_j \neq 0$ and $A = b_j$. Then, if the equality holds we have $Bb_k = a_k A$ for all k. Conversely, suppose that $Aa_k = Bb_k$ for all k, where we suppose that $A \neq 0$. Then $a_j b_k - a_k b_j =$ $\frac{B}{A} b_j b_k - \frac{B}{A} b_k b_j = 0$ and the equality above holds. If $A = 0$, then $B \neq 0$ and we proceed in a similar manner.

3.8.23 Theorem. Let $r > 0$. Then $M_r(a) < M_{2r}(a)$ unless all the a_j's are equal, in which case $M_r(a) = M_{2r}(a)$.

Proof. Using Cauchy's inequality, with $a_j = q_j^{1/2}$ and $b_j = q_j^{1/2}a_j^r$, we obtain $(M_r(a))^{2r} = (\sum_{j=1}^n q_j a_j^r)^2 \leq$ $(\sum_{j=1}^n (q_j^{1/2})^2)(\sum_{j=1}^n (q_j^{1/2}a_j^r)^2) = 1 \cdot \sum_{j=1}^n q_j a_j^{2r} = (M_{2r}(a))^{2r}$.

Hence $M_r(a) \leq M_{2r}(a)$. If the equality holds then for some A and B, not both zero, $A\, q_j^{1/2} = B\, q_j^{1/2}\, a_j^r$ for $j = 1, 2, \ldots, n$. Evidently, $B \neq 0$ for if $B = 0$ then $A \neq 0$ and hence $q_j = 0$, contrary to hypothesis. Hence $a_j^r = \frac{B}{A}$ or $a_j = \sqrt[r]{\frac{B}{A}}$ for all j; that is, all the a_j's are equal. Similarly, if all the a_j's are equal, we see that $M_r(a) = M_{2r}(a)$.

3.8.24 Theorem (Theorem of the arithmetic and geometric means). $M_1(a) > G(a)$ unless all of the a_j's are equal; in this case, $M_1(a) = G(a)$.

Proof. If $a_j = t$ for all j, then $M_1(a) = G(a) = t$. Otherwise, by 3.8.23, $M_1(a) > M_{1/2}(a) > \ldots > M_{1/2^n}(a) > \ldots$. Thus by 3.8.21, $G(a) = \lim_{n\to\infty} M_{1/2^n}(a) < M_1(a)$.

3.8.3 Theorem (Hölder's inequality). Let $\mathcal{L}_1(X, \mathfrak{M}, \mu)$ be an arbitrary measure space, and let $f_1, \ldots, f_n$ be non-negative functions in $\mathcal{L}_1(X, \mathfrak{M}, \mu)$. Let $\{q_1, \ldots, q_n\}$ be a finite sequence of positive numbers such that

$\sum_{j=1}^n q_j = 1$. Then

$$\int_X f_1^{q_1}(x) \ldots f_n^{q_n}(x)d\mu(x) < \left(\int_X f_1(x)d\mu(x)\right)^{q_1} \ldots \left(\int_X f_n(x)d\mu(x)\right)^{q_n},$$

unless either some f_j vanishes a.e. or, for all j and k, $(j \neq k)$, there exist A and B (depending on j and k), neither zero, such that $Af_j(x) = Bf_k(x)$ a.e.

<u>Proof</u>. In this proof we will sometimes write $\int f$ to denote $\int_X f(x)d\mu(x)$.

If some $f_j = 0$ a.e., then both sides are zero. Hence suppose that $\int_X f_j(x)d\mu(x) > 0$ for $j = 1, 2, \ldots, n$; suppose also that each f_j is finite everywhere. For each fixed $x \in X$ we have, by 3.8.24,

$$\left(\frac{f_1(x)}{\int f_1}\right)^{q_1} \cdots \left(\frac{f_n(x)}{\int f_n}\right)^{q_n} < \frac{q_1 f_1(x)}{\int f_1} + \cdots + \frac{q_n f_n(x)}{\int f_n} \quad \text{(A)}$$

unless

$$\frac{f_1(x)}{\int f_1} = \frac{f_2(x)}{\int f_2} = \cdots = \frac{f_n(x)}{\int f_n}, \quad \text{(B)}$$

in which case equality holds.

If (B) does not hold a.e. on X, then (A) holds on a set of positive measure. Then, integrating both sides of (A), we obtain,

$$\int_X \frac{f_1^{q_1}(x) \cdots f_n^{q_n}(x)}{(\int f_1)^{q_1} \cdots (\int f_n)^{q_n}} d\mu(x) < 1 \qquad \text{or}$$

$$\int_X f_1^{q_1}(x) \cdots f_n^{q_n}(x)\, d\mu(x) < (\int f_1)^{q_1} \cdots (\int f_n)^{q_n}. \quad \text{(C)}$$

If (B) holds a.e., then (A) holds with equality a.e. and hence (C) holds with equality.

3.8.31 Corollary (Hölder's inequality). Let $p > 1$, and write $p' = \frac{p}{p-1}$ so that $\frac{1}{p} + \frac{1}{p'} = 1$. If $f \varepsilon \mathcal{L}_p(X, \mathfrak{M}, \mu)$, and $g \varepsilon \mathcal{L}_{p'}(X, \mathfrak{M}, \mu)$, then $fg \varepsilon \mathcal{L}_1$ and

$$\int_X |f(x)g(x)|d\mu(x) < \left(\int_X |f(x)|^p d\mu(x)\right)^{\frac{1}{p}} \left(\int_X |g(x)|^{p'} d\mu(x)\right)^{\frac{1}{p'}}$$

unless either f or g vanishes a.e. or there exist constants A and B, neither equal to zero, such that $A|f|^p = B|g|^{p'}$ a.e.

Proof. We use 3.8.3 with $n = 2$, $q_1 = \frac{1}{p}$, and $q_2 = \frac{1}{p'}$. Then $\int_X (|f(x)|^p)^{1/p} (|g(x)|^{p'})^{1/p'} d\mu(x) <$ $\left(\int_X |f(x)|^p d\mu(x)\right)^{1/p} \left(\int_X |g(x)|^{p'} d\mu(x)\right)^{1/p'}$ unless $f = 0$ a.e., $g = 0$ a.e., or $\frac{|f(x)|^p}{\int_X |f(x)|^p d\mu(x)} = \frac{|g(x)|^{p'}}{\int_X |g(x)|^{p'} d\mu(x)}$ a.e. In these exceptional cases equality prevails.

3.8.32 Remark. We note that for $h \varepsilon \mathcal{L}_1$, $\left|\int_X h(x)d\mu(x)\right| = \int_X |h(x)|d\mu(x)$ if and only if h is of constant sign a.e.; that is, either h is non-negative a.e. or h is non-positive a.e. With this in mind we see from 3.8.31 that $\left|\int_X f(x)g(x)d\mu(x)\right| = \|f\|_p \cdot \|g\|_{p'}$ if and only if there exist constants A and B, not both zero, such that $A|f|^p = B|g|^{p'}$ a.e. and fg is of constant sign a.e.

3.8.4 Theorem. Let $f + g$ and αf be defined pointwise

($f, g \in \mathcal{L}_{p,K}$ and $\alpha \in K$). With these operations and the norm of 3.8.12, $\mathcal{L}_{p,K}$ is a normed linear space.

Proof. We first verify that $f, g \in \mathcal{L}_{p,K}$ and $\alpha \in K$ imply that $f + g \in \mathcal{L}_{p,K}$ and $\alpha f \in \mathcal{L}_{p,K}$. We have $|f(x) + g(x)|^p \leq (|f(x)| + |g(x)|)^p \leq (2 \max(|f(x)|, |g(x)|))^p = 2^p \max(|f(x)|^p, |g(x)|^p) \leq 2^p(|f(x)|^p + |g(x)|^p)$. Therefore $|f + g|^p \in \mathcal{L}_{1,K}$ so that $f + g \in \mathcal{L}_{p,K}$. We have the identity $\|\alpha f\|_p = (\int_X |\alpha f(x)|^p d\mu(x))^{1/p} = (|\alpha|^p \int_X |f(x)|^p d\mu(x))^{1/p} = |\alpha| \cdot \|f\|_p$. Hence $\alpha f \in \mathcal{L}_{p,K}$. Moreover, we have property (ii) of 3.7.41. It is easy to see that property (i) is also satisfied; that is, $\|f\|_p > 0$ unless $f = 0$ a.e., and $\|f\|_p = 0$ if $f = 0$ a.e. Property (iii) is contained in the following theorem.

3.8.41 Theorem (Minkowski's inequality). For $f, g \in \mathcal{L}_{p,K}(X, \mathfrak{M}, \mu)$, we have $\|f + g\|_p \leq \|f\|_p + \|g\|_p$.

Proof. If $f + g = 0$ a.e., the inequality is clear. Hence we may suppose that $\|f + g\|_p > 0$. Let $p' = \frac{p}{p - 1}$. Now $\|f + g\|_p^p = \int_X |f(x) + g(x)|^p d\mu(x) =$
$\int_X |f(x) + g(x)| \cdot |f(x) + g(x)|^{p-1} d\mu(x) \leq$
$\int_X |f(x)| \cdot |f(x) + g(x)|^{p-1} d\mu(x) + \int_X |g(x)| \cdot |f(x) + g(x)|^{p-1} d\mu(x)$. Since $[(f + g)^{p-1}]^{p'} = (f + g)^{(p-1) \cdot \frac{p}{p-1}} = (f + g)^p \in \mathcal{L}_{1,K}$, we have $(f + g)^{p-1} \in \mathcal{L}_{p',K}$. By hypothesis, $f, g \in \mathcal{L}_{p,K}$. Thus, using Hölder's inequality (3.8.31), we obtain $\|f + g\|_p^p \leq \|f\|_p \cdot \|(f + g)^{p-1}\|_{p'} +$

$\|g\|_p \cdot \|(f + g)^{p-1}\|_{p'}$. Now $\|(f + g)^{p-1}\|_{p'} =$ $\left(\int_X |f(x) + g(x)|^{(p-1)\frac{p}{p-1}} d\mu(x)\right)^{\frac{p-1}{p}} = \|f + g\|_p^{p-1}$. Hence $\|f + g\|_p^p \leq (\|f\|_p + \|g\|_p)(\|f + g\|_p^{p-1})$. Consequently, $\|f + g\|_p \leq \|f\|_p + \|g\|_p$.

3.8.42 __Exercise__. Find the conditions for equality to hold in Minkowski's inequality.

3.8.5 __Theorem__. The spaces $\mathcal{L}_{p,K}(X, \mathcal{M}, \mu)$ and $\mathcal{L}_p(X, \mathcal{M}, \mu)$ are complete. That is, if $\{f_n\}_{n=1}^{\infty}$ is a sequence of functions in $\mathcal{L}_{p,K}(\mathcal{L}_p)$ such that $\lim_{m,n\to\infty} \|f_n - f_m\|_p = 0$, then there exists $g \in \mathcal{L}_{p,K}(\mathcal{L}_p)$ such that $\lim_{n\to\infty} \|f_n - g\|_p = 0$.

__Proof__. We prove the theorem for $\mathcal{L}_{p,K}$; $\mathcal{L}_p$ is treated similarly. Choose n_1 such that $n \geq n_1$ implies $\|f_n - f_{n_1}\|_p < \frac{1}{2}$. When $n_1, \ldots, n_k$ have been chosen, let $n_{k+1} > n_k$ be such that $\|f_n - f_{n_{k+1}}\|_p < \frac{1}{2^{k+1}}$ whenever $n \geq n_{k+1}$. Hence the sequence of integers $\{n_k\}_{k=1}^{\infty}$ is defined and, moreover, we have $\|f_{n_1}\|_p + \sum_{k=1}^{\infty} \|f_{n_{k+1}} - f_{n_k}\|_p <$ $\|f_{n_1}\|_p + 1 < \infty$. For $k = 1, 2, \ldots$, let $\phi_k = |f_{n_1}| +$ $|f_{n_2} - f_{n_1}| + \ldots + |f_{n_{k+1}} - f_{n_k}|$; ϕ_k is defined and finite valued everywhere--recall that functions in $\mathcal{L}_{p,K}$ are taken to be finite valued everywhere. We have $\phi_k \geq 0$ and $\phi_k^p \leq \phi_{k+1}^p$ for all k. We infer from 3.8.41 that $\|\phi_k^p\|_1 = \|\phi_k\|_p^p \leq (\|f_{n_1}\|_p + \sum_{j=1}^{k} \|f_{n_{j+1}} - f_{n_j}\|_p)^p <$

$(\|f_{n_1}\|_p + 1)^p < \infty$ for all k. Let $\phi = \lim_{k\to\infty} \phi_k = |f_{n_1}| + \sum_{k=1}^{\infty} |f_{n_{k+1}} - f_{n_k}|$. Then by 3.5.1, $\int_X [\phi(x)]^p d\mu(x) = \int_X \lim_{k\to\infty} [\phi_k(x)]^p d\mu(x) = \lim_{k\to\infty} \int_X [\phi_k(x)]^p d\mu(x) < (\|f_{n_1}\|_p + 1)^p < \infty$. It follows from this and 3.3.21 that $\phi(x) < \infty$ a.e. on X. Since an absolutely convergent series is convergent, $f_{n_1}(x) + \sum_{k=1}^{\infty} [f_{n_{k+1}}(x) - f_{n_k}(x)]$ converges a.e. The functions $f_{n_{k+1}}$ are partial sums of this series, and hence $\lim_{k\to\infty} f_{n_k}(x) = g(x)$ exists a.e.

Fix $\varepsilon > 0$ and let n_k be so large that for $m \geq n_k$, $\int_X |f_m(x) - f_{n_k}(x)|^p d\mu(x) < \varepsilon^p$. Then by 3.5.2, we have $\int_X |f_m(x) - g(x)|^p d\mu(x) = \int_X \underline{\lim}_{k\to\infty} |f_m(x) - f_{n_k}(x)|^p d\mu(x) \leq \underline{\lim}_{k\to\infty} \int_X |f_m(x) - f_{n_k}(x)|^p d\mu(x) \leq \varepsilon^p$ for $m \geq n_k$. Hence $f_{n_k} - g \in \mathcal{L}_{p,K}$ so that $g = f_{n_k} - (f_{n_k} - g) \in \mathcal{L}_{p,K}$. Furthermore, $\|f_m - g\|_p \leq \varepsilon$ for $m \geq n_k$ and since ε is arbitrary, we conclude that $\lim_{m\to\infty} \|f_m - g\|_p = 0$.

3.8.51 __Remark__. For $X = \{1, 2, \ldots\}$ and μ such that $\mu(n) = 1$ for all $n \in X$, the space $\mathcal{L}_{p,K}(X, \mathfrak{M}, \mu)$ is the space of all sequences $a = \{a_n\}_{n=1}^{\infty}$ such that $\sum_{n=1}^{\infty} |a_n|^p < \infty$. This space is denoted by the symbol ℓ_p. Minkowski's inequality for ℓ_p assumes the form $(\sum_{n=1}^{\infty} |a_n + b_n|^p)^{1/p} \leq (\sum_{n=1}^{\infty} |a_n|^p)^{1/p} + (\sum_{n=1}^{\infty} |b_n|^p)^{1/p}$. Moreover, ℓ_p is complete.

3.8.6 <u>Theorem</u>. Suppose that $\mu(X) < \infty$. Let $1 \leq q < p$. Then $\mathcal{L}_{p,K} \subset \mathcal{L}_{q,K}$ and there exists a constant A such that $\|f\|_q \leq A\|f\|_p$ for all $f \in \mathcal{L}_{p,K}$.

<u>Proof</u>. Suppose that $f \in \mathcal{L}_{p,K}$; then $\int_X |f(x)|^p d\mu(x) < \infty$. We have $\|f\|_q^q = \int_X |f(x)|^q d\mu(x) = \int_X |f(x)|^q \cdot 1\, d\mu(x)$. Evidently, $|f(x)|^q \in \mathcal{L}_{p/q,K}$ and $1 \in \mathcal{L}_{(p/q)',K}$ where $(p/q)'$ is as defined in 3.8.31. Now Hölder's inequality (3.8.31) shows that $\|f\|_q^q \leq \left(\int_X |f(x)|^{q\cdot p/q} d\mu(x)\right)^{q/p} \cdot$

$$\left(\int_X 1\, d\mu(x)\right)^{\frac{1}{(p/q)'}} = \|f\|_p^q \cdot A^q \quad \text{where } A^q = \left(\int_X d\mu(x)\right)^{\frac{1}{(p/q)'}} < \infty$$

since $\mu(X) < \infty$. Consequently, $\|f\|_q \leq \|f\|_p \cdot A < \infty$ and $f \in \mathcal{L}_{q,K}$.

3.8.61 <u>Theorem</u>. If $1 \leq p < q$, then $\ell_p \subset \ell_q$.

<u>Proof</u>. Suppose that $\sum_{n=1}^{\infty} |a_n|^p < \infty$. Then for some t, $|a_n| < t$ for all n. Then $\sum_{n=1}^{\infty} |a_n|^q = \sum_{n=1}^{\infty} |a_n|^p \cdot |a_n|^{q-p} \leq$

$$\sum_{n=1}^{\infty} |a_n|^p t^{q-p} = t^{q-p} \sum_{n=1}^{\infty} |a_n|^p < \infty.$$

3.8.7 <u>Exercises</u>.

3.8.71 <u>Final Exercise # 13</u>. Let $f \in \mathcal{L}_2([0,\infty[)$ be a real-valued continuous function defined on $[0,\infty[$ and suppose that $f(x) = \int_0^x f'(t)d\lambda(t)$ for all $x \geq 0$. Prove that

$$\int_0^{\infty} f^2(x)d\lambda(x) < 2\left(\int_0^{\infty} x^2 f^2(x)d\lambda(x)\right)^{1/2} \cdot \left(\int_0^{\infty} [f'(x)]^2 d\lambda(x)\right)^{1/2}$$

unless $f(x)$ has the form Be^{-cx^2} with $c > 0$, in which case equality holds. Hint: Suppose that the integrals on the right are finite. Then $\lim_{x\to\infty} x|f(x)| = 0$, and one can integrate by parts over $[0, x_k]$, where $\{x_k\}_{k=1}^{\infty}$ is an appropriate sequence with limit ∞. Now use Hölder's inequality with special attention to the possibility for equality.

3.8.72 Exercise. Let $1 \leq q < p < \infty$ and suppose that $f \in \mathcal{L}_p \cap \mathcal{L}_q$. Prove that $f \in \mathcal{L}_r$ for all $q < r < p$, and find a bound on the $\mathcal{L}_r$ norms.

3.8.73 Exercise. (a) Prove that $(x \log^2 \frac{1}{x})^{-1} \in \mathcal{L}_p(0,\frac{1}{2})\,(p \geq 1)$ if and only if $p = 1$.

(b) Prove that $[x^{1/2}(1 + |\log x|)]^{-1} \in \mathcal{L}_p(0,\infty)$ $(p \geq 1)$ if and only if $p = 2$.

3.8.731 Definition. Suppose that $\{f_n\}_{n=1}^{\infty}$ is a sequence of functions in $\mathcal{L}_p(X, \mathfrak{M}, \mu)$ and that $f \in \mathcal{L}_p$. Then the sequence $\{f_n\}_{n=1}^{\infty}$ is said to converge in the $\mathcal{L}_p$-sense (briefly, $f_n \to f(\mathcal{L}_p)$) to f if $\lim_{n\to\infty} \|f_n - f\|_p = 0$.

3.8.74 Exercise. Suppose X is a σ-finite measure space and that $f, f_1, f_2, \ldots \in \mathcal{L}_p$. If $f_n \to f(\mathcal{L}_p)$ and $f_n(x) \to q(x)$ a.e., then $f(x) = q(x)$ a.e. Hint: Use Egorov's Theorem.

3.8.75 Exercise. If $f_n \to f(\mathcal{L}_p)$ and $g_n \to g(\mathcal{L}_{p'})$, then $\lim_{n\to\infty} \int_X f_n(x)g_n(x)d\mu(x) = \int_X f(x)g(x)d\mu(x)$.

3.9 Abstract Hilbert spaces and the spaces $\mathcal{L}_{2,K}(X, \mathfrak{M}, \mu)$.

3.9.1 <u>Definition</u>. A (complex) inner product space is a linear space H over K with a function, called the inner product function, on $H \times H$ to K whose value at $\langle x,y \rangle \in H \times H$ is written as (x,y), with the following properties:

i) $(x_1 + x_2, y) = (x_1, y) + (x_2, y)$ for $x_1, x_2, y \in H$;

ii) $(\alpha x, y) = \alpha(x,y)$ for $x,y \in H$ and $\alpha \in K$;

iii) $(x,y) = \overline{(y,x)}$ for $x,y \in H$ ($\bar{z}$ is the complex conjugate of z);

iv) $(x,x) > 0$ if $x \neq 0$.

If, in addition, we have

v) If $\lim_{m,n\to\infty} (x_m - x_n, x_m - x_n) = 0$, then there is an $x \in H$ for which $\lim_{n\to\infty} (x_n - x, x_n - x) = 0$;

then the inner product space is said to be a (complex) Hilbert space.

We emphasize that in this context (x,y) is not an ordered pair, but is a complex number determined by $x,y \in H$. Hence we used $\langle x,y \rangle$ to denote an ordered pair.

Throughout all of section 3.9, we will write $\mathcal{L}_p$ (or $\mathcal{L}_p(X, \mathfrak{M}, \mu)$) for $\mathcal{L}_{p,K}$ (or $\mathcal{L}_{p,K}(X, \mathfrak{M}, \mu)$), $1 \leq p < \infty$.

3.9.11 <u>Theorem</u>. If H is an inner product space, then

i) $(x, y_1 + y_2) = (x, y_1) + (x, y_2)$ for $x, y_1, y_2 \in H$;

ii) $(x, \alpha y) = \bar{\alpha}(x,y)$ for $x,y \in H$ and $\alpha \in K$;

iii) $(x,0) = (0,x) = 0$ for all $x \in H$;

iv) $(x,y) = 0$ for all $x \in H$ implies that $y = 0$.

The proof is left to the reader.

3.9.12 Theorem (Cauchy-Schwarz-Bunyakovskiĭ). If H is an inner product space, then $|(x,y)|^2 \leq (x,x)(y,y)$ with strict inequality unless $\alpha x = \beta y$ for some $\alpha,\beta \in K$, not both zero, in which case equality holds.

Proof. If $y = 0$, then equality holds trivially; moreover $0 \cdot x = 1 \cdot y$. Suppose that $y \neq 0$. The identity $(x - \lambda y, x - \lambda y) = (x,x) - \bar{\lambda}(x,y) - \lambda(y,x) + |\lambda|^2(y,y)$ is easily verified. Let $\lambda = \frac{(x,y)}{(y,y)}$; then $\bar{\lambda} = \frac{\overline{(x,y)}}{(y,y)}$, and $(x,x) - \bar{\lambda}(x,y) - \lambda(y,x) + |\lambda|^2(y,y) = (x,x) - \frac{\overline{(x,y)}}{(y,y)}(x,y) - \frac{(x,y)}{(y,y)}(y,x) + \frac{(x,y)\overline{(x,y)}}{(y,y)^2}(y,y) = (x,x) - \frac{2|(x,y)|^2}{(y,y)} + \frac{|(x,y)|^2}{(y,y)} = (x,x) - \frac{|(x,y)|^2}{(y,y)}$. Combining equalities, we have $(x,x) - \frac{|(x,y)|^2}{(y,y)} = (x - \lambda y, x - \lambda y) \geq 0$ and equality holds only if $x = \lambda y$. Hence $|(x,y)|^2 \leq (x,x)(y,y)$, with strict inequality unless $x = \lambda y$.

It remains to prove that whenever there exist $\alpha,\beta \in K$ not both zero, such that $\alpha x = \beta y$, then equality holds. Suppose that $\alpha \neq 0$. Then $x = \frac{\beta}{\alpha}y$ and $|(x,y)|^2 = |(\frac{\beta}{\alpha}y,y)|^2 = |\frac{\beta}{\alpha}(y,y)|^2 = |\frac{\beta}{\alpha}|^2|(y,y)|^2 = |\frac{\beta}{\alpha}|^2(y,y)(y,y) = (\frac{\beta}{\alpha}y,\frac{\beta}{\alpha}y)(y,y) = (x,x)(y,y)$. If $\alpha = 0$, then $\beta \neq 0$ and the proof is similar.

3.9.13 Theorem. If H is an inner product space and if we define $\|x\| = \sqrt{(x,x)}$, then H is a normed linear space.

Proof. As usual, the only postulate that is not obviously

satisfied is the triangle inequality: $\|x + y\| \leq \|x\| + \|y\|$ for all $x,y \in H$. We have $\|x + y\|^2 = (x + y, x + y) = [(x,x) + (x,y) + (y,x) + (y,y)] = |(x,x) + (x,y) + (y,x) + (y,y)| \leq (x,x) + |(x,y)| + |(y,x)| + (y,y) \leq \|x\|^2 + \|x\| \cdot \|y\| + \|y\| \cdot \|x\| + \|y\|^2 = (\|x\| + \|y\|)^2$. Hence $\|x + y\| \leq \|x\| + \|y\|$.

Note that the inequality $|(x,y)| \leq \|x\| \cdot \|y\|$ is a restatement of 3.9.12.

3.9.131 Examples. i) Let H be the set of all complex-valued sequences $x = (x_1, \ldots, x_n, \ldots)$ such that $x_n = 0$ for all but a finite number of integers n. Define $(x,y) = \sum_{n=1}^{\infty} x_n \bar{y}_n$. This is an inner product space but not a Hilbert space. To see this consider the sequence $\{x^{(r)}\}_{r=1}^{\infty}$ of points in H such that $x^{(r)} = (1, \frac{1}{2}, \ldots, \frac{1}{r}, 0, \ldots)$. Now for any r and s, say $r < s$,

$$\|x^{(r)} - x^{(s)}\|^2 = \sum_{n=r+1}^{s} |x_n^{(r)} - x_n^{(s)}|^2 = \sum_{n=r+1}^{s} \frac{1}{n^2} \leq \sum_{n=r+1}^{\infty} \frac{1}{n^2}.$$

Since the series $\sum_{n=1}^{\infty} \frac{1}{n^2}$ converges, we see that $\lim_{r,s\to\infty} \|x^{(r)} - x^{(s)}\| = 0$. However, if some point $y \in H$ has the property that $\lim_{r\to\infty} \|x^{(r)} - y\| = 0$ then, as one can easily check, $y_n = \frac{1}{n}$ for all n. This means that $y \notin H$.

ii) By 3.8.4 and 3.8.5, ℓ_2 is a Hilbert space.

3.9.132 Final Exercise # 14. Let P consist of all $x \in \ell_2$

such that $|x_n| \leq \frac{1}{n}$ for all n. (P is often called the Hilbert parallelotope or Hilbert cube.) Then P is compact in the following sense: every sequence in P has a subsequence which converges to a point of P in the ℓ_2 sense. An equivalent assertion is the following. P is complete and totally bounded. Total boundedness means that for every $\varepsilon > 0$, there is a finite subset $\{y_1, \ldots, y_m\} \subset P$ such that for all $x \in P$, $\min\{\|x - y_1\|, \ldots, \|x - y_m\|\} < \varepsilon$.

3.9.14 Theorem. Every closed subspace M of a Hilbert space H is a Hilbert space.

Proof. It is clear that the closed subspace M is an inner product space. Suppose that $\{x_n\}_{n=1}^{\infty}$ is a Cauchy sequence in M. Then there exists an $x \in H$ such that $\lim_{n\to\infty} \|x_n - x\| = 0$. Thus x is a limit point of M and hence $x \in M$.

3.9.2 Theorem (Beppo Levi). Let H be an inner product space, M a subspace of H, and $x \in H$. Let $d = \inf\{\|x - y\|: y \in M\}$. If $y_1, y_2 \in M$, then $\|y_1 - y_2\| \leq \sqrt{\|x - y_1\|^2 - d^2}$ $\sqrt{\|x - y_2\|^2 - d^2}$.

Proof. We first show that $\|x - y_1 - \lambda(x - y_2)\|^2 \geq |1 - \lambda|^2 d^2$ for all $\lambda \in K$. If $\lambda = 1$, the inequality is clear. Suppose that $\lambda \neq 1$. Then $\frac{y_1 - \lambda y_2}{1-\lambda} \in M$. Hence $\|x - \frac{y_1 - \lambda y_2}{1-\lambda}\|^2 \geq d^2$. Thus $\|(1 - \lambda)x - (y_1 - \lambda y_2)\|^2 \geq$

$|1-\lambda|^2 d^2$. Writing $x - y_1 = z_1$ and $x - y_2 = z_2$, the last inequality becomes $\|z_1 - \lambda z_2\|^2 \geq |1-\lambda|^2 d^2$. Thus $|1-\lambda|^2 d^2 \leq \|z_1 - \lambda z_2\|^2 = (z_1 - \lambda z_2, z_1 - \lambda z_2) = \|z_1\|^2 - \bar{\lambda}(z_1,z_2) - \lambda(z_2,z_1) + \lambda\bar{\lambda}\|z_2\|^2$. Moreover, $|1-\lambda|^2 d^2 = (1 - \bar{\lambda} - \lambda + |\lambda|^2)d^2$. Hence $(1-\bar{\lambda}-\lambda+|\lambda|^2)d^2 \leq \|z_1\|^2 - \bar{\lambda}(z_1,z_2) - \lambda(z_2,z_1) + |\lambda|^2 \cdot \|z_2\|^2$, so that

$$(*)\quad [\|z_1\|^2 - d^2] - \bar{\lambda}[(z_1,z_2) - d^2] - \lambda[(z_2,z_1) - d^2] + |\lambda|^2[\|z_2\|^2 - d^2] \geq 0.$$

Suppose that $\|z_2\|^2 - d^2 \neq 0$. Inequality (*) holds for all complex λ, and in particular for $\lambda = \dfrac{(z_1,z_2)-d^2}{\|z_2\|^2 - d^2}$. That is, $[\|z_1\|^2 - d^2] - \dfrac{|(z_1,z_2)-d^2|^2}{\|z_2\|^2 - d^2} - \dfrac{|(z_1,z_2)-d^2|^2}{\|z_2\|^2 - d^2} + \dfrac{|(z_1,z_2)-d^2|^2}{(\|z_2\|^2 - d^2)^2}[\|z_2\|^2 - d^2] \geq 0$. So $[\|z_1\|^2 - d^2] - \dfrac{|(z_1,z_2)-d^2|^2}{(\|z_2\|^2 - d^2)} \geq 0$ and hence

$$(**)\quad |(z_1,z_2) - d^2|^2 \leq (\|z_1\|^2 - d^2)(\|z_2\|^2 - d^2).$$

The inequality (**) holds also if $\|z_2\|^2 - d^2 = 0$. To see this we will show that $|(z_1,z_2) - d^2| = 0$ in this case. Let $\lambda = \mu[(z_1,z_2) - d^2]$, where μ is a real number. Substituting λ in (*), we obtain $[\|z_1\|^2 - d^2] - \mu|(z_1,z_2) - d^2|^2 - \mu|(z_1,z_2) - d^2|^2 \geq 0$. Thus $2\mu|(z_1,z_2) - d^2| \leq [\|z_1\|^2 - d^2]$. Since this is true for all real μ, we conclude that $|(z_1,z_2) - d^2| = 0$.

Now, using (**), we obtain $\|y_1 - y_2\|^2 = \|y_1 - x + x - y_2\|^2 = \|z_1 - z_2\|^2 = (z_1 - z_2, z_1 - z_2) = \|z_1\|^2 - (z_1,z_2) - (z_2,z_1) + \|z_2\|^2 = [\|z_1\|^2 - d^2] - [(z_1,z_2) - d^2] - [(z_2,z_1) - d^2] + [\|z_2\|^2 - d^2] \leq \|z_1\|^2 - d^2 + 2|(z_1,z_2) - d^2| + \|z_2\|^2 - d^2 \leq \|z_1\|^2 - d^2 + 2\sqrt{\|z_1\|^2 - d^2} \cdot \sqrt{\|z_2\|^2 - d^2} + \|z_2\|^2 - d^2 = (\sqrt{\|z_1\|^2 - d^2} + \sqrt{\|z_2\|^2 - d^2})^2$. Hence $\|y_1 - y_2\| \leq \sqrt{\|x - y_1\|^2 - d^2} + \sqrt{\|x - y_2\|^2 - d^2}$, and the proof is complete.

3.9.21 Definition. Let H be an inner product space. If $x,y \in H$ and $(x,y) = 0$, x and y are said to be orthogonal to each other; we write $x \perp y$. For $A \subset H$, we write $x \perp A$ if $x \perp y$ for all $y \in A$.

Note that $0 \perp H$ and that $x \perp x$ only if $x = 0$.

3.9.22 Theorem. Let H be a Hilbert space, and let M be a closed linear subspace of H. For every $x \in H$, there is a unique $x' \in M$ such that $(x - x') \perp M$.

Proof. Let $d = \inf\{\|x - y\|: y \in M\}$. There exists a sequence $\{y_n\}_{n=1}^{\infty}$, $y_n \in M$, such that $\lim_{n\to\infty} \|x - y_n\| = d$. By 3.9.2, we have $\|y_n - y_m\| \leq [\|x - y_n\|^2 - d^2]^{1/2} + [\|x - y_m\|^2 - d^2]^{1/2}$ for all m and n, and hence $\lim_{m,n\to\infty} \|y_n - y_m\| = 0$ since $\lim_{m,n\to\infty} [\|x - y_n\|^2 - d^2] = 0$ and $\lim_{m,n\to\infty} [\|x - y_m\|^2 - d^2] = 0$.

By 3.9.14 M is complete; thus there exists an $x' \in M$ such that $\lim_{n\to\infty} \|y_n - x'\| = 0$. By the definition of d, $d \leq \|x - x'\|$. Moreover, $\|x - x'\| \leq \|x - y_n\| + \|y_n - x'\|$ for all n and hence $\|x - x'\| \leq \lim_{n\to\infty} [\|x - y_n\| + \|y_n - x'\|] = d + 0 = d$. Thus $\|x - x'\| = d$.

Write $x'' = x - x'$. We wish to prove that $x'' \perp M$. Clearly $x'' \perp 0$; hence suppose that $y \in M$ and $y \neq 0$. Let t be any complex number. Then $x' - ty \in M$. Therefore we have $d^2 \leq \|x - (x' - ty)\|^2 = \|x'' + ty\|^2 = (x'' + ty, x'' + ty) = (x'', x'') + t(y, x'') + \bar{t}(x'', y) + t\bar{t}(y, y) = d^2 + t(y, x'') + \bar{t}(x'', y) + t\bar{t}(y, y)$. Choose $t = -\frac{(x'', y)}{(y, y)}$. Then $d^2 \leq d^2 - \frac{|(x'', y)|^2}{(y, y)} - \frac{|(x'', y)|^2}{(y, y)} + \frac{|(x'', y)|^2}{(y, y)}$. Consequently $0 \leq -\frac{|(x'', y)|^2}{(y, y)}$ and hence $(x'', y) = 0$. Since $x'' \perp y$ for all $y \in M$, $x'' \perp M$.

To prove uniqueness, suppose that $x = x' + x'' = y' + y''$ where $x', y' \in M$, $x'' \perp M$, and $y'' \perp M$. Then $x' - y' = y'' - x'' \in M$ and $y'' - x'' \perp M$. So $x' - y' \perp x' - y'$ and hence $x' - y' = 0$. Thus $x' = y'$.

3.9.23 <u>Theorem</u>. Let H and M be as in 3.9.22. Then for each $x \in H$, there exist unique elements $x' \in M$ and $x'' \perp M$ such that $x = x' + x''$.

<u>Proof</u>. This merely restates 3.9.22 except for the uniqueness of x''. If $x = x' + x'' = y' + y''$, then $x' = y'$ by 3.9.22, so that $x'' = y''$.

3.9.231 Definition. Let L be a linear space. If A and B are linear subspaces of L such that $A \cap B = \{0\}$ and such that every element of L can be written in (exactly) one way as $x' + x''$, where $x' \in A$ and $x'' \in B$, then we say that L is the direct sum of A and B; we write $L = A \oplus B$.

3.9.24 Theorem. Let H and M be as in 3.9.22. Let $M^{\perp}$ be the set $\{x\colon\ x \in H \text{ and } x \perp M\}$. Then $M^{\perp}$ is a closed linear subspace of H, and $H = M \oplus M^{\perp}$.

Proof. This restates 3.9.23 except to prove that $M^{\perp}$ is a closed linear subspace. Suppose that $x_1, x_2 \in M^{\perp}$ and $\alpha, \beta \in K$. Then for $y \in M$, $(\alpha x_1 + \beta x_2, y) = \alpha(x_1, y) + \beta(x_2, y) = 0 + 0 = 0$. Thus $\alpha x_1 + \beta x_2 \in M^{\perp}$. Suppose that $\{x_n\}_{n=1}^{\infty}$ is a sequence in $M^{\perp}$ and that $\lim_{n\to\infty} \|x - x_n\| = 0$ for some $x \in H$. Then for $y \in M$, we have $|(x,y)| = |(x,y) - (x_n,y)| = |(x - x_n, y)| \leq \|x - x_n\| \cdot \|y\|$ so that $|(x,y)| \leq \lim_{n\to\infty} \|x - x_n\| \cdot \|y\| = 0$. Thus $(x,y) = 0$ and hence $x \in M^{\perp}$.

3.9.25 Theorem. Let H and M be as in 3.9.22. Then $M^{\perp\perp} = M$.

Proof. Suppose that $x \in M$. For all $y \in M^{\perp}$, we have $(x,y) = 0$ and hence $x \in M^{\perp\perp}$. Suppose conversely that $x \in M^{\perp\perp}$. Then by 3.9.23, $x = x' + x''$ where $x' \in M$ and $x'' \in M^{\perp}$. For all $y \in M^{\perp}$, we have $(x'', y) = (x - x', y) = (x,y) - (x',y) = 0$. Hence $x'' \in M^{\perp}$ and $x'' \perp M^{\perp}$. Thus $x'' = 0$ and $x = x' \in M$.

3.9.26 Theorem. A subspace M of the Hilbert space H is dense in H if and only if $M^{\perp} = \{0\}$. (Note: A set $A \subset H$ is dense in H if for each $x \in H$ and each $\varepsilon > 0$, there exists an $a \in A$ such that $\|x - a\| < \varepsilon$.)

The proof is left as an exercise for the reader.

3.9.3 Definition. A linear functional f on any complex linear space L is a complex-valued function such that $f(\alpha x + \beta y) = \alpha f(x) + \beta f(y)$ for all $\alpha, \beta \in K$ and $x, y \in L$. If L is a normed linear space and if there exists a positive number A such that $|f(x)| \leq A \cdot \|x\|$ for all $x \in L$, f is said to be a bounded linear functional.

3.9.31 Example. Let H be an inner product space and let $y \in H$ be fixed. Let f be the function such that $f(x) = (x,y)$ for all $x \in H$. Clearly f is a linear functional. By 3.9.12, $|f(x)| = |(x,y)| \leq \|y\| \cdot \|x\|$ for all $x \in H$, so that f is a bounded linear functional.

3.9.32 Theorem. Let f be a bounded linear functional on a normed linear space L. Then $\sup\left\{\frac{|f(x)|}{\|x\|}: x \in L, x \neq 0\right\} < \infty$; we define $\|f\| = \sup\left\{\frac{|f(x)|}{\|x\|}: x \in L, x \neq 0\right\}$. Then $|f(x)| \leq \|f\| \cdot \|x\|$ for all $x \in L$ and $\|f\|$ is the least number with this property.

The proof is omitted.

3.9.33 Theorem. Let L be a normed linear space and f be a bounded linear functional on L. Then $Z_f = \{x: x \in L, f(x) = 0\}$ is a closed linear subspace of L.

Proof. If $x, y \in Z_f$ and $\alpha, \beta \in K$, then $f(\alpha x + \beta y) =$

$\alpha f(x) + \beta f(y) = 0$ so that $\alpha x + \beta y \in Z_f$. Suppose that $\{x_n\}_{n=1}^{\infty}$ is a sequence in Z_f converging to a point $x \in L$. Since $|f(x)| = |f(x) - f(x_n)| = |f(x - x_n)| \leq \|f\| \cdot \|x - x_n\|$, we have $|f(x)| \leq \lim_{n\to\infty} \|f\| \cdot \|x - x_n\| = 0$. Thus $f(x) = 0$ and $x \in Z_f$.

3.9.34 Theorem. (F. Riesz). Let H be a Hilbert space. Let f be a bounded linear functional on H. Then there is a unique $y \in H$ such that $f(x) = (x,y)$ for all $x \in H$.

Proof. Case I. Suppose that $f = 0$. Then $f(x) = (x,0)$ for all x and, moreover, 0 is unique since for $y \neq 0$, we have $(y,y) \neq 0$.

Case II. Suppose that $f \neq 0$. Then Z_f is a proper closed linear subspace of H. By 3.9.26, $Z_f^{\perp} \neq \{0\}$. Choose $w \in Z_f^{\perp}$ such that $w \neq 0$; thus $f(w) \neq 0$. For any $x \in H$, $x - \frac{f(x)}{f(w)} w \in Z_f$ since $f(x - \frac{f(x)}{f(w)} w) = f(x) - \frac{f(x)}{f(w)} f(w) = 0$. Since $w \in Z_f^{\perp}$, we have $(x - \frac{f(x)}{f(w)} w, w) = 0$ and so $(x,w) - (\frac{f(x)}{f(w)} w, w) = 0$. Hence $\frac{f(x)}{f(w)} (w,w) = (x,w)$ or $f(x) = (x, \frac{\overline{f(w)}}{(w,w)} w)$. Thus $\frac{\overline{f(w)}}{(w,w)} w$ is the y required by the theorem. To prove uniqueness, suppose that $(x,y) = (x,y')$ for all $x \in H$. Then $(x,y - y') = 0$ for all $x \in H$. Thus $y - y' = 0$, i.e., $y = y'$.

3.9.4 Definition. Let H be a Hilbert space. A subset E of

H is said to be orthogonal if $(e_1,e_2) = 0$ for all $e_1,e_2 \in E$ such that $e_1 \neq e_2$. If we also have $(e,e) = 1$ for all $e \in E$, then E is called orthonormal. From this point to the end of 3.9, H will denote a Hilbert space, unless the contrary is explicitly stated.

3.9.411 Theorem. If $\{x_1, \ldots, x_n\}$ is an orthogonal subset of H, then $\|x_1 + \ldots + x_n\|^2 = \|x_1\|^2 + \ldots + \|x_n\|^2$.

Proof. We have $\|x_1 + \ldots + x_n\|^2 = (\sum_{j=1}^{n} x_j, \sum_{k=1}^{n} x_k) = \sum_{j=1}^{n} \sum_{k=1}^{n} (x_j,x_k) = \sum_{j=1}^{n} (x_j,x_j) = \sum_{j=1}^{n} \|x_j\|^2$.

3.9.412 Theorem. Suppose that $\{x_1, \ldots, x_n, \ldots\}$ is an orthogonal subset of H. Then $\lim_{n\to\infty} \sum_{k=1}^{n} x_k$ exists in H if and only if $\sum_{k=1}^{\infty} \|x_k\|^2 < \infty$. When this limit exists, we write it as $\sum_{k=1}^{\infty} x_k$.

Proof. For $n > m$ we have $\|\sum_{k=1}^{n} x_k - \sum_{k=1}^{m} x_k\|^2 = \|\sum_{k=m+1}^{n} x_k\|^2 = \sum_{k=m+1}^{n} \|x_k\|^2$; the last equality follows from 3.9.411. Now $\sum_{k=1}^{\infty} \|x_k\|^2 < \infty$ if and only if $\lim_{m,n\to\infty} \sum_{k=m+1}^{n} \|x_k\|^2 = 0$ and hence if and only if $\left\{\sum_{k=1}^{n} x_k\right\}_{n=1}^{\infty}$ forms a Cauchy sequence. Clearly this is equivalent to the existence of $\lim_{n\to\infty} \sum_{k=1}^{n} x_k$.

3.9.413 Definition. A subset E of a linear space L is said to be linearly independent if $\sum_{k=1}^{n} \alpha_k x_k = 0$ $(\alpha_k \in K)$ implies that each $\alpha_k = 0$, for every finite subset $\{x_1, \ldots, x_k\}$ of E.

3.9.414 Definition. The smallest linear subspace of a linear space L that contains a given subset A of L is said to be spanned by A.

3.9.415 Theorem. Any finite orthogonal subset $\{x_1, \ldots, x_k\}$ of H not containing 0 is linearly independent.

Proof. Suppose that $\sum_{k=1}^{n} \alpha_k x_k = 0$. Then for $\ell = 1, 2, \ldots, n$ we have $0 = (0, x_\ell) = (\sum_{k=1}^{n} \alpha_k x_k, x_\ell) = \alpha_\ell (x_\ell, x_\ell)$. Hence $\alpha_\ell = 0$ for $\ell = 1, 2, \ldots, n$, and $\{x_1, \ldots, x_k\}$ is linearly independent.

3.9.42 Definition. Let E be an orthonormal set in H, $x \in H$, and $e \in E$. Then (x,e) is called a Fourier coefficient of x with respect to E.

3.9.421 Note. The foregoing definition is an abstraction from the theory of Fourier series. Let $H = \mathcal{L}_2(-\pi,\pi)$ and define $(f,g) = \frac{1}{2\pi} \int_{-\pi}^{\pi} f(x) \overline{g(x)}\, d\lambda(x)$. For $n = 0, \pm 1, \pm 2, \ldots,$ let $e_n(x) = e^{inx}$. Then $(f, e_n) = \frac{1}{2\pi} \int_{-\pi}^{\pi} f(x) e^{-inx} d\lambda($ for all $f \in \mathcal{L}_2(-\pi,\pi)$, and 3.9.42 thus yields the classical Fourier coefficients in this case.

3.9.43 Theorem. Let $\{e_1, \ldots, e_n\}$ be any finite orthonormal subset of H, and let $x \in H$. Then $\min \left\{ \|x - \sum_{k=1}^{n} \alpha_k e_k\| : \alpha_1, \ldots, \alpha_n \in K \right\}$ is attained precisely when each $\alpha_k = (x, e_k)$. Furthermore,

$$(*)\quad \sum_{k=1}^{n} |(x,e_k)|^2 \leq \|x\|^2;$$

this is a special case of Bessel's inequality.

Proof. We have $\|x - \sum_{k=1}^{n} \alpha_k e_k\|^2 = (x - \sum_{k=1}^{n} \alpha_k e_k,$ $x - \sum_{k=1}^{n} \alpha_k e_k) = (x,x) - \sum_{k=1}^{n} (x,\alpha_k e_k) - \sum_{k=1}^{n} (\alpha_k e_k,x) +$ $\sum_{k=1}^{n} (\alpha_k e_k,\alpha_k e_k) = \|x\|^2 - \sum_{k=1}^{n} \bar{\alpha}_k (x,e_k) - \sum_{k=1}^{n} \alpha_k \overline{(x,e_k)} + \sum_{k=1}^{n} |\alpha_k|^2 =$ $\|x\|^2 + \sum_{k=1}^{n} |(x,e_k)|^2 - \sum_{k=1}^{n} \bar{\alpha}_k (x,e_k) - \sum_{k=1}^{n} \alpha_k \overline{(x,e_k)} +$ $\sum_{k=1}^{n} |\alpha_k|^2 - \sum_{k=1}^{n} |(x,e_k)|^2 = \|x\|^2 + \sum_{k=1}^{n} |(x,e_k) - \alpha_k|^2 -$ $\sum_{k=1}^{n} |(x,e_k)|^2.$

The above computation shows that as a function of $\alpha_1, \ldots, \alpha_n$, $\|x - \sum_{k=1}^{n} \alpha_k e_k\|^2$ attains its minimum when $\alpha_k = (x,e_k)$ for all k, and for no other values of $\alpha_1, \ldots, \alpha_n$. Setting $\alpha_k = (x,e_k)(k = 1, 2, \ldots, n)$ we see also that $0 \leq \|x - \sum_{k=1}^{n} (x,e_k)e_k\|^2 = \|x\|^2 - \sum_{k=1}^{n} |(x,e_k)|^2$

or

$$(*)\quad \sum_{k=1}^{n} |(x,e_k)|^2 \leq \|x\|^2.$$

3.9.44 Theorem. Let E be any orthonormal subset of H and let $x \in H$. Then $(x,e) = 0$ for all but a countable number of $e \in E$, and Bessel's inequality obtains:

$$\sum_{e \in E} |(x,e)|^2 \leq \|x\|^2.$$

Proof. For a finite subset $\{e_1, \ldots, e_n\}$ of E we

have $\sum_{k=1}^{n} |(x,e_k)|^2 \leq \|x\|^2$ by 3.9.43. Hence, using the definition of $\sum_{e\varepsilon E}$ we infer that $\sum_{e\varepsilon E} |(x,e)|^2 = \sup\left\{\sum_{k=1}^{n} |(x,e_k)|^2 : \{e_1, \ldots, e_n\} \text{ is a finite subset of } E\right\} \leq \|x\|^2$.

For every positive integer n, $\{e: |(x,e)|^2 \geq \frac{1}{n}\}$ must be finite; otherwise $\sum_{e\varepsilon E} |(x,e)|^2 = \infty \leq \|x\|^2$, which is absurd. Consequently, $\{e: |(x,e)|^2 > 0\} = \bigcup_{n=1}^{\infty} \{e: |(x,e)|^2 \geq \frac{1}{n}\}$ is countable.

3.9.45 Theorem. Let $\{e_k\}_{k=1}^{\infty}$ be a countably infinite orthonormal set in H, and suppose that $x \varepsilon H$. Then $y = \sum_{k=1}^{\infty} (x,e_k)e_k$ exists and $x - y$ is orthogonal to all of the e_k $(k = 1, 2, \ldots)$.

Proof. By 3.9.44 we have $\sum_{k=1}^{\infty} |(x,e_k)|^2 < \infty$. Hence by 3.9.412, y exists. Fix n; we will prove that $(y,e_n) = (x,e_n)$. Choose $N \geq n$. Then $(y,e_n) = (\sum_{k=1}^{N} (x,e_k)e_k, e_n) + (\sum_{n=N+1}^{\infty} (x,e_k)e_k, e_n) = (x,e_n) + (\sum_{k=N+1}^{\infty} (x,e_k)e_k, e_n)$.

Thus $|(y,e_n) - (x,e_n)| = |(\sum_{k=N+1}^{\infty} (x,e_k)e_k, e_n)| \leq \|\sum_{k=N+1}^{\infty} (x,e_k)e_k\| \cdot \|e_n\| = \|\sum_{k=N+1}^{\infty} (x,e_k)e_k\|$. Thus $|(y,e_n) - (x,e_n)| \leq \lim_{N\to\infty} \|\sum_{k=N+1}^{\infty} (x,e_k)e_k\| = 0$ and $(y,e_n) = (x,e_n)$. Therefore, $(y,e_n) = (x,e_n)$ for all n so that $(x - y, e_n) = 0$ for all n.

3.9.5 Definition. An orthonormal set $E \subset H$ is said to be complete if $x \perp E$ implies $x = 0$.

3.9.51 Theorem. Every Hilbert space H, $H \neq \{0\}$, contains a complete orthonormal set.

Proof. Let $\mathcal{E}$ be the family of all non-void orthonormal sets in H. For any $x \in H$, $x \neq 0$, $\left\{\frac{x}{\|x\|}\right\} \in \mathcal{E}$; hence $\mathcal{E}$ is non-void. Partially order $\mathcal{E}$ by inclusion. Consider a completely ordered subfamily $\{E_\lambda\}_{\lambda \in \Lambda}$ of $\mathcal{E}$. The set $E = \bigcup_{\lambda \in \Lambda} E_\lambda$ is an upper bound for $\{E_\lambda\}_{\lambda \in \Lambda}$; we now show that $E \in \mathcal{E}$. If $e \in E$, then $e \in E_\lambda$ for some λ and hence $(e,e) = 1$. If e_1, e_2 are distinct members of E, then $e_1 \in E_{\lambda_1}$ and $e_2 \in E_{\lambda_2}$ for $\lambda_1, \lambda_2 \in \Lambda$. Either $E_{\lambda_1} \subset E_{\lambda_2}$ or $E_{\lambda_2} \subset E_{\lambda_1}$; suppose that $E_{\lambda_1} \subset E_{\lambda_2}$. Then $e_1, e_2 \in E_{\lambda_2}$ and hence $(e_1, e_2) = 0$.

By Theorem 1.5.7, there exists a maximal orthonormal set E_0. Suppose that $x \in H$, $x \neq 0$, and $x \perp E_0$. Then $\frac{x}{\|x\|} \notin E_0$ and $\frac{x}{\|x\|} \perp E_0$; hence $\left\{\frac{x}{\|x\|}\right\} \cup E_0$ is an orthonormal set properly containing E_0. This contradicts the maximality of E_0. Hence E_0 is complete.

3.9.52 Theorem. Let $H \neq \{0\}$ be a Hilbert space containing a countable dense subset. Then H contains a countable complete orthonormal subset, which can be constructed without appealing to 1.5.7.

Proof. Let $D = \{x_1, \ldots, x_n, \ldots\}$ be dense in H; we may suppose that $x_n \neq 0$ for all n. Let $j_1 = 1$. Suppose that positive integers $j_1 < j_2 < \ldots < j_k$ have been chosen so that the set $\{x_{j_1}, x_{j_2}, \ldots, x_{j_k}\}$ is linearly independent. If there does not exist a $q > j_k$ such that $\{x_q, x_{j_1}, \ldots, x_{j_k}\}$ is linearly independent, then the process stops. Otherwise define j_{k+1} to be the least integer q such that $q > j_k$ and $\{x_{j_1}, \ldots, x_{j_k}, x_q\}$ is linearly independent.

Write $y_n = x_{j_n}$ for $n = 1, 2, \ldots$. Let S be the linear subspace of H spanned by $\{y_1, y_2, \ldots\}$. Evidently, each $x_n \in S$ by the construction of the x_{j_n}. Consequently, S is dense in H. Let $e_1 = \frac{y_1}{\|y_1\|}$. Let $f_2 = y_2 - (y_2, e_1) \cdot e_1$. Then let $e_2 = \frac{f_2}{\|f_2\|}$. Suppose $e_1, \ldots, e_k$ have been defined to be orthonormal and to span the same subspace as $y_1, \ldots, y_k$. Then let $f_{k+1} = y_{k+1} - [(y_{k+1}, e_1)e_1 + \ldots + (y_{k+1}, e_k)e_k]$. For $\ell = 1, 2, \ldots, k$, it is clear that $(f_{k+1}, e_\ell) = 0$. Let $e_{k+1} = \frac{f_{k+1}}{\|f_{k+1}\|}$. Then $\{e_1, \ldots, e_k, e_{k+1}\}$ is orthonormal and spans the same subspace as $\{y_1, \ldots, y_k, y_{k+1}\}$. Thus there are as many e_k's as y_k's. Also, $\{e_k\}_{k=1}^{n}$ (n is a positive integer or ∞) spans S. By 3.9.26, we see that $S^\perp = \{0\}$. Consequently, if $x \in H$ and $x \perp e_k$ for all k, then $x \perp S$ and $x = 0$. Hence

$\{e_k\}_{k=1}^{n}$ is complete.

The construction used in the above proof is called the Gram-Schmidt process.

3.9.521 Theorem. A Hilbert space H is a finite-dimensional complex Euclidean space if and only if the Gram-Schmidt process yields a finite complete orthonormal set.

Proof. Suppose that $\{e_1, \ldots, e_n\}$, where n is a positive integer, is the complete orthonormal set produced by the Gram-Schmidt process. Then for every $x \in H$, write $x' = \sum_{j=1}^{n} (x, e_j) e_j$. For $k = 1, \ldots, n$, $(x' - x, e_k) =$
$(\sum_{j=1}^{n} (x, e_j) e_j - x, e_k) = \sum_{j=1}^{n} ((x, e_j) e_j, e_k) - (x, e_k) =$
$\sum_{j=1}^{n} (x, e_j)(e_j, e_k) - (x, e_k) = (x, e_k)(e_k, e_k) - (x, e_k) = 0.$
Thus $x' - x \perp \{e_1, \ldots, e_n\}$. Therefore $x - x' = 0$ and $x = x' = \sum_{j=1}^{n} (x, e_j) e_j$. This means that H is finite-dimensional.

If H is finite-dimensional, say the dimension is n, then there can be only n y's and hence only n e's.

3.9.522 Exercise. Suppose that $y_1, \ldots, y_n, \ldots$ are given as in 3.9.52. Prove that the e_n's are given by

$$e_n = \frac{1}{\sqrt{D_{n-1} D_n}} \begin{vmatrix} (y_1, y_1) & (y_2, y_1) & \cdots & (y_n, y_1) \\ \cdots & & & \\ (y_1, y_{n-1}) & (y_2, y_{n-1}) & \cdots & (y_n, y_{n-1}) \\ y_1 & y_2 & \cdots & y_n \end{vmatrix}$$

where $D_0 = 1$ and

$$D_n = \begin{vmatrix} (y_1,y_1) & (y_2,y_1) & \cdots & (y_n,y_1) \\ (y_1,y_2) & (y_2,y_2) & \cdots & (y_n,y_2) \\ \cdots & & & \\ (y_1,y_n) & (y_2,y_n) & \cdots & (y_n,y_n) \end{vmatrix},$$

for $n = 1, 2, \ldots$.

3.9.523 Example. Let $H = \mathcal{L}_2(-\pi,\pi)$ and let $e_n(x) = e^{inx}$ for $x \in [-\pi,\pi]$ and $n = 0, \pm 1, \pm 2, \ldots$. We define $(f,g) = \frac{1}{2\pi}\int_{-\pi}^{\pi} f(x)\overline{g(x)}\,d\lambda(x)$ for $f,g \in \mathcal{L}_2(-\pi,\pi)$. Then the e_n's are orthonormal, as a simple computation shows. They are also complete: this will be proved in 3.9.7.

3.9.524 Example. Let $H = \mathcal{L}_2(-1,1)$ and let $f_n(x) = x^n$ for $x \in [-1,1]$ and $n = 0, 1, 2, \ldots$. Then the f_n are linearly independent, since if $\sum_{k=0}^{n} \alpha_k x^k = 0$ for all $x \in [-1,1]$, then $\alpha_k = 0$ for all k. The set of linear combinations of the x^n is dense in $\mathcal{L}_2(-1,1)$. For $f,g \in \mathcal{L}_2(-1,1)$, define $(f,g) = \int_{-1}^{1} f(x)\overline{g(x)}\,d\lambda(x)$. The orthogonal functions obtained from the x^k's are the Legendre polynomials:

$P_0(x) = 1$

$P_n(x) = \frac{1}{2^n n!}\frac{d^n}{dx^n}[(x^2-1)^n]$ for $n = 1, 2, \ldots$.

The equality, $\int_{-1}^{1} P_n(x)x^m d\lambda(x) = 0$ for $m = 0, 1, 2, \ldots, n-1$, can be verified by integrating by parts. As a result, $\int_{-1}^{1} P_n(x)P_m(x)d\lambda(x) = 0$ for $n \neq m$. One may also check that $\int_{-1}^{1} P_n^2(x)d\lambda(x) = \frac{2}{2n+1}$.

3.9.525 Example. Let $\mathcal{B}$ be the Borel sets in $[-1,1]$ and define $\mu(A) = \int_A \frac{1}{\sqrt{1-x^2}} d\lambda(x)$ for $A \in \mathcal{B}$. Then for every Lebesgue measurable function f defined on $[-1,1]$, we have $\int_{-1}^{1} f(x) \frac{1}{\sqrt{1-x^2}} d\lambda(x) = \int_{[-1,1]} f(x)d\mu(x)$, whenever either integral exists. This equality is obvious for simple measurable functions and is proved for arbitrary Lebesgue measurable functions by applying 3.2.12 and 3.4.21. Let $H = \mathfrak{L}_2([-1,1], \mathcal{B}, \mu)$. For $f,g \in H$, let $(f,g) = \int_{[-1,1]} f(x)\,\overline{g(x)}\,d\mu(x) = \int_{[-1,1]} f(x)\,\overline{g(x)}\,\frac{1}{\sqrt{1-x^2}} d\lambda(x)$.
Then when the set $\{1,x,x^2,\ldots\}$ is orthogonalized by the Gram-Schmidt process, we obtain the Čebyšev polynomials of the first kind:

$T_0(x) = 1,$

$T_n(x) = \frac{1}{2^{n-1}} \cos [n \text{ arc cos } x]$ for $n = 1,2,\ldots$.

3.9.526 Example. Let $\mathcal{B}$ be the Borel sets of R and let $\mu(A) = \int_A e^{-x^2} d\lambda(x)$ for $A \in \mathcal{B}$. As in 3.9.525, we see readily that $\int_R f(x)d\mu(x) = \int_{-\infty}^{\infty} f(x)e^{-x^2}d\lambda(x)$ whenever either integral exists. The functions $1, x, x^2, \ldots$

are all in $\mathcal{L}_2(R, \mathcal{B}, \mu)$ and are clearly linearly independent. For $f,g \in \mathcal{L}_2(R, \mathcal{B}, \mu)$, define $(f,g) = \int_{]-\infty,\infty[} f(x)\,\overline{g(x)}\,d\mu(x) = \int_{]-\infty,\infty[} f(x)\,\overline{g(x)}\,e^{-x^2}\,d\lambda(x)$.

We shall identify the orthonormal functions obtained from these functions. The functions obtained are $\frac{1}{\sqrt{2^n n!\,\sqrt{\pi}}} H_n$, where the H_n are the Hermite polynomials defined by

$H_n(x) = (-1)^n e^{x^2} \frac{d^n}{dx^n}(e^{-x^2})$ $(n = 0, 1, 2, \ldots)$. For example, $H_0(x) = 1$, $H_1(x) = 2x$, and $H_2(x) = 4x^2 - 2$.

It will be convenient to use the notation $f(x)^{(n)}$ to mean $\frac{d^n}{dx^n} f(x)$. To show that the Hermite polynomials are orthogonal, i.e. $\int_R H_m(x)H_n(x)d\mu(x) = 0$ whenever $m \neq n$, we will show that the Hermite functions $\phi_n(x) = H_n(x)e^{-\frac{x^2}{2}}$ satisfy the relation $\int_{-\infty}^{\infty} \phi_m(x)\phi_n(x)dx = 0$ for $m \neq n$. We first show that $\phi_n''(x) = (x^2 - 2n - 1)\phi_n(x$

For this we need the relation $(e^{-x^2})^{(n+2)} = (-2xe^{-x^2})^{(n+1)}$

$\sum_{k=0}^{n+1} \binom{n+1}{k} (-2x)^{(k)} (e^{-x^2})^{(n+1-k)} = -2x(e^{-x^2})^{(n+1)} - 2(n+1)(e^{-x^2}$

we use Leibniz's rule here. Now $\phi_n(x) = (-1)^n e^{x^2/2}(e^{-x^2})^{(}$

so that $\phi_n'(x) = (-1)^n \left\{ xe^{x^2/2}(e^{-x^2})^{(n)} + e^{x^2/2}(e^{-x^2})^{(n+1)} \right\}$.

Hence $\phi_n''(x) = (-1)^n \left\{ e^{x^2/2}(e^{-x^2})^{(n)} + x^2e^{x^2/2}(e^{-x^2})^{(n)} + xe^{x^2/2}(e^{-x^2})^{(n+1)} + xe^{x^2/2}(e^{-x^2})^{(n+1)} + e^{x^2/2}(e^{-x^2})^{(n+2)} \right\} =$

$(-1)^n\Big\{e^{x^2/2}\ (e^{-x^2})^{(n)} + x^2e^{x^2/2}(e^{-x^2})^{(n)} + 2xe^{x^2/2}\cdot$
$(e^{-x^2})^{(n+1)} + e^{x^2/2}[-2x(e^{-x^2})^{(n+1)} - 2(n+1)(e^{-x^2})^{(n)}]\Big\} =$
$(-1)^n e^{x^2/2}(e^{-x^2})^{(n)}(1 + x^2 - 2n - 2) = (x^2 - 2n - 1)\phi_n(x).$

We now compute $\phi_m''(x)\phi_n(x) - \phi_m(x)\phi_n''(x) = \{(x^2 - 2m - 1) - (x^2 - 2n - 1)\}\ \phi_m(x)\phi_n(x) = 2(n - m)\phi_m(x)\phi_n(x)$. Using this and integrating by parts, we obtain for $m \neq n$,

$$2(n - m) \int_{-\infty}^{\infty}\phi_m(x)\phi_n(x)dx = \int_{-\infty}^{\infty}\phi_m''(x)\phi_n(x)dx - \int_{-\infty}^{\infty}\phi_m(x)\phi_n''(x)dx =$$
$$\phi_m'(x)\phi_n(x)\Big|_{-\infty}^{\infty} - \int_{-\infty}^{\infty}\phi_m'(x)\phi_n'(x)dx - \phi_m(x)\phi_n'(x)\Big|_{-\infty}^{\infty} +$$
$$\int_{-\infty}^{\infty}\phi_m'(x)\phi_n'(x)dx = 0;$$ the last equality follows since $\phi_m'(x)\phi_n(x) \to 0$ as $x \to \pm\infty$.

We now proceed to show that $\int_{-\infty}^{\infty} H_n^2(x)e^{-x^2}dx = 2^n n!\sqrt{\pi}$. Let $\psi(t,x) = e^{-t^2+2tx} =$

$$e^{x^2}e^{-(t-x)^2} = \sum_{n=0}^{\infty} e^{x^2}\ \frac{d^n}{dt^n}(e^{-(t-x)^2})\Big|_{t=0}\ \frac{t^n}{n!} =$$

$$\sum_{n=0}^{\infty} \frac{H_n(x)}{n!}t^n.$$ We have $$\frac{\partial\psi}{\partial x} = \sum_{n=0}^{\infty}\frac{H_n'(x)}{n!}\ t^n = \sum_{n=1}^{\infty}\frac{H_n'(x)}{n!}\ t^n.$$

We also have $$\frac{\partial\psi}{\partial x} = 2t\ \psi(t,x) = \sum_{n=0}^{\infty}\frac{2H_n(x)}{n!}t^{n+1} = \sum_{n=1}^{\infty}\frac{2nH_{n-1}(x)}{n!}t^n.$$

Equating coefficients, we obtain $H_n'(x) = 2nH_{n-1}(x)$. Then

$$\int_{-\infty}^{\infty}H_n^2(x)e^{-x^2}dx = (-1)^n \int_{-\infty}^{\infty}H_n(x)(e^{-x^2})^{(n)}dx = (-1)^nH_n(x)\cdot$$
$$(e^{-x^2})^{(n-1)}\Big|_{-\infty}^{\infty} + (-1)^{n-1}\int_{-\infty}^{\infty} 2nH_{n-1}(x)(e^{-x^2})^{(n-1)}dx =$$
$$2n\int_{-\infty}^{\infty} H_{n-1}^2(x)e^{-x^2}dx = \ \dots\ = 2^n n!\int_{-\infty}^{\infty} e^{-x^2}dx = 2^n n!\sqrt{\pi}\ ;$$

$$(-1)^n H_n(x)(e^{-x^2})^{(n-1)}\Big|_{-\infty}^{\infty} = 0 \text{ since } x^k e^{-x^2} \to 0 \text{ as}$$

$x \to \pm\infty$, for every positive integer k.

We have thus shown that the family of functions

$\dfrac{1}{\sqrt{2^n n!\sqrt{\pi}}} H_n$ are orthonormal.

3.9.53 Theorem. Let H be a Hilbert space and E an orthonormal set in H. Then the following conditions are equivalent:

i) E is complete;

ii) $x = \sum_{e \varepsilon E} (x,e)e$ for all $x \varepsilon H$;

iii) $\|x\|^2 = \sum_{e \varepsilon E} |(x,e)|^2$ for all $x \varepsilon H$;

iv) $(x,y) = \sum_{e \varepsilon E} (x,e)\overline{(y,e)}$ for all $x,y \varepsilon H$.

Proof. Suppose that E is complete; we will prove ii). For each $x \varepsilon H$, $[x - \sum_{e \varepsilon E} (x,e)e] \perp E$ by 3.9.44 and 3.9.45. Hence by completeness, $x - \sum_{e \varepsilon E} (x,e)e = 0$ or $x = \sum_{e \varepsilon E} (x,e)e$.

We now prove that ii) implies iv). Let $x,y \varepsilon H$. Let $\{e_1, e_2, \ldots\}$ be the subset of E for which (x,e) or (y,e) is different from zero. Let $y_n = \sum_{k=1}^{n} (y,e_k)e_k$ and $x_n = \sum_{k=1}^{n} (x,e_k)e_k$. Then $(x_n,y_n) = \sum_{k=1}^{n} (x,e_k)\overline{(y,e_k)}$;

we need to show that $\lim_{n\to\infty} |(x,y) - (x_n,y_n)| = 0$. However, this follows from the relations $|(x,y) - (x_n,y_n)| = |(x,y) - (x_n,y) + (x_n,y) - (x_n,y_n)| = |(x - x_n,y) + (x_n,y - y_n)| \leq \|x - x_n\| \cdot \|y\| + \|x_n\| \cdot \|y - y_n\| \leq \|x - x_n\| \cdot \|y\| + \|x\| \cdot \|y - y_n\|$.

Suppose that (iv) holds; we will prove iii). By iv), $\|x\|^2 = (x,x) = \sum_{e\varepsilon E} |(x,e)|^2$ for all $x \varepsilon H$.

Finally, we prove that iii) implies i). Suppose $x \perp E$. Then $(x,e) = 0$ for all $e \varepsilon E$. Thus $\|x\|^2 = \sum_{e\varepsilon E} 0 = 0$, and hence $x = 0$. Consequently E is complete.

3.9.531 <u>Definition</u>. Suppose that L is a linear space. If $\{x_1, \ldots, x_n\}$ is a linearly independent subset of L that spans L, then $\{x_1, \ldots, x_n\}$ is said to be a basis for L.

3.9.54 <u>Theorem</u>. Any two complete orthonormal sets in a Hilbert space H have the same cardinal number.

<u>Proof</u>. Part I. Suppose that $H = \{0\}$. Then H does not have any complete orthonormal sets.

Part II. We need the following result. Let L be a linear space and $\{x_1, \ldots, x_m\}$ a finite subset spanning L. Suppose that $\{y_1, \ldots, y_r\}$ is a linearly independent subset of L. Then $m \geq r$. (This result is called the Exchange Theorem (Steinitz's <u>Austanschsatz</u>).) Evidently, $\{y_1, x_1, x_2, \ldots, x_m\}$ is linearly dependent. Thus some

x_i is a linear combination of the preceding vectors; by relabelling if necessary, we may suppose that x_m is a linear combination of preceding vectors. Then $\{y_1, x_1, \ldots, x_{m-1}\}$ spans L. Consequently $\{y_2, y_1, x_1, x_2, \ldots, x_{m-1}\}$ is linearly dependent. Since $\{y_1, \ldots, y_r\}$ is linearly independent, y_1 is not a multiple of y_2. Thus some x_i is a linear combination of the preceding vectors; as above we may suppose $x_i = x_{m-1}$. Continue in this manner until the set $\{y_1, \ldots, y_r\}$ is exhausted. If $m < r$, then at the m<u>th</u> step we would obtain $\{y_m, y_{m-1}, \ldots, y_1\}$ as a set spanning L, contradicting the fact that $\{y_1, \ldots, y_r\}$ is linearly independent. (The vectors $y_{m+1}, \ldots, y_r$ are <u>not</u> linear combinations of $y_1, \ldots, y_m$.) Consequently $m \geq r$.

In particular, we see that two finite bases of L must have the same cardinality.

Part III. Suppose that H contains a finite complete orthonormal set $\{e_1, \ldots, e_n\}$. By 3.9.53 and 3.9.415, $\{e_1, \ldots, e_n\}$ is a basis for H. If $\{f_1, \ldots, f_m\}$ is a finite complete orthonormal subset of H, then $\{f_1, \ldots, f_m\}$ is also a basis for H. Hence by part II, $m = n$. If $\{f_1, f_2, \ldots, f_m, \ldots\}$ is a complete orthonormal subset of H, then every finite subset of $n + 1$ elements is linearly independent. This also contradicts part II.

Part IV. Suppose that H is infinite dimensional; that is, every complete orthonormal subset of H is infinite. Let $\mathfrak{m}$ be the least cardinal number such that H has a dense subset of cardinality $\mathfrak{m}$. Let E be any complete orthonormal set. We will prove that $\overline{\overline{E}} = \mathfrak{m}$. Suppose D is a dense subset of H with $\overline{\overline{D}} = \mathfrak{m}$. We note that $\|e_1 - e_2\| = (e_1 - e_2, e_1 - e_2)^{1/2} = \sqrt{2}$ for all $e_1, e_2 \in E, e_1 \neq e_2$. For all $e \in E$, let $\lambda(e) \in D$ be such that $\|\lambda(e) - e\| < \frac{\sqrt{2}}{2}$. The relations $e_1 \neq e_2$, $e_1, e_2 \in E$, imply that $\lambda(e_1) \neq \lambda(e_2)$. Otherwise, $\sqrt{2} = \|e_1 - e_2\| = \|e_1 - \lambda(e_1) + \lambda(e_2) - e_2\| \leq \|e_1 - \lambda(e_1)\| + \|\lambda(e_2) - e_2\| < \sqrt{2}$, which is impossible. Consequently, λ is a one-to-one map of E into D, from which it follows that $\overline{\overline{E}} \leq \overline{\overline{D}} = \mathfrak{m}$.

For the reverse inequality, let $S = \{\alpha_1 e_1 + \ldots + \alpha_n e_n : \alpha_j = r_j + is_j$ where r_j, s_j are rational numbers and $e_j \in E$ $(j = 1, 2, \ldots, n)\}$. Since E is infinite, it is easy to see that $\overline{\overline{S}} = \overline{\overline{E}}$. Moreover, S is dense in H. This is seen by noting that S is dense in the set of all finite linear combinations of E and that this set is dense in H. Thus $\overline{\overline{E}} = \overline{\overline{S}} \geq \mathfrak{m}$ and consequently, $\overline{\overline{E}} = \mathfrak{m}$.

We have shown that in this case every complete orthonormal subset of H has cardinality $\mathfrak{m}$.

3.9.6 Theorem. Let H_1 and H_2 be Hilbert spaces containing complete orthonormal sets E_1 and E_2, respectively, such that $\overline{\overline{E}}_1 = \overline{\overline{E}}_2$. Then there exists a one-to-one mapping τ of H_1 onto H_2 such that

i) $\tau(\alpha x + \beta y) = \alpha\tau(x) + \beta\tau(y)$ for $x, y \in H$ and $\alpha, \beta \in K$;

ii) $(\tau(x), \tau(y)) = (x, y)$ for $x, y \in H$.

Conversely, if such a τ exists, then $\bar{\bar{E}}_1 = \bar{\bar{E}}_2$ for all complete orthonormal sets $E_1 \subset H_1$ and $E_2 \subset H_2$.

Proof. We outline a proof; the details are easily filled in. Let τ be any one-to-one map of E_1 onto E_2. For all $\alpha_1 e_1 + \ldots + \alpha_n e_n \in H_1$ ($\alpha_j \in K$ and $e_j \in E$), define $\tau(\alpha_1 e_1 + \ldots + \alpha_n e_n) = \alpha_1\tau(e_1) + \ldots + \alpha_n\tau(e_n)$. τ maps the subspace S_1 spanned by E_1 onto the subspace S_2 spanned by E_2; moreover, τ preserves inner products on S_1. Now for any $x \in H_1$, we have $x = \lim_{n\to\infty} x_n$, where $x_n \in S_1$. Define $\tau(x) = \lim_{n\to\infty} \tau(x_n)$; this limit exists since τ preserves inner products on S_1. We see that this defines τ uniquely by noting that if $\lim_{n\to\infty} x_n = \lim_{n\to\infty} y_n = x$, then $\lim_{n\to\infty}\tau(x_n) = \lim_{n\to\infty} \tau(y_n)$. Now assertions i) and ii) may be verified. Finally, τ maps H_1 onto H_2 since $\tau(H_1)$ is a closed dense subset of H_2.

The converse follows from 3.9.54. If H_1 and H_2 are Hilbert spaces connected by a mapping τ with properties i) and ii), then H_1 and H_2 are indistinguishable as inner product spaces, and the proof of 3.9.54 may be repeated verbatim to prove that any complete orthonormal sets in H_1 and H_2 have the same cardinal number.

Remark. If H_1 and H_2 are Hilbert spaces and there exists a one-to-one mapping τ of H_1 onto H_2 satisfying i) and ii) above, we say that H_1 and H_2 are equivalent (as Hilbert spaces).

3.9.61 Theorem. Let $H \neq \{0\}$ be a Hilbert space. Then H is equivalent as a Hilbert space to some $\mathcal{L}_2(X, \mathcal{M}, \mu)$, where X is a non-void set, $\mathcal{M}$ is all subsets of X, and μ is defined by $\mu(A) = \begin{cases} \overline{\overline{A}} & \text{for } A \text{ finite} \\ \infty & \text{for } A \text{ infinite} \end{cases}$.

Proof. For any such $\mathcal{L}_2(X, \mathcal{M}, \mu)$, the family of functions $e_x (x \in X)$ is a complete orthonormal set: we define $e_x(y) = \begin{cases} 1 & \text{if } y = x \\ 0 & \text{if } y \neq x \end{cases}$. Thus $\mathcal{L}_2(X, \mathcal{M}, \mu)$ has a complete orthonormal set of cardinality $\overline{\overline{X}}$. By 3.9.51, H has a complete orthonormal set E. Hence by 3.9.6, H is equivalent to $\mathcal{L}_2(X, \mathcal{M}, \mu)$ if and only if $\overline{\overline{X}} = \overline{\overline{E}}$.

3.9.62 Remarks. Theorem 3.9.61 shows that every $\mathcal{L}_2$ space is equivalent to an $\mathcal{L}_2$ space of a particularly simple kind. The writer does not know if an analogous result holds for $\mathcal{L}_p$ spaces $(1 < p < \infty,\ p \neq 2)$. It is known that the conjugate space of $\mathcal{L}_p$ can be identified with $\mathcal{L}_{p'}$: every bounded linear functional on $\mathcal{L}_p(X, \mathcal{M}, \mu)$ has the form $f \to \int_X f(x)\overline{g(x)}d\mu(x) = T_g f$ for some $g \in \mathcal{L}_{p'}(X, \mathcal{M}, \mu)$. Also $\|T_g\| = \|g\|_{p'}$. This theorem strangely enough is considerably harder to prove than theorem 3.9.34; we postpone the proof to Ch. 4.

3.9.7 Theorem. Let $f \in \mathcal{L}_1(-\pi, \pi)$. If $c_n = \frac{1}{2\pi}\int_{-\pi}^{\pi} f(x)e^{-inx}d\lambda(x) = 0$ for all $n = 0, \pm 1, \pm 2, \ldots,$ then $f(x) = 0$ a.e. in $[-\pi, \pi]$.

The following proof is due to H. Lebesgue.

<u>Proof</u>. Case I. Suppose that f is continuous. Let $T(x) = \sum_{k=-n}^{n} \alpha_k e^{ikx}$ be any trigonometric polynomial. If all of the c_n's are 0, then clearly $\int_{-\pi}^{\pi} f(x)T(x)d\lambda(x) = 0$. If $f \neq 0$, then $f(x_o) \neq 0$ for some $x_o \in]-\pi,\pi[$. Multiplying f by a constant, we may suppose that $\Re f(x_o) > 0$. Let $g = \Re f$. Since g is continuous, there exist $\delta > 0$ and $\eta > 0$ such that $g(x) \geq \eta$ for all $x \in [x_o - \delta, x_o + \delta] \subset [-\pi,\pi]$. Let $t(x) = 1 + \cos(x - x_o) - \cos\delta$ for $x \in [-\pi,\pi]$. Evidently, t is a trigonometric polynomial and so t^n is a trigonometric polynomial for $n = 1, 2, \ldots$. Consequently, $\int_{-\pi}^{\pi} t^n(x)f(x)d\lambda(x) = 0$ for $n = 1, 2, \ldots$. Since $\int_{-\pi}^{\pi} t^n(x)f(x)d\lambda(x) =$ $\int_{-\pi}^{\pi} t^n(x)g(x)d\lambda(x) + i\int_{-\pi}^{\pi} t^n(x)\Im f(x)d\lambda(x)$, it follows that

$$\int_{-\pi}^{\pi} t^n(x)g(x)d\lambda(x) = 0 \quad \text{for} \quad n = 1, 2, \ldots . \qquad (*)$$

We now observe the following relations:

$t(x) \geq 1$ for $x \in [x_o - \delta, x_o + \delta]$

$t(x) < 1$ for $x \notin [x_o - \delta, x_o + \delta]$

$t(x) > -1$ for $x \in [-\pi,\pi]$.

There exists an $\varepsilon > 0$ and a closed subinterval I of $[x_o - \delta, x_o + \delta]$ having positive length such that $t(x) \geq 1 + \varepsilon$ for $x \in I$. Now $\lim_{n\to\infty} \int_{[x_o-\delta,x_o+\delta]} t^n(x)g(x)d\lambda(x$

$\lim_{n\to\infty} \int_I t^n(x)g(x)d\lambda(x) \geq \lim_{n\to\infty} (1 + \varepsilon)^n \eta\lambda(I) = \infty$. We have

$|t^n(x)g(x)| \le |g(x)|$ for all $x \in [x_0 - \delta,\ x_0 + \delta]'$; note that $g \in \mathcal{L}_1(-\pi,\pi)$. Hence by 3.5.21,

$$\lim_{n\to\infty} \int_{[x_0-\delta,x_0+\delta]} t^n(x)g(x)d\lambda(x) = \int_{[x_0-\delta,x_0+\delta]'} \lim_{n\to\infty} t^n(x)g(x)d\lambda(x) = \int_{[x_0-\delta,x_0+\delta]'} 0 = 0.$$

The two limits just obtained clearly contradict equality (*). Consequently, $f(x) = 0$ for all $x \in [-\pi,\pi]$.

Case II. Suppose that f is any function in $\mathcal{L}_1(-\pi,\pi)$. Let $F(x) = \int_{-\pi}^{x} f(t)d\lambda(t)$ for $x \in [-\pi,\pi]$. We have $F(-\pi) = 0$ and, by hypothesis, $F(\pi) = \int_{-\pi}^{\pi} f(t)d\lambda(t) = 2\pi c_0 = 0$. Let C_n for $n = 0, \pm 1, \pm 2, \ldots$ be the Fourier coefficients for F; we will prove that $C_n = 0$ for $n = 0, \pm 1, \pm 2, \ldots$. Integrating by parts, we obtain $C_n = \int_{-\pi}^{\pi} F(x)e^{-inx}d\lambda(x) = F(x)(\frac{-1}{in} e^{-inx}) \Big|_{-\pi}^{\pi} + \frac{1}{in}\int_{-\pi}^{\pi} f(x)e^{-inx}d\lambda(x) = 0$, for $n \ne 0$. The function $F - C_0$ has each of its Fourier coefficients equal to 0. Moreover, $F - C_0$ is continuous so that by case I, $F(x) - C_0 = 0$ for all $x \in [-\pi,\pi]$. In particular, $F(-\pi) - C_0 = 0$ or $C_0 = F(-\pi) = 0$. Thus $C_n = 0$ for $n = 0, \pm 1, \pm 2, \ldots$. Hence $F(x) = 0$ for all $x \in [-\pi,\pi]$. Thus $\int_{-\pi}^{x} f(t)d\lambda(t) = 0$ for all $x \in [-\pi,\pi]$. By 3.6.32 applied to $\Re f$ and $\Im f$, we have $f(t) = 0$ a.e. in $[-\pi,\pi]$.

3.9.71 Theorem (Parseval's equality). Let $f,g \in \mathcal{L}_2(-\pi,\pi)$. For $n = 0, \pm 1, \pm 2, \ldots,$ let $c_n = \frac{1}{2\pi}\int_{-\pi}^{\pi} f(x)e^{-inx}d\lambda(x)$ and $d_n = \frac{1}{2\pi}\int_{-\pi}^{\pi} g(x)e^{-inx}d\lambda(x)$; these are the Fourier coefficients of f and g, respectively. Then

$$\frac{1}{2\pi}\int_{-\pi}^{\pi} f(x)\overline{g(x)}d\lambda(x) = \sum_{n=-\infty}^{\infty} c_n\bar{d}_n.$$

In particular, we have

$$\frac{1}{2\pi}\int_{-\pi}^{\pi} |f(x)|^2 d\lambda(x) = \sum_{n=-\infty}^{\infty} |c_n|^2.$$

Proof. The functions $e^{inx}(n = 0, \pm 1, \pm 2, \ldots)$ are orthonormal on $[-\pi,\pi]$ as pointed out in 3.9.523, and complete by 3.9.7; note that $\mathcal{L}_2(-\pi,\pi) \subset \mathcal{L}_1(-\pi,\pi)$. By 3.9.523 and 3.9.53, iv),

$$(f,g) = \frac{1}{2\pi}\int_{-\pi}^{\pi} f(x)\overline{g(x)}d\lambda(x) =$$

$$\sum_{n=-\infty}^{\infty} \left(\frac{1}{2\pi}\int_{-\pi}^{\pi} f(x)e^{-inx}d\lambda(x)\right)\cdot\overline{\left(\frac{1}{2\pi}\int_{-\pi}^{\pi} g(x)e^{-inx}d\lambda(x)\right)} =$$

$$\sum_{n=-\infty}^{\infty} c_n\bar{d}_n.$$

This is the desired equality.

3.9.72 Theorem (Riesz-Fischer Theorem). Let $\{a_n\}_{n=-\infty}^{\infty}$ be any sequence of complex numbers such that $\sum_{n=-\infty}^{\infty} |a_n|^2 < \infty$.

Then there exists a unique function $h \in \mathcal{L}_2(-\pi,\pi)$ such that $\frac{1}{2\pi}\int_{-\pi}^{\pi} h(x)e^{-inx}d\lambda(x) = a_n$ for $n = 0, \pm 1, \pm 2, \ldots$.

Proof. Define $h_n = \sum_{k=-n}^{n} a_k e^{ikx}$. For $m > n$, we have $\|h_n - h_m\|_2^2 = \sum_{n<|k|\leq m} |a_k|^2$ and hence $\lim_{m,n\to\infty} \|h_n - h_m\|_2 = 0$. Since $\mathcal{L}_2(-\pi,\pi)$ is complete, $h = \lim_{n\to\infty} h_n$ exists in $\mathcal{L}_2(-\pi,\pi)$. Plainly the Fourier coefficients of h are the a_n's.

Chapter 4.

LEBESGUE-STIELTJES INTEGRALS

4.1 Another representation theorem of F. Riesz. As before, we write $\mathfrak{C}([0,1])$ for the class of all continuous real-valued functions on $[0,1]$. We are interested in studying non-negative linear functionals I on $\mathfrak{C}([0,1])$, that is, linear functionals such that $I(f) \geq 0$ for all $f \geq 0$. An obvious source of such functionals is the class of all Riemann-Stieltjes integrals. Let α be any monotone increasing finite valued function on $[0,1]$. Then the ordinary Riemann-Stieltjes integral $I_\alpha(f) = \int_0^1 f(x)d\alpha(x)$ is plainly a non-negative linear functional on $\mathfrak{C}([0,1])$. F. Riesz proved in 1910 that every non-negative linear functional on $\mathfrak{C}([0,1])$ can be represented in this form. Furthermore, if the weight-function α is normalized so that it is right continuous, say, then the α that represents a given non-negative linear functional is uniquely determined by the linear functional that it represents.

Riesz's theorem was generalized by Radon in 1914 to continuous functions defined on a cube in n-dimensional Euclidean space $(n = 2, 3, \ldots)$. Here the monotone function α must be replaced by a non-negative countably additive Borel measure defined on all Borel subsets of the cube in question. Other generalizations and analogues of Riesz's theorem were obtained by P. J. Daniell (1918), by J. v. Neumann (1935), S. Kakutani (1941), and others.

The currently most popular context for Riesz's theorem is the continuous complex-valued functions on a locally compact Hausdorff space, each of which vanishes outside of some compact subset. In the present section, we shall confine ourselves formally to the line, but will state only theorems that are valid for the general case.

4.1.1 Definition. Let $\mathfrak{C}_{00}(R)$ denote the set of all complex-valued continuous functions x on R such that $x(t) = 0$ for $|t| \geq A$, where A is a positive number depending on x. The symbol $\mathfrak{C}_r$ will denote the set of all $x \in \mathfrak{C}_{00}(R)$ such that $x(t)$ is real for all $t \in R$, and $\mathfrak{C}_+$ will denote the set of all $x \in \mathfrak{C}_r$ such that $x(t) \geq 0$ for all $t \in R$. Addition and scalar multiplication are defined pointwise:

$(x + y)(t) = x(t) + y(t)$ for all $x,y \in \mathfrak{C}_{00}(R)$,

$(\alpha x)(t) = \alpha(x(t))$ for all $x \in \mathfrak{C}_{00}(R)$ and $\alpha \in K$.

For each $x \in \mathfrak{C}_{00}(R)$, we write $S_x = \{t: t \in R, x(t) \neq 0\}^-$; S_x is called the support of x. We note that S_x is closed and bounded, and hence compact. For each $x \in \mathfrak{C}_{00}(R)$, let $\|x\|_u = \max\{|x(t)|: t \in R\}$. We see that $\mathfrak{C}_{00}(R)$ is a normed linear space. Let I be a complex-valued functional defined on $\mathfrak{C}_{00}(R)$ such that $I(\alpha x + \beta y) = \alpha I(x) + \beta I(y)$ for all $x,y \in \mathfrak{C}_{00}(R)$ and $\alpha,\beta \in K$; $I(x) \geq 0$ if $x \in \mathfrak{C}_+$. Such a functional is called a non-negative linear functional.

Remark. Suppose that I is a non-negative linear functional and that $x \in \mathfrak{C}_r$. Then $x = \max(x,0) - (-\min(x,0))$ so that $I(x) = I(\max(x,0)) - I(-\min(x,0))$; each of these numbers is real. Consequently, we have that if $x \in \mathfrak{C}_r$, then $I(x)$ is real. We note also that $x \leq y$ implies $I(x) \leq I(y)$ for $x,y \in \mathfrak{C}_r$.

The aim of this section is to show that for every non-negative linear functional I on $\mathfrak{C}_{\infty\infty}(R)$, there exists a countably additive non-negative, possibly infinite, measure μ defined for all Borel sets in R, and finite for all compact sets, such that

$$I(x) = \int_R x(t)d\mu(t) \quad \text{for all} \quad x \in \mathfrak{C}_{\infty\infty}(R).$$

Here are two simple examples. If I is the non-negative linear functional $I(x) = \int_{-\infty}^{\infty} x(t)dt$, then μ is Lebesgue measure λ. If I is the functional defined by $I(x) = \sum_{n=-\infty}^{\infty} x(n)$, then the corresponding measure for Borel sets is $\mu(A) = \left\{ \begin{array}{ll} \overline{\overline{A \cap \{0,\pm1,\pm2,\ldots\}}} & \text{if this is finite} \\ \infty & \text{otherwise} \end{array} \right\}$.

Throughout § 4.1, I will represent a fixed non-negative linear functional on $\mathfrak{C}_{\infty\infty}(R)$.

4.1.11 Theorem. For all $x \in \mathfrak{C}_{\infty\infty}(R)$, we have $|I(x)| \leq I(|x|)$.

Proof. (K. Itô). Suppose that $x \in \mathfrak{C}_{\infty\infty}(R)$. We have $I(x) = \rho e^{i\theta}$, $\rho \geq 0$ and $0 \leq \theta < 2\pi$. Now $\rho = e^{-i\theta}I(x) =$

$I(e^{-i\theta}x) = I(y_1 + iy_2) = I(y_1) + iI(y_2)$. Equating real parts, we obtain $\rho = I(y_1)$ and hence $|I(x)| = \rho = I(y_1)$. We have $y_1 \leq |y_1| \leq |y_1 + iy_2| = |e^{-i\theta}x| = |x|$. Noting that $y_1 \in \mathfrak{C}_r$, we conclude that $|I(x)| = I(y_1) \leq I(|x|)$.

4.1.12 Theorem. Let A be a compact subset of R. Then there exists a non-negative real number β (depending only on A) such that $|I(x)| \leq \beta \|x\|_u$ for all $x \in \mathfrak{C}_{\infty\infty}(R)$ such that $S_x \subset A$.

Proof. Let $A \subset R$ be compact. Then there exists a function $y \in \mathfrak{C}_+$ such that $y(t) = 1$ for all $t \in A$. For example, if u and v are upper and lower bounds for A, the function whose graph is sketched below has these properties.

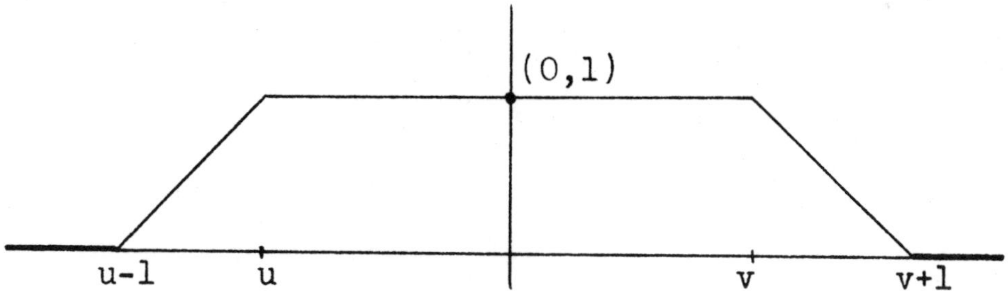

For $t \in A$, we have $0 \leq |x(t)| \leq \|x\|_u = \|x\|_u \cdot y(t)$ and, for $t \notin A$, we have $0 = |x(t)| \leq \|x\|_u y(t)$. Thus, for all $x \in \mathfrak{C}_{\infty\infty}(R)$ such that $S_x \subset A$, we have $0 \leq |x| \leq \|x\|_u \cdot y$. Hence $|I(x)| \leq I(|x|) \leq \|x\|_u I(y)$; this proves the theorem.

4.1.13 Theorem. Let $\mathfrak{X}$ be any subset of $\mathfrak{C}_+$ such that for $x_1, x_2 \in \mathfrak{X}$, there exists an $x_3 \in \mathfrak{X}$ such that

$x_3 \leq \min(x_1, x_2)$. Suppose also that for all $t \in R$, $\inf\{x(t): x \in \mathfrak{X}\} = 0$. Then for every $\varepsilon > 0$, there is an $x_\varepsilon \in \mathfrak{X}$ such that $x_\varepsilon(t) < \varepsilon$ for all $t \in R$. Moreover, $\inf\{I(x): x \in \mathfrak{X}\} = 0$.

Proof. Let ε be any fixed positive real number. Let $A_x = \{t: x(t) \geq \varepsilon\}$ for all $x \in \mathfrak{X}$. By the continuity of x, A_x is closed. Thus A_x is compact since $A_x \subset S_x$ and S_x is bounded. Since $\inf\{x(t): x \in \mathfrak{X}\} = 0$, we see that $\bigcap_{x \in \mathfrak{X}} A_x = 0$. By virtue of Exercise 1.8.61, there exist $x_1, \ldots, x_n$ such that $A_{x_1} \cap \ldots \cap A_{x_n} = 0$. Let x_ε be a function in $\mathfrak{X}$ such that $x_\varepsilon \leq \min(x_1, \ldots, x_n)$; the existence of x_ε can be shown by an easy induction. Evidently, $x_\varepsilon(t) < \varepsilon$ for all $t \in R$.

It remains to verify that $\inf\{I(x): x \in \mathfrak{X}\} = 0$. Let y be fixed in $\mathfrak{X}$. Let ε be any positive number. Then there exists an $x \in \mathfrak{X}$ such that $x \leq \min(y, x_\varepsilon)$. Now, using 4.1.12 there exists a β, depending only on y, such that $I(x) \leq \beta \|x\|_u \leq \beta\varepsilon$. Since ε is arbitrary, we infer that $\inf\{I(x): x \in \mathfrak{X}\} = 0$.

4.1.14 Definition. A non-negative, real-valued (possibly infinite) function x on R is said to be lower semi-continuous if the following hold. If $x(t_o) < \infty$, then for every $\varepsilon > 0$, there exists a $\delta > 0$ such that $x(t) > x(t_o) - \varepsilon$ whenever $|t - t_o| < \delta$. If $x(t_o) = \infty$, then for every positive real number A, there is a $\delta > 0$ such that

$x(t) > A$ if $|t - t_o| < \delta$. The class of all such functions will be denoted by $\mathfrak{M}_+$. For each $x \in \mathfrak{M}_+$, let $\mathcal{Y}_x = \{y: y \in \mathfrak{C}_+, y \leq x\}$.

A non-negative, real-valued (possibly infinite) function x on R is said to be upper semi-continuous if the following holds. For every $t_o \in R$ and $\varepsilon > 0$, there exists a $\delta > 0$ such that $x(t) \leq x(t_o) + \varepsilon$ for $|t - t_o| < \delta$. Let $\mathfrak{N}_+$ be the class of all such functions.

4.1.141 <u>Theorem</u>. (i) If $x \in \mathfrak{M}_+$ and $\alpha \geq 0$, then $\alpha x \in \mathfrak{M}_+$; (ii) if $x_1, \ldots, x_n \in \mathfrak{M}_+$, then $\min (x_1, \ldots, x_n) \in \mathfrak{M}_+$; (iii) if $\mathfrak{X} \subset \mathfrak{M}_+$, then $\sup \{x: x \in \mathfrak{X}\} \in \mathfrak{M}_+$; (iv) if $x_1, \ldots, x_n \in \mathfrak{M}_+$, then $x_1 + \ldots + x_n \in \mathfrak{M}_+$.

The proof is omitted.

4.1.142 <u>Theorem</u>. For $x \in \mathfrak{M}_+$, $x = \sup \{y: y \in \mathcal{Y}_x\}$.

<u>Proof</u>. It is obvious that $x \geq \sup \{y: y \in \mathcal{Y}_x\}$. We note that $0 \in \mathcal{Y}_x$. If $x(t_o) = 0$, then clearly $x(t_o) = \sup \{y(t_o): y \in \mathcal{Y}_x\}$. Suppose that $x(t_o) > 0$. Then for every ε, $0 < \varepsilon < x(t_o)$, there exists a $\delta > 0$ such that $x(t) > x(t_o) - \varepsilon$ whenever $|t - t_o| < \delta$. Consequently, the function y sketched below is such that $y(t_o) = x(t_o) - \varepsilon$ and $y(t) \leq x(t)$ for all $t \in R$; that is, $y \in \mathcal{Y}_x$. Since ε is arbitrary, we have $x(t_o) \leq \sup \{y(t_o): y \in \mathcal{Y}_x\}$. Since t_o is arbitrary, this proves the theorem.

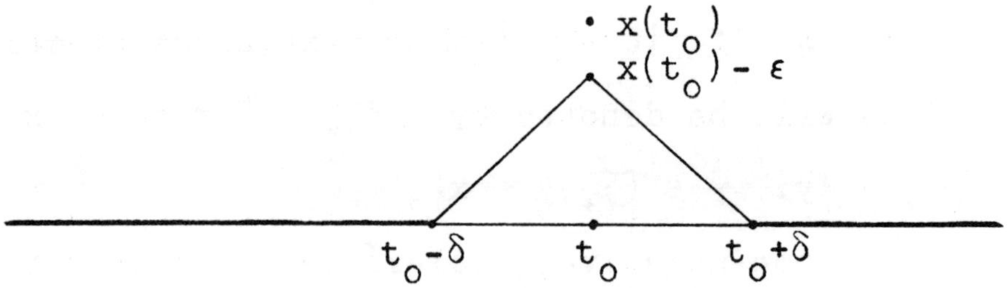

The function y.

4.1.15 Definition. For $x \in \mathfrak{M}_+$, let $\bar{I}(x) = \sup\{I(y): y \in \mathcal{Y}_x\}$.

4.1.151 Theorem. (i) If $x \in \mathfrak{C}_+$, then $I(x) = \bar{I}(x)$;

(ii) if $x_1 \leq x_2$ and $x_1, x_2 \in \mathfrak{M}_+$, then $\bar{I}(x_1) \leq \bar{I}(x_2)$;

(iii) for $x \in \mathfrak{M}_+$ and $\alpha \geq 0$, $\bar{I}(\alpha x) = \alpha \bar{I}(x)$.

The proof is omitted.

4.1.152 Theorem. Let $\mathfrak{X}$ be any subset of $\mathfrak{M}_+$ such that for all $x_1, x_2 \in \mathfrak{X}$, there exists an $x_3 \in \mathfrak{X}$ such that $x_3 \geq \max(x_1, x_2)$. Then $\bar{I}(\sup\{x: x \in \mathfrak{X}\}) = \sup\{\bar{I}(x): x \in \mathfrak{X}\}$.

In particular, if $x_1 \leq x_2 \leq \cdots \leq x_n \leq \cdots$ and each $x_n \in \mathfrak{M}_+$, then $\bar{I}(\lim_{n\to\infty} x_n) = \lim_{n\to\infty} \bar{I}(x_n)$.

Proof. Let $x_o = \sup\{x: x \in \mathfrak{X}\}$.

Case I. Suppose that $\mathfrak{X} \subset \mathfrak{C}_+$ and $x_o \in \mathfrak{C}_+$. We will prove that $I(x_o) = \sup\{I(x): x \in \mathfrak{X}\}$. We have $\inf\{x_o - x: x \in \mathfrak{X}\} = 0$ and hence the set $\{x_o - x: x \in \mathfrak{X}\}$ satisfies the hypotheses of 4.1.13. Hence we have $\inf\{I(x_o - x): x \in \mathfrak{X}\} = \inf\{I(x_o) - I(x): x \in \mathfrak{X}\} =$ This is equivalent to the equality $I(x_o) = \sup\{I(x): x \in \mathfrak{X}\}$.

Case II. Suppose that $\mathfrak{X} \subset \mathfrak{M}_+$. It is evident that $\bar{I}(x) \leq \bar{I}(x_o)$ for all $x \in \mathfrak{X}$, so that $\sup\{\bar{I}(x):$

$x \in \mathfrak{X}\} \leq \bar{I}(x_o)$. To prove the inequality $\bar{I}(x_o) \leq \sup\{\bar{I}(x): x \in \mathfrak{X}\}$, it suffices to prove that $I(y_o) \leq \sup\{\bar{I}(x): x \in \mathfrak{X}\}$ for all $y_o \in \mathcal{Y}_{x_o}$. Consider a fixed $y_o \in \mathcal{Y}_{x_o}$. Letting $\mathcal{Y} = \bigcup_{x \in \mathfrak{X}} \mathcal{Y}_x$ and using 4.1.142, we obtain the relations $x_o = \sup\{x: x \in \mathfrak{X}\} = \sup_{x \in \mathfrak{X}} \{\sup_{y \in \mathcal{Y}_x} y\} = \sup_{y \in \mathcal{Y}} y$. We thus have $y_o = \min(y_o, x_o) = \sup_{y \in \mathcal{Y}} \{\min(y_o, y)\}$. Since y_o and each of the y belong to $\mathfrak{C}_+$, Case I applies and hence

$$I(y_o) = \sup_{y \in \mathcal{Y}} I(\min(y_o, y)) \leq \sup_{y \in \mathcal{Y}} I(y) = \sup_{x \in \mathfrak{X}} \{\sup_{y \in \mathcal{Y}_x} I(y)\} = \sup_{x \in \mathfrak{X}} \{\bar{I}(x)\}.$$

The theorem is proved.

4.1.153 Theorem. Let $x_1, x_2 \in \mathfrak{M}_+$. Then $\bar{I}(x_1 + x_2) = \bar{I}(x_1) + \bar{I}(x_2)$.

Proof. Let $\mathfrak{X} = \{y_1 + y_2: y_j \in \mathfrak{C}_+ \text{ and } y_j \leq x_j \text{ for } j = 1, 2\}$. We have $\sup\{x: x \in \mathfrak{X}\} = x_1 + x_2$ and, moreover, it is easy to see that $\mathfrak{X}$ satisfies the hypotheses of 4.1.152. Therefore $\bar{I}(x_1 + x_2) = \sup\{I(y_1 + y_2): y_j \in \mathfrak{C}_+ \text{ and } y_j \leq x_j \text{ for } j = 1, 2\} = \sup\{I(y_1) + I(y_2): y_j \in \mathfrak{C}_+ \text{ and } y_j \leq x_j \text{ for } j = 1, 2\} = \sup\{I(y_1): y_1 \in \mathfrak{C}_+ \text{ and } y_1 \leq x_1\} + \sup\{I(y_2): y_2 \in \mathfrak{C}_+ \text{ and } y_2 \leq x_2\} = \bar{I}(x_1) + \bar{I}(x_2)$.

4.1.154 Theorem. Let $\mathfrak{X} \subset \mathfrak{M}_+$ and define the function $\sum_{x \in \mathfrak{X}} x$ by $(\sum_{x \in \mathfrak{X}} x)(t) = \sup\{x_1(t) + \ldots + x_m(t): \{x_1, \ldots, x_m\} \text{ is a finite subset of } \mathfrak{X}\}$ for $t \in R$. Then $\bar{I}(\sum_{x \in \mathfrak{X}} x) = \sum_{x \in \mathfrak{X}} \bar{I}(x)$.

Proof. For every finite subset $\{x_1, \ldots, x_m\}$ of $\mathcal{X}$, we have $\bar{I}(x_1 + \ldots + x_m) = \bar{I}(x_1) + \ldots + \bar{I}(x_m)$ by 4.1.153. It is clear that $\{x_1 + \ldots + x_m: \{x_1, \ldots, x_m\} \subset \mathcal{X}\}$ satisfies the hypotheses of 4.1.152. Consequently,

$$\sum_{x \varepsilon \mathcal{X}} \bar{I}(x) = \sup\{\bar{I}(x_1) + \ldots + \bar{I}(x_m): \{x_1, \ldots, x_m\} \subset \mathcal{X}\} =$$

$$\sup\{\bar{I}(x_1 + \ldots + x_m): \{x_1, \ldots, x_m\} \subset \mathcal{X}\} =$$

$$\bar{I}(\sup\{(x_1 + \ldots + x_m): \{x_1, \ldots, x_m\} \subset \mathcal{X}\}) = \bar{I}(\sum_{x \varepsilon \mathcal{X}} x).$$

4.1.2 Definition. Let z be any non-negative, possibly infinite function defined on R. Let $\bar{\bar{I}}(z) = \inf\{\bar{I}(y): y \varepsilon \mathfrak{M}_+$ and $y \geq z\}$.

4.1.21 Theorem. If $z \varepsilon \mathfrak{M}_+$, then $\bar{\bar{I}}(z) = \bar{I}(z)$.

Proof. Since $z \geq z$ and $z \varepsilon \mathfrak{M}_+$, we have $\bar{\bar{I}}(z) \leq \bar{I}(z)$. If $y \varepsilon \mathfrak{M}_+$ and $y \geq z$, then $\bar{I}(y) \geq \bar{I}(z)$ and therefore $\bar{\bar{I}}(z) = \inf\{\bar{I}(y): y \varepsilon \mathfrak{M}_+$ and $y \geq z\} \geq \bar{I}(z)$. Hence $\bar{\bar{I}}(z) = \bar{I}(z)$.

4.1.22 Theorem. Let z_1 and z_2 be any non-negative functions defined on R. Then

i) $z_1 \leq z_2$ implies $\bar{\bar{I}}(z_1) \leq \bar{\bar{I}}(z_2)$;

ii) $\bar{\bar{I}}(\alpha z_1) = \alpha\bar{\bar{I}}(z_1)$ if $\alpha \geq 0$.

The proof is omitted.

The functional $\bar{\bar{I}}$ is not in general additive. However, we do have the following theorem.

4.1.23 Theorem. Let z_1 and z_2 be any non-negative functions defined in R. Then $\bar{\bar{I}}(z_1 + z_2) \leq \bar{\bar{I}}(z_1) + \bar{\bar{I}}(z_2)$.

Proof. Suppose that $y_j \geq z_j$ and $y_j \in \mathfrak{M}_+$ for $j = 1,2$. Then $z_1 + z_2 \leq y_1 + y_2$, so that $\bar{\bar{I}}(z_1 + z_2) \leq \bar{\bar{I}}(y_1 + y_2) = \bar{I}(y_1 + y_2) = \bar{I}(y_1) + \bar{I}(y_2)$. Therefore $\bar{\bar{I}}(z_1 + z_2) \leq \inf\left\{\bar{I}(y_1) + \bar{I}(y_2): \ y_j \geq z_j \text{ and } y_j \in \mathfrak{M}_+ \text{ for } j = 1,2\right\} = \inf\left\{\bar{I}(y_1): \ y_1 \geq z_1 \text{ and } y_1 \in \mathfrak{M}_+\right\} + \inf\left\{\bar{I}(y_2): \ y_2 \geq z_2 \text{ and } y_2 \in \mathfrak{M}_+\right\} = \bar{\bar{I}}(z_1) + \bar{\bar{I}}(z_2)$.

4.1.24 Theorem. Let $\{z_n\}_{n=1}^{\infty}$ be a monotone increasing sequence of non-negative functions on R. Then $\bar{\bar{I}}(\sup z_n) = \sup\left\{\bar{\bar{I}}(z_n)\right\}$. (All suprema in the present theorem are to be taken over the positive integers.)

Proof. Since $z_n \leq \sup z_n$ for $n = 1, 2, \ldots$, we have $\bar{\bar{I}}(z_n) \leq \bar{\bar{I}}(\sup z_n)$ for $n = 1, 2, \ldots$. Consequently, $\sup\left\{\bar{\bar{I}}(z_n)\right\} \leq \bar{\bar{I}}(\sup z_n)$. It remains to prove that $\sup\left\{\bar{\bar{I}}(z_n)\right\} \geq \bar{\bar{I}}(\sup z_n)$. Since this inequality is trivial if $\sup\left\{\bar{\bar{I}}(z_n)\right\} = \infty$, we suppose from here on that $\sup\left\{\bar{\bar{I}}(z_n)\right\} < \infty$. This implies, in particular, that $\bar{\bar{I}}(z_n) < \infty$ for each n.

Let ε be an arbitrary positive number. For each n, choose $y_n \in \mathfrak{M}_+$ such that $y_n \geq z_n$ and $\bar{I}(y_n) < \bar{\bar{I}}(z_n) + \frac{\varepsilon}{2^n}$. For each n, let $u_n = \max\left\{y_1, \ldots, y_n\right\}$. Then $u_1 \leq u_2 \leq \ldots \leq u_n \leq \ldots$ and, for each n, $z_n \leq y_n \leq u_n$. We also note that $u_n \in \mathfrak{M}_+$ for $n = 1,2, \ldots$. Now $u_{n+1} + \min(u_n, y_{n+1}) = \max(u_n, y_{n+1}) + \min(u_n, y_{n+1}) = u_n + y_{n+1}$. Hence $\bar{I}(u_{n+1}) + \bar{I}(\min(u_n, y_{n+1})) = \bar{I}(u_n) + \bar{I}(y_{n+1})$, by 4.1.153. Since $\bar{I}(\min(u_n, y_{n+1})) \leq \bar{I}(y_{n+1}) < \infty$, we may write this equality as $\bar{I}(u_{n+1}) = \bar{I}(u_n) + \bar{I}(y_{n+1}) - \bar{I}(\min(u_n, y_{n+1}))$. Since $u_n \geq z_n$ and

$y_{n+1} \geq z_{n+1} \geq z_n$ for all n, we have $\min(u_n, y_{n+1}) \geq z_n$ and so $\bar{I}(\min(u_n, y_{n+1})) \geq \bar{\bar{I}}(z_n)$. We thus have $\bar{I}(u_{n+1}) < \bar{I}(u_n) + \bar{\bar{I}}(z_{n+1}) + \frac{\varepsilon}{2^{n+1}} - \bar{\bar{I}}(z_n)$. We now obtain $\bar{I}(u_2) + \ldots + \bar{I}(u_{m+1}) < \bar{I}(u_1) + \ldots + \bar{I}(u_m) + \bar{\bar{I}}(z_{m+1}) - \bar{\bar{I}}(z_1) + \frac{\varepsilon}{2}\cdot(\frac{1}{2} + \frac{1}{4} + \ldots + \frac{1}{2^m})$ and hence $\bar{I}(u_{m+1}) < \bar{I}(u_1) + \bar{\bar{I}}(z_{m+1}) - \bar{\bar{I}}(z_1) + \frac{\varepsilon}{2}$ for $m = 1, 2, \ldots$. We also have $\bar{I}(u_1) - \bar{\bar{I}}(z_1) = \bar{I}(y_1) - \bar{\bar{I}}(z_1) < \frac{\varepsilon}{2}$. Therefore $\bar{I}(u_m) < \bar{\bar{I}}(z_m) + \varepsilon$ for $m = 2, 3, \ldots$. Consequently $\sup \bar{I}(u_n) \leq \sup \bar{\bar{I}}(z_n) + \varepsilon$. By 4.1.152 we have $\sup \bar{I}(u_n) = \bar{I}(\sup u_n)$ and, recalling that $u_n \geq z_n$ for $n = 1, 2, \ldots$, we also have $\sup u_n \geq \sup z_n$. Since $\sup u_n \in \mathfrak{M}_+$, $\bar{I}(\sup u_n) \geq \bar{\bar{I}}(\sup z_n)$ (4.1.2). Therefore $\bar{\bar{I}}(\sup z_n) \leq \sup \bar{\bar{I}}(z_n) + \varepsilon$. Since ε is arbitrary, $\bar{\bar{I}}(\sup z_n) \leq \sup \bar{\bar{I}}(z_n)$.

4.1.25 <u>Remark</u>. The conclusion of Theorem 4.1.24 can be written as $\lim\limits_{n\to\infty} \bar{\bar{I}}(z_n) = \bar{\bar{I}}(\lim\limits_{n\to\infty} z_n)$.

4.1.26 <u>Remark</u>. Theorem 4.1.24 is a far-reaching generalization of 3.5.11.

4.1.27 <u>Theorem</u>. Let $\{x_n\}_{n=1}^{\infty}$ be any sequence of non-negative functions on R. Then $\bar{\bar{I}}(\sum_{n=1}^{\infty} x_n) \leq \sum_{n=1}^{\infty} \bar{\bar{I}}(x_n)$.

<u>Proof</u>. By 4.1.23, we have $\bar{\bar{I}}(\sum_{n=1}^{m} x_n) \leq \sum_{n=1}^{m} \bar{\bar{I}}(x_n)$ for $m = 1, 2, \ldots$. Thus, applying 4.1.25, we obtain

$$\bar{\bar{I}}(\sum_{n=1}^{\infty} x_n) = \bar{\bar{I}}(\lim_{m\to\infty} \sum_{n=1}^{m} x_n) = \lim_{m\to\infty} \bar{\bar{I}}(\sum_{n=1}^{m} x_n) \leq \lim_{m\to\infty} \sum_{n=1}^{m} \bar{\bar{I}}(x_n) =$$

$\sum_{n=1}^{\infty} \bar{\bar{I}}(x_n)$.

4.1.28 Definition. If x is a non-negative function defined on R such that $\bar{\bar{I}}(x) = 0$, then x is called a null function.

4.1.29 Exercise.

i) If $0 \leq x \leq y$ and y is null, then x is null and for $\alpha \varepsilon R$, $\alpha \geq 0$, αy is null.

ii) If $\{x_n\}_{n=1}^{\infty}$ is an increasing sequence of null functions, then $\sup x_n$ is a null function. The sum of an infinite series of null functions is a null function.

iii) Produce an example to show that $\sup \{x: x \varepsilon \mathfrak{X}\}$ need not be null if $\mathfrak{X}$ is an uncountable collection of null functions closed under the formation of countable suprema. Begin by defining I on $\mathfrak{C}_{\infty\infty}(R)$.

4.1.3 Definition. For $A \subset R$, let $\mu(A) = \bar{\bar{I}}(\chi_A)$.

4.1.31 Theorem. The set-function μ is a Carathéodory outer measure on the subsets of R:

i) $0 \leq \mu(A) \leq \infty$ for all $A \subset R$;

ii) $\mu(A) \leq \mu(B)$ whenever $A \subset B \subset R$;

iii) $\mu(\bigcup_{n=1}^{\infty} A_n) \leq \sum_{n=1}^{\infty} \mu(A_n)$ for all sequences $\{A_n\}_{n=1}^{\infty}$ where $A_n \subset R$;

iv) $\mu(0) = 0$.

Proof. Properties i) and ii) are immediate consequences of the definitions. For property iii), we use 4.1.22 and

4.1.27 to get $\mu(\bigcup_{n=1}^{\infty} A_n) = \bar{\bar{I}}(\chi_{\bigcup_{n=1}^{\infty} A_n}) \leq \bar{\bar{I}}(\sum_{n=1}^{\infty} \chi_{A_n}) \leq$ $\sum_{n=1}^{\infty} \bar{\bar{I}}(\chi_{A_n}) = \sum_{n=1}^{\infty} \mu(A_n)$. Since $\chi_0 \in \mathfrak{T}_{\infty\infty}(R)$, $\mu(0) = \bar{\bar{I}}(\chi_0) = \bar{I}(0) = 0$.

4.1.32 Theorem. Let $\{G_\lambda\}_{\lambda\in\Lambda}$ be any family of pairwise disjoint open sets. Then $\mu(\bigcup_{\lambda\in\Lambda} G_\lambda) = \sum_{\lambda\in\Lambda} \mu(G_\lambda)$.

Proof. We first show that if H is open, then χ_H is lower semi-continuous. We thus require that for every $x \in R$ and $\varepsilon > 0$, there exist a $\delta > 0$ such that $\chi_H(y) > \chi_H(x) - \varepsilon$ for all $y \in]x - \delta, x + \delta[$. This condition is obviously satisfied for $x \notin H$. For $x \in H$, there exists a $\delta > 0$ such that $]x - \delta, x + \delta[\subset H$. Then for any $\varepsilon > 0$, $y \in]x - \delta, x + \delta[$ implies that $\chi_H(y) = 1 > 1 - \varepsilon = \chi_H(x) - \varepsilon$.

Consequently we may apply 4.1.154 to obtain $\mu(\bigcup_{\lambda\in\Lambda} G_\lambda) = \bar{\bar{I}}(\chi_{\bigcup_{\lambda\in\Lambda} G_\lambda}) = \bar{I}(\chi_{\bigcup_{\lambda\in\Lambda} G_\lambda}) = \bar{I}(\sum_{\lambda\in\Lambda} \chi_{G_\lambda}) = \sum_{\lambda\in\Lambda} \bar{I}(\chi_{G_\lambda}) =$ $\sum_{\lambda\in\Lambda} \bar{\bar{I}}(\chi_{G_\lambda}) = \sum_{\lambda\in\Lambda} \mu(G_\lambda)$.

4.1.33 Remark. Any family of pairwise disjoint non-void open subsets of R is countable. For suppose $\{G_\lambda\}_{\lambda\in\Lambda}$ is such a family. To each G_λ there corresponds a rational r_λ contained in G_λ. This correspondence is one-to-one and into the rationals. Consequently Λ is countable. All of the results of the present section are valid if

R is replaced by an arbitrary locally compact Hausdorff space; in these spaces, families of non-void pairwise disjoint open sets can have arbitrary cardinal number.

4.1.34 Theorem. Suppose that $A \subset R$ is compact. Then $\mu(A) < \infty$.

Proof. As in the proof of 4.1.12, we see that there exists a function $y \in \mathfrak{C}_+$ such that $y(t) = 1$ for all $t \in A$. Noting that $\chi_A \leq y$ and that I is real-valued on $\mathfrak{C}_+$, we see that $\mu(A) = \bar{\bar{I}}(\chi_A) \leq \bar{I}(y) = I(y) < \infty$.

4.1.35 Theorem. Let $A \subset R$; then $\mu(A) = \inf\{\mu(G): G$ is open and $G \supset A\}$.

Proof. Clearly $\mu(A) \leq \inf\{\mu(G): G$ open and $G \supset A\}$; it remains to verify the reverse inequality. This is clear if $\mu(A) = \infty$; suppose that $\mu(A) = \bar{\bar{I}}(\chi_A) < \infty$. Choose $0 < \varepsilon < 1$. There exists an $x \in \mathfrak{M}_+$ such that $x \geq \chi_A$ and $\bar{I}(x) - \varepsilon < \bar{\bar{I}}(\chi_A) = \mu(A)$. Let $G = \{t: x(t) > 1 - \varepsilon\} \supset A$. Since x is lower semi-continuous, G is open. Evidently $\frac{1}{1-\varepsilon} x \in \mathfrak{M}_+$ and $\frac{1}{1-\varepsilon}x \geq \chi_G$. Now $\mu(G) = \bar{\bar{I}}(\chi_G) \leq \bar{I}(\frac{1}{1-\varepsilon} x) = \frac{1}{1-\varepsilon} \bar{I}(x) <$ $\frac{1}{1-\varepsilon}[\mu(A) + \varepsilon] = \frac{\varepsilon}{1-\varepsilon} + \frac{1}{1-\varepsilon} \mu(A)$. For ε sufficiently small, the right hand term is arbitrarily close to $\mu(A)$. Consequently, $\inf\{\mu(G): G$ open and $G \supset A\} \leq \mu(A)$.

4.1.36 Definition. If $A \subset R$ and $\mu(A) = 0$, then A is said to be a null set.

4.1.361 Theorem. Subsets of a null set are null and countable unions of null sets are null.

This follows at once from 4.1.31.

4.1.362 Final Exercise # 15. A non-negative function x is null if and only if $\{t: x(t) > 0\}$ is a null set.

4.1.363 Final Exercise # 16. Let x be a non-negative function on R. If $\bar{\bar{I}}(x) < \infty$, then $\{t: x(t) = \infty\}$ is a null set.

4.1.37 Definition. Let x_1 and x_2 be complex-valued functions defined on R. If $\{t: t \varepsilon R \text{ and } x_1(t) \neq x_2(t)\}$ is null, then we say that $x_1 = x_2$ a.e. (almost everywhere) on R. If y is a complex-valued (or an extended real-valued) function defined on R except for a null set, y is said to be defined a.e. on R.

4.1.371 Theorem. i) If $x_1 = x_2$ a.e. on R, then $\alpha x_1 = \alpha x_2$ a.e. on R for $\alpha \varepsilon K$.

ii) If $x_1 = x_2$ a.e. on R and $y_1 = y_2$ a.e. on R, then $x_1 + y_1 = x_2 + y_2$ a.e. on R.

iii) If $x_1 = x_2$ a.e. on R and $x_2 = x_3$ a.e. on R, then $x_1 = x_3$ a.e. on R.

The proofs are easy and are omitted.

4.1.4 Definitions. Suppose that x and x' are functions defined a.e. on R. Then we define $x \sim x'$ if $x = x'$ a.e. on R. This relation is an equivalence relation; see 4.1.371 (iii). Let $\mathfrak{J}_1$ be the set of all equivalence classes ξ of complex-valued functions x defined a.e. on R such that ξ contains some function x, defined everywhere on R, for which $\bar{\bar{I}}(|x|) < \infty$.

For ξ, $\eta \in \mathfrak{J}_1$, let $\xi + \eta$ be the class containing $x + y$ for all $x \in \xi$ and $y \in \eta$. This is single-valued by 4.1.371 (ii). To see that $\xi + \eta \in \mathfrak{J}_1$, let $x \in \xi$ and $y \in \eta$ be such that $\bar{\bar{I}}(|x|) < \infty$ and $\bar{\bar{I}}(|y|) < \infty$. Then $x + y \in \xi + \eta$ and $\bar{\bar{I}}(|x + y|) \leq \bar{\bar{I}}(|x| + |y|) \leq \bar{\bar{I}}(|x|) + \bar{\bar{I}}(|y|) < \infty$. Hence $\xi + \eta \in \mathfrak{J}_1$.

For $\xi \in \mathfrak{J}_1$ and $\alpha \in K$, let $\alpha\xi$ be the class containing αx for all $x \in \xi$. As above, this is single-valued and $\alpha\xi \in \mathfrak{J}_1$.

Finally, we define a norm on $\mathfrak{J}_1$ as follows: for $\xi \in \mathfrak{J}_1$, let $\|\xi\|_1 = \bar{\bar{I}}(|x|)$ for any $x \in \xi$ such that x is defined everywhere on R and $\bar{\bar{I}}(|x|) < \infty$. That this is a well-defined norm is shown in the following theorem.

4.1.401 <u>Theorem</u>. For $\xi \in \mathfrak{J}_1$, let x and x' be elements of ξ, defined everywhere, such that $\bar{\bar{I}}(|x|) < \infty$ and $\bar{\bar{I}}(|x'|) < \infty$. Then $\bar{\bar{I}}(|x|) = \bar{\bar{I}}(|x'|)$.

<u>Proof</u>. Let y and y' be non-negative real-valued functions on R such that $y = y'$ a.e. Now $y = y - y' + y'$ so that $|y| \leq |y - y'| + |y'|$ or $y \leq |y - y'| + y'$. Thus $\bar{\bar{I}}(y) \leq \bar{\bar{I}}(|y - y'|) + \bar{\bar{I}}(y')$. By 4.1.362, $\bar{\bar{I}}(|y - y'|) = 0$. Consequently $\bar{\bar{I}}(y) \leq \bar{\bar{I}}(y')$. By symmetry we have

$\bar{\bar{I}}(y') \leq \bar{\bar{I}}(y)$, so that $\bar{\bar{I}}(y) = \bar{\bar{I}}(y')$.

Let x and x' be as in the hypotheses of the theorem. Then $|x| = |x'|$ a.e., since $x = x'$ a.e. Thus the above paragraph applies and we obtain $\bar{\bar{I}}(|x|) = \bar{\bar{I}}(|x'|)$.

4.1.41 Theorem. With the definitions of sum, scalar product, and norm given in 4.1.4, $\mathfrak{I}_1$ is a complex normed linear space.

Proof. The algebraic properties are obvious. The zero Ω of $\mathfrak{I}_1$ is the class containing the function that is identically zero. Suppose $\xi \neq \Omega$. There exists an $x \varepsilon \xi$ such that x is defined everywhere and $\bar{\bar{I}}(|x|) < \infty$. Since the relation $x = 0$ a.e. fails, $\{t: \ |x(t)| > 0\}$ is not null. Consequently, by 4.1.362, $\bar{\bar{I}}(|x|) \neq 0$; that is, $\|\xi\|_1 \neq 0$. The remaining two postulates for a norm are easily verified.

4.1.411 Convention. Two functions are said to be equal if they are defined almost everywhere and they are equal almost everywhere. We will write $x, y, z, \ldots$ to denote the equivalence classes $\xi, \eta, \zeta, \ldots$ containing these functions.

4.1.42 Theorem. Let $\{x_n\}_{n=1}^{\infty}$ be a sequence of functions in $\mathfrak{I}_1$ such that $\sum_{n=1}^{\infty} \|x_n\|_1 < \infty$. Let s be defined as follows: $s(t) = \sum_{n=1}^{\infty} x_n(t)$ for $t \varepsilon R$ such that $x_n(t)$ exists for all n and $\sum_{n=1}^{\infty} x_n(t) < \infty$; $s(t) = 0$ otherwise. Then

i) $\sum_{n=1}^{\infty} |x_n(t)| < \infty$ for almost all $t \in R$;

ii) $s \in \mathfrak{J}_1$;

iii) $\lim_{k\to\infty} \|s - \sum_{n=1}^{k} x_n\|_1 = 0$.

Proof. The sum $\sum_{n=1}^{\infty} |x_n(t)|$ is defined a.e. since each x_n is defined a.e. Applying 4.1.27, we have $\bar{\bar{I}}(\sum_{n=1}^{\infty} |x_n|) \leq \sum_{n=1}^{\infty} \bar{\bar{I}}(|x_n|) = \sum_{n=1}^{\infty} \|x_n\|_1 < \infty$. Thus by 4.1.363, $\sum_{n=1}^{\infty} |x_n(t)|$ is finite for almost all $t \in R$. Therefore i) holds.

To prove assertion ii), we must show that $\bar{\bar{I}}(|s|) < \infty$. By assertion i), $s(t) = \sum_{n=1}^{\infty} x_n(t)$ a.e. on R. For almost all $t \in R$, $|s(t)| = \lim_{k\to\infty} |\sum_{n=1}^{k} x_n(t)| \leq \sum_{n=1}^{\infty} |x_n(t)|$. By 4.1.22 i), $\bar{\bar{I}}(|s|) \leq \bar{\bar{I}}(\sum_{n=1}^{\infty} |x_n|) < \infty$. Consequently, $s \in \mathfrak{J}_1$.

Finally, we have $\|s - \sum_{n=1}^{k} x_n\|_1 = \|\sum_{n=k+1}^{\infty} x_n\|_1 = \bar{\bar{I}}(|\sum_{n=k+1}^{\infty} x_n|) \leq \sum_{n=k+1}^{\infty} \bar{\bar{I}}(|x_n|) = \sum_{n=k+1}^{\infty} \|x_n\|_1$. Therefore $\lim_{k\to\infty} \|s - \sum_{n=1}^{k} x_n\|_1 \leq \lim_{k\to\infty} \sum_{n=k+1}^{\infty} \|x_n\|_1 = 0$ and assertion iii) is proved.

4.1.43 Theorem. The normed linear space $\mathfrak{J}_1$ is complete; i.e., $\mathfrak{J}_1$ is a complex Banach space.

Proof. This proof is very like the proof of 3.7.5. Let $\{x_n\}_{n=1}^{\infty}$ be any sequence of functions in $\mathfrak{J}_1$ such that $\lim_{m,n\to\infty} \|x_n - x_m\|_1 = 0$. There exists a subsequence $\{x_{n_k}\}_{k=1}^{\infty}$ of $\{x_n\}_{n=1}^{\infty}$ such that $\|x_m - x_{n_k}\|_1 < \frac{1}{2^k}$ for all $m \geq n_k$. Then $\|x_{n_1}\| + \sum_{k=1}^{\infty} \|x_{n_{k+1}} - x_{n_k}\|_1 < \infty$. By 4.1.42 i), we see that $\lim_{\ell\to\infty} [x_{n_1}(t) + \sum_{k=1}^{\ell} (x_{n_{k+1}}(t) - x_{n_k}(t))]$ exists and is finite for almost all $t \in R$. Then $\lim_{\ell\to\infty} x_{n_{\ell+1}}(t)$ exists and is finite a.e.; let $x(t) = \lim_{\ell\to\infty} x_{n_{\ell+1}}(t)$ where this limit exists and let $x(t) = 0$ elsewhere. By 4.1.42 ii) and iii), we have $x \in \mathfrak{J}_1$ and $\lim_{k\to\infty} \|x - x_{n_k}\|_1 = 0$. From this it follows that $\lim_{m\to\infty} \|x - x_m\|_1 = 0$, completing the proof.

4.1.44 Definition. Let $\mathfrak{L}_1(R,I)$ (written $\mathfrak{L}_1$ where no confusion should occur) be the space of all functions $x \in \mathfrak{J}_1$ such that for some sequence $\{y_n\}_{n=1}^{\infty}$, $y_n \in \mathfrak{C}_{\infty\infty}(R)$, we have $\lim_{n\to\infty} \| y_n - x\|_1 = 0$. The elements of $\mathfrak{L}_1$ will be called summable functions.

Remark. By definition, $\mathfrak{L}_1$ is the closure of $\mathfrak{C}_{\infty\infty}(R)$ in $\mathfrak{J}_1$. The class $\mathfrak{L}_1$ is in general a much smaller class of functions than $\mathfrak{J}_1$. While $\mathfrak{L}_1$ is a much studied Banach space, little attention seems up to now to have been given to $\mathfrak{J}_1$. It would be of considerable interest to know the detailed structure of $\mathfrak{J}_1$.

4.1.441 <u>Theorem</u>. $\mathcal{L}_1$ is a complex Banach space with the linear operations and norm that it inherits from $\mathfrak{J}_1$; $\mathfrak{C}_{\infty\infty}(R)$ is a dense linear subspace of $\mathcal{L}_1$. Furthermore, the functional I admits an extension, which we again call I, over $\mathcal{L}_1$ such that I is linear on $\mathcal{L}_1$ and $|I(x)| \leq \|x\|_1$ for all $x \in \mathcal{L}_1$. This extension I is unique under the restrictions that it be linear and satisfy the inequality $|I(x)| \leq A\|x\|_1$, for some $A > 0$ and all $x \in \mathcal{L}_1$.

<u>Proof</u>. Suppose that $x, x' \in \mathcal{L}_1$. Then $x = \lim_{n\to\infty} y_n$ and $x' = \lim_{n\to\infty} y_n'$, where $y_n, y_n' \in \mathfrak{C}_{\infty\infty}(R)$ for $n = 1, 2, \ldots$. Then $x + x' = \lim_{n\to\infty} (y_n + y_n')$ where $y_n + y_n' \in \mathfrak{C}_{\infty\infty}(R)$. Thus $\mathcal{L}_1$ is closed under addition. In like manner, we see that $\mathcal{L}_1$ is closed under scalar multiplication. Therefore, $\mathcal{L}_1$ is a linear subspace of $\mathfrak{J}_1$.

Let $\{x_n\}_{n=1}^{\infty}$ be a Cauchy sequence in $\mathcal{L}_1$; i.e., $\lim_{m,n\to\infty} \|x_n - x_m\|_1 = 0$. We must show that $\{x_n\}_{n=1}^{\infty}$ has a limit in $\mathcal{L}_1$. Since $\mathfrak{J}_1$ is complete, there is a $z \in \mathfrak{J}_1$ such that $\lim_{n\to\infty} \|x_n - z\|_1 = 0$. For each x_n there exists $y_n \in \mathfrak{C}_{\infty\infty}(R)$ such that $\|x_n - y_n\|_1 < \frac{1}{n}$. Now $\|z - y_n\|_1 \leq \|z - x_n\|_1 + \|x_n - y_n\|_1$ for $n = 1, 2, \ldots$, so that $\lim_{n\to\infty} \|z - y_n\|_1 \leq \lim_{n\to\infty} \|z - x_n\|_1 + \lim_{n\to\infty} \|x_n - y_n\|_1 = 0$. Consequently $z \in \mathcal{L}_1$.

To extend I from $\mathcal{C}_{\infty\infty}(R)$ to $\mathcal{L}_1$, let $x \in \mathcal{L}_1$

and let $\{y_n\}_{n=1}^{\infty}$ be a sequence from $\mathcal{C}_{\infty\infty}(R)$ such that

$\lim\limits_{n\to\infty} \|x - y_n\|_1 = 0$. We first show that the sequence

$\{I(y_n)\}_{n=1}^{\infty}$ is Cauchy in K. For $m = 1, 2, \ldots$ and

$n = 1, 2, \ldots,$ we have $|I(y_n) - I(y_m)| = |I(y_n - y_m)| \leq$

$I(|y_n - y_m|) = \bar{\bar{I}}(|y_n - y_m|) = \|y_n - y_m\|_1 \leq \|y_n - x\|_1 +$

$\|x - y_m\|_1$ and consequently, $\lim\limits_{m,n\to\infty} |I(y_n) - I(y_m)| \leq$

$\lim\limits_{m,n\to\infty} [\|y_n - x\|_1 + \|x - y_m\|_1] = 0$. Since K is complete,

$\{I(y_n)\}_{n=1}^{\infty}$ has a limit; let $I(x)$ be this limit. This

is well-defined, for suppose that $\{y_n\}_{n=1}^{\infty}$ and $\{z_n\}_{n=1}^{\infty}$

are sequences in $\mathcal{C}_{\infty\infty}(R)$ for which $\lim\limits_{n\to\infty} \|y_n - x\|_1 = 0$

and $\lim\limits_{n\to\infty} \|z_n - x\|_1 = 0$. Then $|I(z_n) - I(y_n)| \leq I(|z_n - y_n|$

$\|z_n - y_n\|_1 \leq \|z_n - x\|_1 + \|x - y_n\|_1$. Thus $\lim\limits_{n\to\infty} |I(z_n) -$

$I(y_n)| = 0$ and $\lim\limits_{n\to\infty} I(z_n) = \lim\limits_{n\to\infty} I(y_n)$. It is easy to

show that I is a linear functional on $\mathcal{L}_1$.

Now we show that $|I(x)| \leq \|x\|_1$ for all $x \in \mathcal{L}_1$.
Assume that $|I(x)| > \|x\|_1$ and let $\alpha = |I(x)| - \|x\|_1$.
There is a sequence $\{y_n\}_{n=1}^{\infty}$ in $\mathcal{C}_{\infty\infty}(R)$ such that

$\lim\limits_{n\to\infty} \|y_n - x\|_1 = 0$, and hence $\lim\limits_{n\to\infty} |I(y_n) - I(x)| = 0$.

For n sufficiently large, we have $|I(y_n)| > \|x\|_1 + \frac{\alpha}{2}$

and $|\|y_n\|_1 - \|x\|_1| \leq \|y_n - x\|_1 < \frac{\alpha}{2}$. Thus for sufficiently

large n, we have $\frac{\alpha}{2} + \|x\|_1 < |I(y_n)| \leq I(|y_n|) = \|y_n\|_1 <$

$\|x\|_1 + \frac{\alpha}{2}$. This contradiction proves the assertion.

We see that I must be unique by proving that $\lim_{n\to\infty} I(y_n) = I(x)$ if $\lim_{n\to\infty} \|y_n - x\|_1 = 0$, using only the supposition that I is a linear extension over $\mathcal{L}_1$ of the original I such that $|I(x)| \leq A\|x\|_1$. But we have $|I(y_n) - I(x)| = |I(y_n - x)| \leq I(|y_n - x|) \leq A \cdot \|y_n - x\|_1$, for a positive constant A.

4.1.45 <u>Exercises</u>.

4.1.451 <u>Exercise</u>. Let $x \in \mathcal{L}_1$. Then $|x| \in \mathcal{L}_1$ and $|I(x)| \leq I(|x|)$.

4.1.452 <u>Exercise</u>. Suppose $x \in \mathcal{L}_1$ and $x \geq 0$. Then $\bar{\bar{I}}(x) = \|x\|_1 = I(x)$, where I is the extension of the original I described in 4.1.441.

4.1.453 <u>Exercise</u>. If $x \in \mathcal{L}_1$ and x is real-valued, then $I(x)$ is a real number. Suppose that $x,y \in \mathcal{L}_1$, that x and y are real-valued, and that $y \leq x$. Then $I(y) \leq I(x)$.

4.1.454 <u>Exercise</u>. Suppose that $\{x_n\}_{n=1}^{\infty}$ is a sequence of non-negative functions in $\mathcal{L}_1$ and that $\sum_{n=1}^{\infty} I(x_n) < \infty$. Then the function $x = \sum_{n=1}^{\infty} x_n$ is finite a.e., belongs to $\mathcal{L}_1$, and $\lim_{m\to\infty} \|\sum_{n=1}^{m} x_n - x\|_1 = 0$. Furthermore, $I(x) = \sum_{n=1}^{\infty} I(x_n)$.

4.1.455 <u>Exercise</u>. If $\{x_n\}_{n=1}^{\infty}$ is an increasing (or decreasing) sequence of real-valued functions in $\mathcal{L}_1$ and the set of numbers $\{I(x_n)\}_{n=1}^{\infty}$ is bounded, then $x = \lim_{n\to\infty} x_n \in \mathcal{L}_1$

and $I(x) = \lim_{n\to\infty} I(x_n)$.

4.1.46 <u>Theorem</u>. Let $x \in \mathfrak{M}_+$. Then $x \in \mathcal{L}_1$ if and only if $\bar{I}(x) < \infty$, and in this case $\bar{I}(x) = I(x)$.

<u>Proof</u>. Suppose that $x \in \mathcal{L}_1$. Then, using 4.1.21, we have $\bar{I}(x) = \bar{\bar{I}}(x) = \|x\|_1 < \infty$.

Suppose that $\bar{I}(x) < \infty$. For $n = 1, 2, \ldots,$ there exists a $y_n \in \mathfrak{C}_+$ such that $y_n \leq x$ and $I(y_n) + \frac{1}{n} > \bar{I}(x)$. In particular, $\bar{\bar{I}}(x) = \bar{I}(x) < I(y_1) + 1 < \infty$, so that $x \in \mathfrak{J}_1$. Since $x - y_n \in \mathfrak{M}_+$ and $\bar{I}$ is additive on $\mathfrak{M}_+$ (4.1.153), $\bar{I}(x) = \bar{I}(x - y_n + y_n) = \bar{I}(x - y_n) + \bar{I}(y_n)$. Hence $\bar{I}(x - y_n) = \bar{I}(x) - \bar{I}(y_n) < \frac{1}{n}$ for $n = 1, 2, \ldots$. We have $\|x - y_n\|_1 = \bar{\bar{I}}(|x - y_n|) = \bar{I}(x - y_n) < \frac{1}{n}$. Consequently, $\lim_{n\to\infty} \|x - y_n\|_1 = 0$. Since each $y_n \in \mathfrak{C}_{\infty\infty}(R)$, it follows that $x \in \mathcal{L}_1$.

4.1.47 <u>Theorem</u>. Let $x \in \mathfrak{N}_+$. Then $x \in \mathcal{L}_1$ if and only if $\bar{\bar{I}}(x) < \infty$.

<u>Proof</u>. If $x \in \mathcal{L}_1$, then $\bar{\bar{I}}(x) = \|x\|_1 < \infty$.

Suppose that $\bar{\bar{I}}(x) < \infty$. There exists a $y \in \mathfrak{M}_+$ such that $y \geq x$ and $\bar{I}(y) < \bar{\bar{I}}(x) + 1 < \infty$. By 4.1.46, $y \in \mathcal{L}_1$. For $t \in R$, let $y(t) - x(t) =$

$$\begin{Bmatrix} y(t) - x(t) & \text{if } x(t) \text{ is finite} \\ 0 & \text{if } x(t) \text{ is infinite} \end{Bmatrix}.$$

Then $y - x \in \mathfrak{M}_+$. Now $\bar{I}(y - x) \leq \bar{\bar{I}}(y + x) \leq \bar{\bar{I}}(y) + \bar{\bar{I}}(x) < \infty$. Thus, by 4.1.46, $y - x \in \mathcal{L}_1$. Finally, $x = y - (y - x) \in \mathcal{L}_1$, since $\mathcal{L}_1$ is a linear space.

4.1.48 <u>Theorem</u>. Let $x \in \mathcal{L}_1$ be a non-negative function and let $\varepsilon > 0$. Then there exist $z \in \mathfrak{N}_+$ and $y \in \mathfrak{M}_+$ such that $y, z \in \mathcal{L}_1$, $0 \leq z \leq x \leq y$, and $I(y - z) < \varepsilon$.

<u>Proof</u>. We first show that there exists a $u \in \mathfrak{C}_+$ such that $\bar{\bar{I}}(|u - x|) < \frac{\varepsilon}{4}$. There exists an $f \in \mathfrak{C}_{\infty\infty}(R)$ such that $\|f - x\|_1 < \frac{\varepsilon}{4}$. Now $|\max(\mathfrak{R}f, 0) - x| \leq |\mathfrak{R}f - x| \leq |f - x|$; let $u = \max(\mathfrak{R}f, 0)$. Clearly $u \in \mathfrak{C}_+$. We thus have $\bar{\bar{I}}(|u - x|) \leq \bar{\bar{I}}(|f - x|) = \|f - x\|_1 < \frac{\varepsilon}{4}$.

There exists a $v \in \mathfrak{M}_+$, $v \geq |u - x|$, such that $\bar{I}(v) < \frac{\varepsilon}{2}$. Since some member of the equivalence class containing x is finite everywhere, we may suppose that x is finite everywhere. Then $-v \leq x - u \leq v$ everywhere or, equivalently, $u - v \leq x \leq u + v$ everywhere. Recall that $u \in \mathfrak{C}_+$ and $v \in \mathfrak{M}_+$. Let $y = u + v$ and $z = \max(u - v, 0)$. Then $y \in \mathfrak{M}_+$ and $z \in \mathfrak{N}_+$. It is evident that $0 \leq z \leq x \leq y$. Since $\bar{I}(y) = \bar{I}(u) + \bar{I}(v) < \bar{I}(\max(\mathfrak{R}f, 0)) + \frac{\varepsilon}{2} \leq \bar{I}(|f|) + \frac{\varepsilon}{2} < \infty$ and $\bar{\bar{I}}(z) \leq \bar{\bar{I}}(x) < \infty$, we infer from 4.1.47 and 4.1.46 that $z \in \mathcal{L}_1$ and $y \in \mathcal{L}_1$. Now $y - z = u + v - \max(u - v, 0) \leq u + v - (u - v) = 2v$, so that $I(y - z) \leq I(2v) = 2I(v) = 2\bar{I}(v) < \varepsilon$.

4.1.49 <u>Final Exercise # 17</u>. For every $x \in \mathcal{L}_1$, $x \geq 0$, there exists an increasing sequence $\{z_n\}_{n=1}^{\infty}$ of functions $z_n \in \mathfrak{N}_+$, each having compact support, and a decreasing sequence $\{y_n\}_{n=1}^{\infty}$ of functions $y_n \in \mathfrak{M}_+$, such that:

$\lim_{n\to\infty} z_n \leq x \leq \lim_{n\to\infty} y_n$; $I(\lim_{n\to\infty} z_n) = I(x) = I(\lim_{n\to\infty} y_n)$; and $\lim_{n\to\infty} z_n = x = \lim_{n\to\infty} y_n$ a.e.

4.1.5 Definition. A subset A of R is said to be summable if $\chi_A \in \mathcal{L}_1$.

Note that for summable sets, $\mu(A) = \bar{\bar{I}}(\chi_A) = I(\chi_A)$.

4.1.51 Theorem. If A is a null set, then A is summable and $\mu(A) = 0$.

Proof. Since $\chi_A = 0$ a.e., $\chi_A \in \mathcal{L}_1$ and $\mu(A) = I(\chi_A) = I(0) = 0$.

4.1.52 Theorem. Let $A_1, \ldots, A_n, \ldots$ be pairwise disjoint summable sets. Then $\mu(\bigcup_{n=1}^{\infty} A_n) = \sum_{n=1}^{\infty} \mu(A_n)$.

Proof. Case I. Suppose that $\sum_{n=1}^{\infty} \mu(A_n) < \infty$. Applying 4.1.452, we have $\sum_{n=1}^{\infty} I(\chi_{A_n}) = \sum_{n=1}^{\infty} \bar{\bar{I}}(\chi_{A_n}) = \sum_{n=1}^{\infty} \mu(A_n) < \infty$. Hence by 4.1.454 we have $\chi_{\bigcup_{n=1}^{\infty} A_n} = \sum_{n=1}^{\infty} \chi_{A_n} \in \mathcal{L}_1$. Now using 4.1.452 and 4.1.454, we obtain $\mu(\bigcup_{n=1}^{\infty} A_n) = \bar{\bar{I}}(\chi_{\bigcup_{n=1}^{\infty} A_n}) =$

$I(\chi_{\bigcup_{n=1}^{\infty} A_n}) = \sum_{n=1}^{\infty} I(\chi_{A_n}) = \sum_{n=1}^{\infty} \mu(A_n)$.

Case II. Suppose that $\sum_{n=1}^{\infty} \mu(A_n) = \infty$. Then

$\mu(\bigcup_{n=1}^{\infty} A_n) \geq \lim_{m\to\infty} \mu(\bigcup_{n=1}^{m} A_n) = \lim_{m\to\infty} \sum_{n=1}^{m} \mu(A_n) = \infty$, by Case I.

4.1.53 Theorem. If A and B are summable, then $A \cap B'$, $A \cap B$, and $A \cup B$ are summable.

Proof. The set $A \cap B'$ is summable since the function $\chi_{A\cap B'} = \max(\chi_A - \chi_B, 0)$ is summable. The identity

$A \cap B = A \cap (A \cap B')'$ shows that $A \cap B$ is summable. Since $\chi_{A\cup B} = \chi_A + \chi_{A'\cap B'}$, $A \cup B$ is summable.

4.1.54 Theorem. A set A that is open or closed is summable if and only if $\bar{\bar{I}}(\chi_A) < \infty$.

Proof. If A is open, then $\chi_A \in \mathfrak{M}_+$ and by 4.1.46 χ_A is summable if and only if $\bar{I}(\chi_A) = \bar{\bar{I}}(\chi_A) < \infty$. If A is closed, then $\chi_A \in \mathfrak{N}_+$ and by 4.1.47 χ_A is summable if and only if $\bar{\bar{I}}(\chi_A) < \infty$.

4.1.541 Exercise. If $A_1 \supset A_2 \supset \ldots \supset A_n \supset \ldots$ is a sequence of summable sets, then $\mu(\bigcap_{n=1}^{\infty} A_n) = \lim_{n\to\infty} \mu(A_n)$. If $A_1 \subset A_2 \subset \ldots \subset A_n \subset \ldots$ is a sequence of summable sets, then $\mu(\bigcup_{n=1}^{\infty} A_n) = \lim_{n\to\infty} \mu(A_n)$.

4.1.55 Theorem. Every compact set is summable.

Proof. This is immediate from 4.1.34 and 4.1.54.

4.1.56 Theorem. A subset A of R is summable if and only if (*) for every $\varepsilon > 0$, there exists an open set G and a compact set F such that $F \subset A \subset G$ and $\mu(G \cap F') < \varepsilon$.

Proof. Suppose that condition (*) holds. Then for every $\varepsilon > 0$, there are an open set G and a compact set $F \subset A$ such that $\|\chi_A - \chi_F\|_1 = \mu(A \cap F') \leq \mu(G \cap F') < \varepsilon$. By 4.1.55, $\chi_F \in \mathcal{L}_1$. Since ε is arbitrary, we conclude that $\chi_A \in \mathcal{L}_1$.

Suppose that A is summable, $\chi_A \in \mathcal{L}_1$. Let $\varepsilon > 0$. By 4.1.35, there exists an open set $G \supset A$ such that $\mu(G) < \mu(A) + \frac{\varepsilon}{2}$. By 4.1.48, there exists a $z \in \mathfrak{N}_+$,

$z \in \mathcal{L}_1$, having compact support such that $z \leq \chi_A$ and $I(\chi_A - z) < \frac{\varepsilon}{4}$. If $\mu(A) = 0$, let $F = 0$; clearly $\mu(G \cap F') = \mu(G) < \frac{\varepsilon}{2}$. Otherwise let $\delta = \min\left(\frac{\varepsilon}{8\mu(A)}, 1\right)$ and let $F = \{t: z(t) \geq \delta\}$. Evidently F is compact and $F \subset A$. We also know that $A \cap F'$ is summable. Now $z \leq \chi_F + \delta\chi_{A \cap F'}$, so that $I(z) \leq I(\chi_F) + \delta I(\chi_{A \cap F'}) \leq \mu(F) + \frac{\varepsilon}{8\mu(A)}\mu(A) < \mu(F) + \frac{\varepsilon}{4}(z, \chi_F$, and $\chi_{A \cap F'}$ are summable). We have $\mu(A) = I(\chi_A) = I(\chi_A - z) + I(z) < \frac{\varepsilon}{4} + I(z) < \frac{\varepsilon}{4} + \mu(F) + \frac{\varepsilon}{4} = \mu(F) + \frac{\varepsilon}{2}$. Finally, $\mu(G \cap F') = \mu(G) - \mu(F) = \mu(G) - \mu(A) + \mu(A) - \mu(F) < \frac{\varepsilon}{2} + \frac{\varepsilon}{2} = \varepsilon$.

4.1.57 __Theorem.__ Let $A \subset R$ be summable. Then there exists a sequence $G_1 \supset G_2 \supset \ldots \supset G_n \supset \ldots$ of open sets where $G_n \supset A$ and $\mu((\bigcap_{n=1}^{\infty} G_n) \cap A') = 0$. Furthermore, there exists a sequence of pairwise disjoint compact sets $\{F_n\}_{n=1}^{\infty}$ such that $F_n \subset A$ and $\mu(A \cap (\bigcup_{n=1}^{\infty} F_n)') = 0$.

__Proof.__ For every positive integer n, let H_n and E_n be open and compact sets, respectively, such that $E_n \subset A \subset H_n$ and $\mu(H_n \cap E_n') < \frac{1}{n}$. For $n = 1, 2, \ldots$, let $G_n = H_1 \cap H_2 \cap \ldots \cap H_n$. Applying 4.1.541, we obtain

$$\mu((\bigcap_{n=1}^{\infty} G_n) \cap A') = \lim_{n\to\infty} \mu(G_n \cap A') \leq \lim_{n\to\infty} \mu(H_n \cap E_n') = 0.$$

Clearly each $G_n \supset A$ is open and $G_1 \supset G_2 \supset \ldots \supset G_n \supset \ldots$

Let $F_1 \subset A$ be a compact set such that $\mu(A \cap F_1') < 1$. Note that $A \cap F_1'$ is summable; hence there exists a compact set $F_2 \subset A \cap F_1'$ such that $\mu((A \cap F_1') \cap F_2') < \frac{1}{2}$. Continuing in this manner, we obtain a sequence of compact sets $\{F_n\}_{n=1}^{\infty}$ such that $F_n \subset A \cap (F_1 \cup \ldots \cup F_{n-1})'$ with $\mu(A \cap (F_1 \cup \ldots \cup F_n)') < \frac{1}{n}$. Evidently the F_n are pairwise disjoint and by 4.1.541, we have $\mu(A \cap (\bigcup_{n=1}^{\infty} F_n)') = \lim_{n\to\infty} \mu(A \cap (F_1 \cup \ldots \cup F_n)') = 0$.

4.1.58 Theorem. Let $A \subset R$ and $\mu(A) < \infty$. Then A is contained in the union of a null set and the union of a countable family of pairwise disjoint compact sets.

Proof. By 4.1.35, there exists a sequence $\{G_n\}_{n=1}^{\infty}$ of open sets such that $G_n \supset A$ and $\mu(G_n) < \mu(A) + \frac{1}{n}$. Let $B = \bigcap_{n=1}^{\infty} G_n$; we have $\mu(B) = \mu(A)$. The set B is summable since $\chi_B = \lim_{n\to\infty} \chi_{G_1 \cap \ldots \cap G_n}$ and these are summable functions (4.1.53 and 4.1.44). Consequently, we may apply 4.1.57 to obtain a sequence $\{F_n\}_{n=1}^{\infty}$ of pairwise disjoint compact sets such that $\mu(B \cap (\bigcup_{n=1}^{\infty} F_n)') = 0$. Since $A \subset (B \cap (\bigcup_{n=1}^{\infty} F_n)') \cup (\bigcup_{n=1}^{\infty} F_n)$, the proof is complete.

4.1.6 Definition. A subset B of R is said to be measurable if $B \cap F$ is summable for all compact sets F. Let $\mathfrak{M}$ be the family of all measurable sets.

4.1.61 Theorem. $\mathfrak{M}$ is a σ-algebra of sets.

Proof. Let $B \in \mathfrak{M}$. For F compact, $\chi_{B' \cap F} = \chi_F - \chi_{B \cap F}$ Thus $B' \cap F$ is summable for all compact sets F; i.e.,

$B' \in \mathfrak{M}$.

Let $\{B_n\}_{n=1}^{\infty}$ be any sequence of sets in $\mathfrak{M}$. Let F be compact. For $m = 1, 2, \ldots$, let $A_m = (\bigcup_{n=1}^{m} B_n) \cap F$. Each χ_{A_m} is in $\mathcal{L}_1(R,I)$ since $(B_1 \cap F) \cup \ldots \cup (B_n \cap F)$ is a finite union of summable sets and hence is summable by 4.1.53. For each n, we have $I(\chi_{A_n}) \leq I(\chi_F) < \infty$; the last inequality follows from 4.1.55. By 4.1.455, we see that $\chi_{(\bigcup_{n=1}^{\infty} B_n) \cap F} = \lim_{m \to \infty} \chi_{A_m} \in \mathcal{L}_1$ and $(\bigcup_{n=1}^{\infty} B_n) \cap F$ is summable. Since F is an arbitrary compact set, it follows that $\bigcup_{n=1}^{\infty} B_n \in \mathfrak{M}$.

4.1.62 Theorem. Every closed set is measurable.

Proof. Let A be a closed set and F be any compact set. Then $A \cap F$ is compact and hence summable. Therefore $A \in \mathfrak{M}$.

4.1.621 Theorem. The σ-algebra $\mathfrak{M}$ contains all Borel sets.

This is immediate from 4.1.62 and 4.1.61.

4.1.63 Theorem. If $A \in \mathfrak{M}$ and $\mu(A) < \infty$, then A is summable.

Proof. In 4.1.58, it was shown that $A \subset N \cup (\bigcup_{n=1}^{\infty} F_n)$, where $\mu(N) = 0$ and the F_n's are compact and pairwise disjoint. Thus $A = (N \cap A) \cup (\bigcup_{n=1}^{\infty} (F_n \cap A))$ and $\chi_A = \lim_{m \to \infty} \chi_{(N \cap A) \cup (\bigcup_{n=1}^{m} (F_n \cap A))}$; each $A_m = (N \cap A) \cup$

$(\bigcup_{n=1}^{m}(F_n \cap A))$ is summable, since $A \varepsilon \mathfrak{M}$. Now for all m, $I(\chi_{A_m}) = \mu(A_m) \leq \mu(A)$. Consequently by 4.1.455, $\chi_A \varepsilon \mathcal{L}_1$.

4.1.631 Theorem. μ is countably additive on $\mathfrak{M}$.

Proof. Let $\{A_n\}_{n=1}^{\infty}$ be a pairwise disjoint family of sets in $\mathfrak{M}$. If $\mu(A_{n_o}) = \infty$ for some n_o, then clearly $\infty = \mu(\bigcup_{n=1}^{\infty} A_n) = \sum_{n=1}^{\infty} \mu(A_n)$. If $\mu(A_n) < \infty$ for all n, then by 4.1.63 and 4.1.52, $\mu(\bigcup_{n=1}^{\infty} A_n) = \sum_{n=1}^{\infty} \mu(A_n)$.

4.1.64 Remark. We shall now apply the foregoing construction of μ and $\mathfrak{M}$, and the general theory of measurable functions (3.1 and 3.2), to show that the functional I is actually a Lebesgue integral. Note that a complex function ϕ is said to be measurable if $\mathfrak{R}\phi$ and $\mathfrak{I}\phi$ are measurable.

4.1.65 Theorem. A complex-valued function x on R is summable if and only if x is $\mathfrak{M}$-measurable and $\bar{\bar{I}}(|x|) < \infty$.

Proof. Suppose that $x \varepsilon \mathcal{L}_1$. Clearly $\bar{\bar{I}}(|x|) < \infty$; we now show that x is $\mathfrak{M}$-measurable. There is a sequence $\{x_n\}_{n=1}^{\infty}$ of functions $x_n \varepsilon \mathfrak{C}_{\infty\infty}(R)$ such that $\lim_{n\to\infty} \|x - x_n\|_1 = 0$. As in the proof of 4.1.43, we can find a subsequence $\{x_{n_k}\}_{k=1}^{\infty}$ such that $\lim_{k\to\infty} x_{n_k}(t) = x(t)$ a.e.

on R. By 3.1.31, it now suffices to prove that every function in $\mathfrak{C}_{\infty\infty}(R)$ is $\mathfrak{M}$-measurable.

Let $y \varepsilon \mathfrak{C}_{\infty\infty}(R)$. Then $y = y_1 + iy_2$ where y_1 and y_2 are real-valued continuous functions. Then $\{t: y_j(t) > \alpha\}$ is open for $j = 1, 2$ and therefore in $\mathfrak{M}$ for every real α. Thus y_1 and y_2 are measurable and, consequently, y is measurable.

Suppose that x is $\mathfrak{M}$-measurable and $\bar{\bar{I}}(|x|) < \infty$. We have $x = \max(\mathfrak{R}x,0) - (-\min(\mathfrak{R}x,0)) + i \max(\mathfrak{J}x,0) - i(-\min(\mathfrak{J}x,0))$ where each of these functions is measurable and $\bar{\bar{I}}$ for each of them is bounded by $\bar{\bar{I}}(|x|)$. Since $\mathcal{L}_1$ is a linear space, it suffices, in view of the above, to suppose that x is real-valued, non-negative, and $\mathfrak{M}$-measurable, and that $\bar{\bar{I}}(x) < \infty$. Since $\bar{\bar{I}}(x) < \infty$, we see that $\mu\{t: x(t) = \infty\} = 0$ (4.1.363), and we may replace x by an equivalent function that is finite-valued everywhere. Thus we may suppose that x is finite-valued everywhere.

Let $a > 0$ and $B = \{t: x(t) > a\}$. Since x is measurable, $B \varepsilon \mathfrak{M}$. Clearly $\chi_B \leq \frac{1}{a}x$ and hence $\mu(B) = \bar{\bar{I}}(\chi_B) \leq \bar{\bar{I}}(\frac{1}{a}x) = \frac{1}{a}\bar{\bar{I}}(x) < \infty$. Thus by 4.1.63, B is summable.

For m and n positive integers, let $A_{nm} = \left\{t: \frac{m}{2^n} < x(t) \leq \frac{m+1}{2^n}\right\}$; A_{nm} is summable since it is of the form $B \cap C'$ where B and C are summable.

For $n = 1, 2, \ldots,$ let $x_n = \sum_{m=1}^{\infty} \frac{m}{2^n} \chi_{A_{nm}}$; since $A_{nm_1} \cap A_{nm_2} = 0$ whenever $m_1 \neq m_2$, each x_n is finite valued everywhere. Evidently $x_1 \leq x_2 \leq \ldots \leq x_n \leq \ldots \leq x$ and $\lim_{n\to\infty} x_n(t) = x(t)$ everywhere. For n and k positive integers, let $x_n^{(k)} = \sum_{m=1}^{k} \frac{m}{2^n} \chi_{A_{nm}}$. Since each $\chi_{A_{mn}}$ is summable, we have $x_n^{(k)} \varepsilon \mathcal{L}_1$. Evidently $x_n^{(k)} \leq x$ so that $I(x_n^{(k)}) \leq \bar{\bar{I}}(x) < \infty$ for all n and k. The sequence $\{x_n^{(k)}\}_{k=1}^{\infty}$ is increasing and the set $\{I(x_n^{(k)})\}_{k=1}^{\infty}$ is bounded so that by 4.1.455, we have $x_n = \lim_{k\to\infty} x_n^{(k)} \varepsilon \mathcal{L}_1$ and $I(x_n) \leq \bar{\bar{I}}(x)$ $(n = 1, 2, 3, \ldots)$. By 4.1.455 again, $x = \lim_{n\to\infty} x_n \varepsilon \mathcal{L}_1$. (Note that the numbers $I(x_n)$ are bounded.)

4.1.66 Discussion. In what follows $\mathcal{L}_1$ will denote, as before, the subset of $\mathcal{J}_1$ defined in 4.1.44. We will write $\mathcal{L}_1(R, \mathfrak{M}, \mu)$ for the class of complex-valued functions which is defined in 3.7.73 for the measure space R, the σ- algebra $\mathfrak{M}$, and the measure μ.

4.1.661 Theorem. Let x be a complex-valued function defined a.e. on R. Then $x \varepsilon \mathcal{L}_1$ if and only if $x \varepsilon \mathcal{L}_1(R,\mathfrak{M},\mu)$ and in this case $I(x) = \int_R x(t)d\mu(t)$.

Proof. As in 4.1.65, it suffices to prove this result for non-negative real-valued functions, finite everywhere on R.

Suppose that $x \in \mathcal{L}_1$. Let A_{nm} and x_n be as in 4.1.65; since x is $\mathfrak{M}$-measurable (4.1.65) each A_{nm} is in $\mathfrak{M}$. We first show that each $x_n \in \mathcal{L}_1(R, \mathfrak{M}, \mu)$. By definition, $x_n = \sum_{m=1}^{\infty} \frac{m}{2^n} \chi_{A_{nm}}$ and consequently,

$$\int_R x_n(t)d\mu(t) = \sum_{m=1}^{\infty} \frac{m}{2^n} \mu(A_{nm}) \leq I(x).$$

Thus we have an increasing sequence $\{x_n\}_{n=1}^{\infty}$ of functions in $\mathcal{L}_1(R, \mathfrak{M}, \mu)$ such that $\lim_{n\to\infty} x_n(t) = x(t)$ everywhere and the sequence $\left\{\int_R x_n(t)d\mu(t)\right\}_{n=1}^{\infty}$ is bounded. We infer from 3.5.11 that

$$\int_R x(t)d\mu(t) = \lim_{n\to\infty} \int_R x_n(t)d\mu(t) < \infty$$

and therefore $x \in \mathcal{L}_1(R, \mathfrak{M}, \mu)$.

Suppose that $x \in \mathcal{L}_1(R, \mathfrak{M}, \mu)$, and that x is a non-negative real-valued function on R. Let A_{nm}, $x_n^{(k)}$, and x_n be as in 4.1.65. Each A_{nm} is $\mathfrak{M}$-measurable and $\mu(A_{nm}) < \infty$ since $\int_R x(t)d\mu(t) < \infty$. Thus A_{nm} is summable for all m and n. The $x_n^{(k)}$ are summable, and

$$I(x_n^{(k)}) = \sum_{m=1}^{n} \frac{m}{2^n} I(\chi_{A_{nm}}) = \sum_{m=1}^{k} \frac{m}{2^n} \mu(A_{nm}) = \int_R x_n^{(k)}(t)d\mu(t) \leq \int_R x(t)d\mu(t) < \infty.$$

By 4.1.455, $x_n = \lim_{k\to\infty} x_n^{(k)} \in \mathcal{L}_1$ and the sequence $\{I(x_n)\}_{n=1}^{\infty}$ is bounded. Again using 4.1.455, we conclude that $x \in \mathcal{L}_1$.

We now prove that if $x \in \mathcal{L}_1 = \mathcal{L}_1(R, \mathfrak{M}, \mu)$, then $I(x) = \int_R x(t)d\mu(t)$. Applying 3.5.11 twice, we have

$\lim_{n\to\infty} (\lim_{k\to\infty} \int_R x_n^{(k)}(t)d\mu(t)) = \int_R x(t)d\mu(t)$ and applying 4.1.455 twice, we have $\lim_{n\to\infty} \lim_{k\to\infty} I(x_n^{(k)}) = I(x)$. Hence $I(x) = \int_R x(t)d\mu(t)$.

4.1.7 Theorem. (F. Riesz) Let I be a complex linear functional on $\mathfrak{C}_{\infty\infty}(R)$ such that $I(x) \geq 0$ for $x \in \mathfrak{C}_+$. Then there is a non-negative, extended real-valued, countably additive Borel measure μ such that $I(x) = \int_R x(t)d\mu(t)$ for all $x \in \mathfrak{C}_{\infty\infty}(R)$.

Proof. This is a restatement of 4.1.661 restricting I to $\mathfrak{C}_{\infty\infty}(R)$.

4.1.71 Remark. Theorem 4.1.7 is known as the Riesz representation theorem. Let E be a subset of R that is either open or closed. Let $\mathfrak{C}_{\infty\infty}(E)$ be the linear space of all complex-valued continuous functions x on E such that $x(t) = 0$ outside of some compact subset of E. The Borel subsets of E are the σ-algebra generated by compact subsets of E. Then the Riesz representation theorem holds with no change in either statement or proof. Riesz proved his original theorem for $E = [0,1]$.

4.1.72 Remark. Let μ_1 and μ_2 be countably additive, non-negative, Borel measures on R both of which are finite for every compact set. If $\int_{-\infty}^{\infty} x(t)d\mu_1(t) = \int_{-\infty}^{\infty} x(t)d\mu_2(t)$ for all $x \in \mathfrak{C}_{\infty\infty}(R)$, then μ_1 and μ_2 are identical measures. We shall not go into the proof of this fact.

4.1.73 <u>Definition</u>. A complex-valued linear functional I on $\mathfrak{C}_{\infty\infty}(R)$ is said to be bounded if there exists a non-negative real number A such that $|I(x)| \leq A\|x\|_u$ for all $x \in \mathfrak{C}_{\infty\infty}(R)$.

4.1.731 <u>Theorem</u>. Let I be a bounded complex-valued linear functional on $\mathfrak{C}_{\infty\infty}(R)$. Then $A_o = \inf\{A: A \geq 0, |I(x)| \leq A\|x\|_u$ for all $x \in \mathfrak{C}_{\infty\infty}(R)\} = \sup\{|I(x)|: \|x\|_u \leq 1$ and $x \in \mathfrak{C}_{\infty\infty}(R)\} = B_o$. (This common value is denoted by $\|I\|$ and is called the norm of I.) The functional I is unbounded if and only if $\sup\{|I(x)|: \|x\|_u = 1, x \in \mathfrak{C}_{\infty\infty}(R)\} = \infty$.

<u>Proof</u>. In this proof, x always denotes a member of $\mathfrak{C}_{\infty\infty}(R)$. For $0 < \|x\|_u \leq 1$, we have $|I(\frac{x}{\|x\|_u})| = \frac{1}{\|x\|_u}|I(x)| \geq |I(x)|$, and $\|\frac{x}{\|x\|_u}\|_u = 1$. Consequently $B_o = \sup\{|I(x)|: \|x\|_u = 1\}$. Let ε be a positive real number. Then $|I(x)| \leq (A_o + \varepsilon)\|x\|_u$ for all x. If $\|x\|_u \leq 1$, we then have $|I(x)| \leq A_o + \varepsilon$, and this implies that $B_o \leq A_o$. To prove the reverse inequality, note that there is an x such that $A_o - \varepsilon < |I(\frac{x}{\|x\|_u})|$ (provided $I \neq 0$). This implies that $A_o \leq B_o$.

If $B_o = \infty$, then clearly I is unbounded. Suppose that $B_o < \infty$. Then for any $x \neq 0$, $|I(\frac{x}{\|x\|_u})| \leq B_o$ so that $|I(x)| \leq B_o\|x\|_u$. This inequality also holds if $x = 0$. Hence I is bounded.

4.1.732 Theorem. Let I be a non-negative real-valued functional on $\mathfrak{C}_{\infty\infty}(R)$ and μ be the measure corresponding to I by 4.1.7. Then I is bounded if and only if $\mu(R) < \infty$.

Proof. Suppose that I is bounded. Then

$\mu(R) = \bar{I}(\chi_R) = \sup\{I(x): x \in \mathfrak{C}_+, x \leq \chi_R\} \leq \sup\{|I(x)|: \|x\|_u \leq 1\} < \infty$.

Conversely, suppose that I is unbounded. Then $|I(x)| \leq I(|x|)$ for all $x \in \mathfrak{C}_{\infty\infty}(R)$ so that

$$\mu(R) = \sup\{I(x): x \in \mathfrak{C}_+, x \leq \chi_R\}$$
$$\geq \sup\{I(|x|): \|x\|_u \leq 1, x \in \mathfrak{C}_{\infty\infty}(R)\}$$
$$\geq \sup\{|I(x)|: \|x\|_u \leq 1, x \in \mathfrak{C}_{\infty\infty}(R)\} = \infty.$$

4.1.74 Examples.

4.1.741 Example. Let $I(x) = \int_{-\infty}^{\infty} x(t)dt$, the ordinary Riemann integral, for $x \in \mathfrak{C}_{\infty\infty}(R)$. I is non-negative, unbounded, and the measure μ obtained is Lebesgue measure λ.

4.1.742 Example. Let $g \in \mathfrak{L}_1(R, \mathfrak{M}, \lambda)$ and $I(x) = \int_{-\infty}^{\infty} x(t)g(t)dt$ for $x \in \mathfrak{C}_{\infty\infty}(R)$. We have

$|I(x)| \leq \int_{-\infty}^{\infty} |x(t)|\,|g(t)|dt \leq \|x\|_u \int_{-\infty}^{\infty} |g(t)|dt$ and

$\int_{-\infty}^{\infty} |g(t)|dt < \infty$. Therefore I is bounded. We note also that I is non-negative if g is non-negative a.e. and that $\mu(R) = \int_{-\infty}^{\infty} g(t)dt$ in this case.

4.1.743 Example. Let $t_0 \in R$ be fixed and let $I(x) = x(t_0)$ for $x \in \mathfrak{C}_{\infty\infty}(R)$. The corresponding measure is called ε_{t_0};

it is not hard to show that $\varepsilon_{t_o}(A) = \chi_A(t_o)$.

4.1.744 Example. Let $I(x) = \sum_{n=1}^{\infty} \alpha_n x(t_n)$ for $x \in \mathfrak{C}_{\infty\infty}(R)$ where $\{t_n\}_{n=1}^{\infty}$ has no finite point of accumulation or, if it does, $\sum_{n=1}^{\infty} |\alpha_n| < \infty$. I is bounded if and only if $\sum_{n=1}^{\infty} |\alpha_n| < \infty$; it is non-negative if and only if $\alpha_n \geq 0$ for all n. Clearly $\mu(R) = \sum_{n=1}^{\infty} \alpha_n$.

4.1.8 Final Exercise # 18. Let I be a bounded linear functional on $\mathfrak{C}_{\infty\infty}(R)$ such that I is real-valued for every $x \in \mathfrak{C}_+$. For $x \in \mathfrak{C}_+$, let $I_+(x) = \sup\{I(y): 0 \leq y \leq x$ $y \in \mathfrak{C}_+\}$ and $I_-(x) = I_+(x) - I(x)$. Show that I_+ and I_- can be extended over $\mathfrak{C}_{\infty\infty}(R)$ so as to be bounded non-negative linear functionals on $\mathfrak{C}_{\infty\infty}(R)$, and such that I is the difference of these two extensions (Show first that I_+ and I_- are non-negative, positively homogeneous, and additive on $\mathfrak{C}_+$.)

4.1.81 Final Exercise # 19. Show from 4.1.8 that every bounded complex linear functional I on $\mathfrak{C}_{\infty\infty}(R)$ has the form $I(x) = \int_{-\infty}^{\infty} x(t)d\mu(t)$ where μ is a complex bounded measure that is, $\mu = \mu_1 - \mu_2 + i(\mu_3 - \mu_4)$ where the μ_k are non-negative real-valued bounded measures $(k = 1, 2, 3, 4)$

4.1.82 Final Exercise # 20. Let μ be any complex bounded Borel measure on R. Then $I(x) = \int_{-\infty}^{\infty} x(t)d\mu(t)$ is a bounded linear functional on $\mathfrak{C}_{\infty\infty}(R)$. For all Borel sets A, let $|\mu|(A) = \sup \left\{ \sum_{j=1}^{k} |\mu(E_j)| : \right.$ $E_1 \cup \ldots \cup E_k = A$, $E_i \cap E_j = 0$ if $i \neq j$, and the E_j's are Borel sets$\left. \right\}$.

Prove:

i) $|\mu|$ is a countably additive measure on Borel sets;

ii) $|\mu|$ is the smallest non-negative real-valued measure such that $|\mu|(A) \geq |\mu(A)|$ for all Borel sets A;

iii) $|\mu|(R) = \|I\|$.

4.1.9 Theorem. Let F be a compact subset of R and $\mathfrak{C}(F)$ be the class of all complex-valued continuous functions on F. Let $\mathfrak{C}_+(F)$ be the class of non-negative real-valued functions in $\mathfrak{C}(F)$. Let I be a linear functional on $\mathfrak{C}(F)$ that is non-negative on $\mathfrak{C}_+(F)$. Then I is bounded.

Proof. If $\|x\|_u \leq 1$, then $|x(t)| \leq 1$ for all $t \in F$. Thus $|x| \leq 1$ so that $|I(x)| \leq I(|x|) \leq I(1) < \infty$; here 1 represents the function identically 1 on F. Hence $\sup \{ |I(x)| : \|x\|_u \leq 1, x \in \mathfrak{C}(F) \} \leq I(1)$ and I is bounded.

Note that since $1 \in \mathfrak{C}(F)$, we have $\|I\| = \sup \{ |I(x)| : \|x\|_u \leq 1, x \in \mathfrak{C}(F) \} = I(1)$.

4.1.91 Remark. Everything in section 4.1 can be extended verbatim to $\mathfrak{C}_{\infty\infty}(T)$ where T is an arbitrary locally compact Hausdorff space, except for Remark 4.1.72, which must be modified. $\mathfrak{C}_{\infty\infty}(T)$ is the collection of complex-valued continuous functions x on T such that the set $\{t \varepsilon T: x(t) \neq 0\}$ is contained in a compact subset of T.

4.2 Monotone functions.

4.2.1 Theorem. Let $-\infty < a < b < \infty$ and let I be a non-negative linear functional on $\mathfrak{C}([a,b])$, the class of complex-valued continuous functions on $[a,b]$. Let μ be the Borel measure on $[a,b]$ corresponding to I by 4.1.7. Let α be the function on $[a,b]$ such that $\alpha(a) = 0$ and $\alpha(t) = \mu([a,t])$ for $a < t \leq b$. Then α is a non-negative, real-valued, increasing function that is right continuous except possibly at a. Furthermore, I and μ are completely determined by α and

$$I(x) = \int_{[a,b]} x(t)d\mu(t) = \int_a^b x(t)d\alpha(t) \quad \text{for all} \quad x \varepsilon \mathfrak{C}([a,b]), \; (*)$$

where $\int_a^b x(t)d\alpha(t)$ is the usual Riemann-Stieltjes integral.

Proof. The function α is obviously non-negative and it is increasing since if $a \leq t_1 < t_2 \leq b$, then $\mu([a,t_2]) = \mu([a,t_1]) + \mu(]t_1,t_2]) \geq \mu([a,t_1])$. Suppose that $a < t < b$. Then $[a,t] = \bigcap_{n=1}^{\infty} [a,t + \frac{1}{n}]$ and

$$\alpha(t) = \mu([a,t]) = \lim_{n\to\infty} \mu([a,t + \frac{1}{n}]) = \lim_{n\to\infty} \alpha(t + \frac{1}{n}) (4.1.541).$$

This, together with the fact that α is increasing, proves that α is right continuous for $t \varepsilon]a,b[$.

We note that α need not be right continuous at a for let $I(x) = x(a)$ for $x \in \mathfrak{C}([a,b])$. Then the corresponding measure μ is ε_a. Thus we see that $\alpha(a + \delta) = \varepsilon_a([a,a + \delta]) = 1$ for all $\delta > 0$, whereas $\alpha(a) = 0$; α clearly fails to be right continuous at a.

Suppose that α is the non-negative, real-valued, increasing function obtained from μ and I by defining $\alpha(a) = 0$ and $\alpha(t) = \mu([a,t])$ for $t \in]a,b]$. We will show that μ and I are completely determined by α. Suppose that $]c,d[\subset [a,b]$. Then $]c,d[= \bigcup_{n=n_0}^{\infty}]c,d - \frac{1}{n}]$ where n_0 is such that $d - \frac{1}{n} > c$ for $n \geq n_0$. Now $\mu(]c,d - \frac{1}{n}]) = \mu([a,d - \frac{1}{n}]) - \mu([a,c]) = \alpha(d - \frac{1}{n}) - \alpha(c)$ and therefore, applying 2.4.2, we obtain $\mu(]c,d[) = \lim_{n\to\infty} \mu(]c,d - \frac{1}{n}]) = \lim_{n\to\infty} \alpha(d - \frac{1}{n}) - \alpha(c)$. In an analogous manner, we see that $\mu([a,c[)$ and $\mu(]d,b])$ depend only on α. Therefore α determines μ for all open subsets of $[a,b]$. By 4.1.35, μ is thus determined for all subsets of $[a,b]$. By virtue of 4.1.7, I is also completely determined by α.

We recall here the definition of the Riemann-Stieltjes integral (see Rudin, <u>Principles of Mathematical Analysis</u>; page 88). Let Δ be a subdivision $a = t_0 < t_1 < \ldots < t_n = b$ of the interval $[a,b]$ and α be a monotonically increasing function. For an arbitrary bounded real-valued function y on $[a,b]$, define

$$U(\Delta,y,\alpha) = \sum_{i=1}^{n} \sup\left\{y(t): t_{i-1} \leq t \leq t_i\right\} [\alpha(t_i) - \alpha(t_{i-1})]$$

and

$$L(\Delta,y,\alpha) = \sum_{i=1}^{n} \inf\left\{y(t): t_{i-1} \leq t \leq t_i\right\} [\alpha(t_i) - \alpha(t_{i-1})].$$

If $\inf\left\{U(\Delta,y,\alpha): \Delta \text{ subdivides } [a,b]\right\} =$ $\sup\left\{L(\Delta,y,\alpha): \Delta \text{ subdivides } [a,b]\right\}$, the common value of these two expressions is called the Riemann-Stieltjes integral of y with respect to α. It is written $\int_a^b y(t)d\alpha(t)$. If y is a complex-valued continuous function, then we define $\int_a^b y(t)d\alpha(t) = \int_a^b \Re y(t)d\alpha(t) +$ $i\int_a^b \Im y(t)d\alpha(t)$.

We first prove equality (*) for continuous real-valued functions on $[a,b]$. If y is a real-valued continuous function on $[a,b]$, then $\int_a^b y(t)d\alpha(t)$ exists (Theorem 6.8, Rudin). Pick $\varepsilon > 0$. There exists a subdivision Δ for which $\int_a^b y(t)d\alpha(t) \geq U(\Delta,y,\alpha) - \varepsilon$. Let S_u be the function $M_1\chi_{[t_o,t_1]} + \sum_{i=2}^{n} M_i\chi_{]t_{i-1},t_i]}$ where $M_1 = \sup\left\{y(t): t \in [t_o,t_1]\right\}$ and $M_i = \sup\left\{y(t): t\in]t_{i-1},t_i]\right\}$ for $i = 2, \ldots, n$. Clearly, $\int_{[a,b]} S_u(t)d\mu(t) = U(\Delta,y,\alpha)$, since y is continuous. Since $y \leq S_u$, we have $\int_{[a,b]} y(t)d\mu(t) \leq$

$\int_{[a,b]} S_u(t)d\mu(t) = U(\Delta,y,\alpha) \leq \int_a^b y(t)d\alpha(t) + \varepsilon$. Thus

$\int_{[a,b]} y(t)d\mu(t) \leq \int_a^b y(t)d\alpha(t)$. The reverse inequality is shown in a similar manner using $L(\Delta,y,\alpha)$, etc.

The equality (*) can now easily be extended to all functions in $\mathfrak{C}([a,b])$.

4.2.11 <u>Theorem</u>. Let J be any interval in R (finite or infinite and with or without endpoints). Let I be any bounded non-negative linear functional on $\mathfrak{C}_{\infty\infty}(R)$. Let μ be the measure that corresponds to I by 4.1.7. Then there exists a bounded, monotone increasing, real-valued function α defined on J such that α is right continuous on J except possibly at $\inf J$ and $I(x) = \int_{\inf J}^{\sup J} x(t)d\alpha(t)$ for all $x \in \mathfrak{C}_{\infty\infty}(J)$. Furthermore, μ and I are determined by α.

<u>Proof</u>. This proof will only be outlined; the details are similar to those in the proof of 4.2.1.

Case 1. Suppose that $-\infty < a = \inf J \in J$. Then define $\alpha(a) = 0$ and $\alpha(t) = \mu([a,t])$ for all $t \in J$, $t > a$.

Case 2. Suppose that $a = \inf J \notin J$. Then define $\alpha(t) = \mu(\{x: x \in J, x \leq t\})$ for all $t \in J$. In this case we see that $\lim_{\substack{t\downarrow a \\ t\in J}} \alpha(t) = \lim_{n\to\infty} \mu(]a,a + \frac{1}{n}]) = \mu(\bigcap_{n=1}^{\infty}]a,a + \frac{1}{n}]) = 0$, if $\inf J > -\infty$. If $\inf J = -\infty$, then $\lim_{t\downarrow -\infty} \alpha(t) =$

$\lim_{n\to\infty} \mu(]-\infty,-n]) = \mu(\bigcap_{n=1}^{\infty}]-\infty,-n]) = 0$ using 4.1.732 and 2.4.3.

4.2.12 <u>Exercise</u>. Discuss in detail the representation by means of a Riemann-Stieltjes integral with respect to an unbounded, monotone increasing, right continuous function α of an unbounded non-negative linear functional I on $\mathfrak{C}_{\infty\infty}(J)$, where J is an arbitrary interval.

<u>Discussion</u>. Let α be a monotone increasing real-valued function on $[a,b]$. For any point $c \in]a,b[$, it is easy to see that $\lim_{t\uparrow c} \alpha(t)$ and $\lim_{t\downarrow c} \alpha(t)$ exist and that $\lim_{t\uparrow c} \alpha(t) \leq \lim_{t\downarrow c} \alpha(t)$. In 4.2.1 and 4.2.11, we have encountered only normalized functions α: $\alpha(c) = \lim_{t\downarrow c} \alpha(t)$ for all $c \in]a,b[$. Two different α's may yield the same non-negative functional on $\mathfrak{C}([a,b])$. We shall now explore this matter.

In the following $\alpha(t_o - 0)$ will denote $\lim_{t\uparrow t_o} \alpha(t)$ and $\alpha(t_o + 0)$ will denote $\lim_{t\downarrow t_o} \alpha(t)$.

4.2.2 <u>Theorem</u>. Let α be any monotone increasing real-valued function defined on $[a,b]$ such that $\alpha(a) = 0$. Then α has only a countable set of discontinuities $\{t_k\}_{k=1}^{\infty}$ and $\sum_{k=1}^{\infty} [\alpha(t_k + 0) - \alpha(t_k - 0)] < \infty$. [We make the convention that $\alpha(a - 0) = \alpha(a)$ and $\alpha(b + 0) = \alpha(b)$.]

Let α_d be the function on $[a,b]$ such that

$\alpha_d(a) = 0$ and $\alpha_d(t) = \alpha(t) - \alpha(t - 0) + \sum_{t_k<t} [\alpha(t_k + 0) - \alpha(t_k - 0)]$ for $t \in]a,b]$. Then α_d is monotone increasing on $[a,b]$, and $\alpha - \alpha_d$ is monotone increasing and continuous on $[a,b]$. [The number $[\alpha(t+0) - \alpha(t-0)]$ is called the saltus of α at t; α_d is called the saltus function of α; and $\alpha - \alpha_d = \alpha_c$ is called the continuous part of α.]

Proof. Let T be the set of discontinuities of α and let $\{t_1, \ldots, t_n\}$ be a finite subset of T, where we assume that $a \leq t_1 < t_2 < \ldots < t_n \leq b$. Then

$$\sum_{k=1}^{n} [\alpha(t_k + 0) - \alpha(t_k - 0)] = \alpha(t_n + 0) - \alpha(t_n - 0) + \sum_{k=1}^{n-1} [\alpha(t_k + 0) - \alpha(t_k - 0)] \leq \alpha(b) - \alpha(t_n - 0) + \sum_{k=1}^{n-1} [\alpha(t_{k+1} - 0) - \alpha(t_k - 0)] = \alpha(b) - \alpha(t_1 - 0) \leq \alpha(b) - \alpha(a).$$

Consequently, $\sum_{t\in T} [\alpha(t + 0) - \alpha(t - 0)] \leq \alpha(b) - \alpha(a) < \infty$. Clearly $t \in T$ implies that $[\alpha(t + 0) - \alpha(t - 0)] > 0$ so by Exercise 1.4.92, T is countable; we write $T = \{t_k\}_{k=1}^{\infty}$.

The function α_d is clearly non-negative, so that if $a < t$, then $\alpha_d(a) = 0 \leq \alpha_d(t)$. Suppose that $a < t < u \leq b$. Then $\alpha_d(u) - \alpha_d(t) = \alpha(u) - \alpha(u - 0) + \sum_{t_k<u} [\alpha(t_k + 0) - \alpha(t_k - 0)] - \alpha(t) + \alpha(t - 0) - \sum_{t_k<t} [\alpha(t_k + 0) - \alpha(t_k - 0)] = [\alpha(u) - \alpha(u - 0)] -$

$[\alpha(t) - \alpha(t - 0)] + \sum_{t \le t_k < u} [\alpha(t_k + 0) - \alpha(t_k - 0)]$.

If $t \ne t_k$ for all k, then $\alpha_d(u) - \alpha_d(t) = [\alpha(u) - \alpha(u - 0)] + \sum_{t \le t_k < u} [\alpha(t_k + 0) - \alpha(t_k - 0)] \ge 0$ and if $t = t_\ell$ for some ℓ, then $\alpha_d(u) - \alpha_d(t) = [\alpha(u) - \alpha(u - 0)] - [\alpha(t) - \alpha(t - 0)] + [\alpha(t_\ell + 0) - \alpha(t_\ell - 0)] + \sum_{t < t_k < u} [\alpha(t_k + 0) - \alpha(t_k - 0)] = [\alpha(u) - \alpha(u - 0)] + [\alpha(t_\ell + 0) - \alpha(t)] + \sum_{t < t_k < u} [\alpha(t_k + 0) - \alpha(t_k - 0)] \ge 0$. Consequently, α_d is a monotone increasing function on $[a,b]$.

We now show that $\alpha_c = \alpha - \alpha_d$ is monotone increasing. For $t \in [a,b]$, we have $\alpha_c(t) = \alpha(t - 0) - \sum_{t_k < t} (\alpha(t_k + 0) - \alpha(t_k - 0))$. Let $a \le t < u \le b$. Consider a finite subset T of $\{t_k\}_{k=1}^{\infty}$ where $t < t_k < u$ for $t_k \in T$; it is merely a notational matter to suppose that $T = \{t_1, \ldots, t_n\}$ and that $t < t_1 < \ldots < t_n < u$. We have $\sum_{k=1}^{n} (\alpha(t_k + 0) - \alpha(t_k - 0)) \le \alpha(t_1 + 0) - \alpha(t_1 - 0) + \alpha(t_2 + 0) - \alpha(t_1 + 0) + \ldots + \alpha(t_n + 0) - \alpha(t_{n-1} + 0) = \alpha(t_n + 0) - \alpha(t_1 - 0) \le \alpha(u - 0) - \alpha(t + 0)$. Consequently, $\sum_{t < t_k < u} (\alpha(t_k + 0) - \alpha(t_k - 0)) \le \alpha(u - 0) - \alpha(t + 0)$. Then $\alpha_c(u) - \alpha_c(t) = \alpha(u - 0) - \alpha(t - 0) - \sum_{t \le t_k < u} (\alpha(t_k + 0) - \alpha(t_k - 0)) =$

$$\alpha(u-0) - \alpha(t+0) - \sum_{t<t_k<u} (\alpha(t_k+0) - \alpha(t_k-0)) \geq 0.$$

Hence α_c is monotone increasing on $[a,b]$.

Finally, we show that α_c is continuous. Suppose that $t \in]a,b[$. We have $\alpha_c(t+0) = \lim_{\delta \downarrow 0} \alpha_c(t+\delta) =$ $\lim_{\delta \downarrow 0} \alpha(t+\delta-0) - \lim_{\delta \downarrow 0} \sum_{t_k<t+\delta} (\alpha(t_k+0) - \alpha(t_k-0)) =$ $\alpha(t+0) - \sum_{t_k \leq t} (\alpha(t_k+0) - \alpha(t_k-0)) = \alpha(t-0) -$ $\sum_{t_k<t} (\alpha(t_k+0) - \alpha(t_k-0))$ and $\alpha_c(t-0) = \lim_{\delta \downarrow 0} \alpha_c(t-\delta-0) -$ $\lim_{\delta \downarrow 0} \sum_{t_k<t-\delta} (\alpha(t_k+0) - \alpha(t_k-0)) = \alpha(t-0) - \sum_{t_k<t} (\alpha(t_k+0) -$ $\alpha(t_k-0))$ and thus $\alpha_c(t+0) = \alpha_c(t-0)$. In a similar manner α_c is seen to be continuous at a and b.

4.2.3 __Theorem__. Let $I_\alpha(x) = \int_a^b x(t)d\alpha(t)$ for $x \in \mathfrak{C}([a,b])$, where α is an arbitrary monotone increasing function on $[a,b]$ such that $\alpha(a) = 0$. Let μ be the Borel measure on $[a,b]$ corresponding to I_α by 4.1.7. Then $\mu = \mu_c - \mu_d$ where $\mu_c(\{t\}) = 0$ for all $t \in [a,b]$, $\mu_d = \sum_{k=1}^{\infty} (\alpha(t_k+0) - \alpha(t_k-0)) \varepsilon_{t_k}$, and $\{t_k\}_{k=1}^{\infty}$ is the set where α is discontinuous.

We need a lemma.

4.2.31 __Lemma__. Let α and β be monotone increasing functions on $[a,b]$ such that $\alpha(a) = \beta(a) = 0$. Then for $x \in \mathfrak{C}([a,b])$, we have $\int_a^b x(t)d(\alpha+\beta)(t) = \int_a^b x(t)d\alpha(t) +$ $\int_a^b x(t)d\beta(t)$.

Proof of 4.2.3. By 4.2.2, we can write α as $\alpha_c + \alpha_d$, where α_c is continuous and $\alpha_d(t) = \alpha(t) - \alpha(t-0) + \sum_{t_k<t} (\alpha(t_k+0) - \alpha(t_k-0))$, $(a < t \leq b)$. By 4.2.31, we have $I_\alpha(x) = \int_a^b x(t)d\alpha_c(t) + \int_a^b x(t)d\alpha_d(t) = I_{\alpha_c}(x) + I_{\alpha_d}(x)$, for all $x \in \mathfrak{C}([a,b])$.

Let μ_c be the measure corresponding to I_{α_c} by 4.1.7. For every $t \in [a,b]$, we have $\mu_c(\{t\}) \leq \inf\{I_{\alpha_c}(x): x \in \mathfrak{C}_+([a,b]),\ x(t) = 1\}$. For $\delta > 0$, let $x(t-\delta) = x(t+\delta) = 0$, if $t-\delta$, $t+\delta \in [a,b]$, $x(a) = 0$, $x(b) = 0$, and $x(t) = 1$. Interpolate linearly between these values. Then $\int_a^b x(t)d\alpha_c(t) \leq \alpha_c(t+\delta) - \alpha_c(t-\delta)$, and since α_c is continuous, it follows that $\mu_c(\{t\}) = 0$. Obvious changes are made if $t = a$ or $t = b$. We now deal with the functional I_{α_d}. We claim that $I_{\alpha_d}(x) = \sum_{k=1}^{\infty} (\alpha(t_k+0) - \alpha(t_k-0))x(t_k)$ for all $x \in \mathfrak{C}([a,b])$; this will prove that $\mu_d = \sum_{k=1}^{\infty} (\alpha(t_k+0) - \alpha(t_k-0))\varepsilon_{t_k}$. Let x be any real-valued function in $\mathfrak{C}([a,b])$. Let η be a positive real number, and δ a positive real number such that $|t - t'| < \delta$ and $t, t' \in [a,b]$ imply $|x(t) - x(t')| < \eta$ (recall that x is uniformly continuous). Let n be a positive integer so large that $\sum_{k=n+1}^{\infty} (\alpha(t_k+0) - \alpha(t_k-0)) < \eta$. It is a notational matter only to suppose that $a \leq t_1 < t_2 < \ldots < t_n \leq b$. Let $\Delta = \{a, t_1', t_1, t_1'', t_2', t_2,$

$t_2'', \ldots, t_n', t_n, t_n'', b\}$ be a subdivision of $[a,b]$ such that $0 < t_k'' - t_k' < \delta$ $(k = 1, 2, \ldots, n)$. Obvious changes are required if a or b is a t_k. Then we have $U(\Delta,x,\alpha_d) \leq \max(x(t): t \in [a,b]) \cdot \{\alpha_d(t_1') - \alpha_d(a) + \sum_{k=1}^{n-1}(\alpha_d(t_{k+1}') - \alpha_d(t_k'')) + \alpha_d(b) - \alpha_d(t_n'')\} + \sum_{k=1}^{n}(x(t_k) + \delta)(\alpha_d(t_k'') - \alpha_d(t_k'))$. The expression in curly brackets is easily shown to be less than or equal to η.

We also have $\sum_{k=1}^{n}(x(t_k) + \delta)(\alpha_d(t_k'') - \alpha_d(t_k')) \leq$

$\sum_{k=1}^{n} x(t_k)(\alpha(t_k + 0) - \alpha(t_k - 0)) + \delta(\alpha_d(b) - \alpha_d(a)) + \eta \cdot \max(x(t): t \in [a,b])$. By choosing η and δ sufficiently small, it is plain that we can make $U(\Delta,x,\alpha_d)$ arbitrarily close to $\sum_{k=1}^{\infty}(\alpha(t_k + 0) - \alpha(t_k - 0))x(t_k)$. Similarly $L(\Delta,x,\alpha_d)$ can be made arbitrarily close to the same value. By definition of the Riemann-Stieltjes integral, it follows that $I_{\alpha_d}(x) = \sum_{k=1}^{\infty}(\alpha(t_k + 0) - \alpha(t_k - 0)) \cdot x(t_k)$ for all $x \in \mathfrak{C}([a,b])$.

4.2.4 Theorem. Let α and β be monotone increasing real-valued functions on $[a,b]$ such that $\alpha(a) = \beta(a) = 0$. Then $I_\alpha = I_\beta$ on $\mathfrak{C}([a,b])$ if and only if $\alpha_c = \beta_c$ and $\alpha(t + 0) - \alpha(t - 0) = \beta(t + 0) - \beta(t - 0)$ for all $t \in [a,b]$.

Proof. The sufficiency of the stated conditions follows from 4.2.3. To prove the necessity, we suppose first that for some $t_1 \in [a,b]$, $A = \alpha(t_1 + 0) - \alpha(t_1 - 0) \neq \beta(t_1 + 0) - \beta(t_1 - 0) = B$; we may suppose that $A > B$. We also suppose that $a < t_1 < b$; obvious changes are required if $t_1 = a$ or $t_1 = b$. Choose $\delta > 0$ so small that

$$\sum_{\substack{t \in]t_1 - \delta, t_1 + \delta[\\ t \neq t_1}} (\alpha(t + 0) - \alpha(t - 0)) < \frac{A - B}{5} ;$$

$$\sum_{\substack{t \in]t_1 - \delta, t_1 + \delta[\\ t \neq t_1}} (\beta(t + 0) - \beta(t - 0)) < \frac{A - B}{5} ;$$

$$\alpha_c(t_1 + \delta) - \alpha_c(t_1 - \delta) < \frac{A - B}{5} ;$$

$$\beta_c(t_1 + \delta) - \beta_c(t_1 - \delta) < \frac{A - B}{5} .$$

Let $x \in \mathfrak{C}([a,b])$ be as sketched:

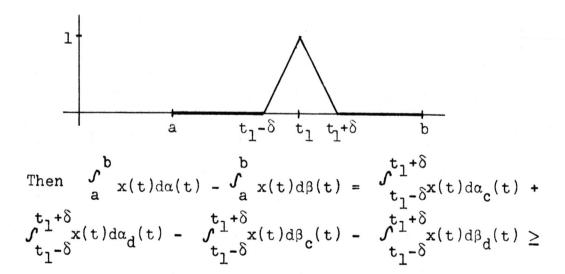

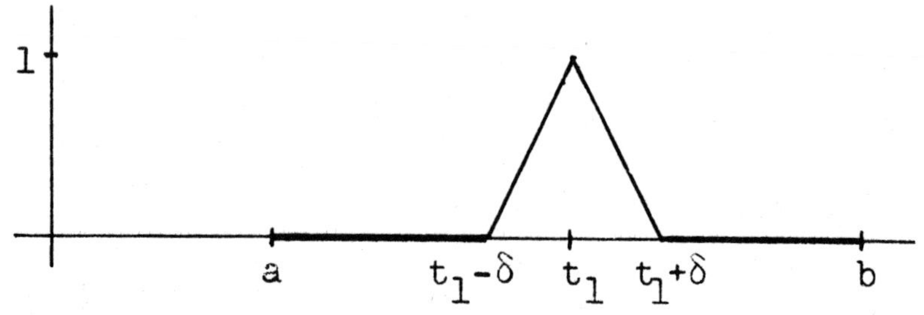

Then $\int_a^b x(t)d\alpha(t) - \int_a^b x(t)d\beta(t) = \int_{t_1-\delta}^{t_1+\delta} x(t)d\alpha_c(t) + \int_{t_1-\delta}^{t_1+\delta} x(t)d\alpha_d(t) - \int_{t_1-\delta}^{t_1+\delta} x(t)d\beta_c(t) - \int_{t_1-\delta}^{t_1+\delta} x(t)d\beta_d(t) \geq$

$- \|x\|_u(\alpha_c(t_1 + \delta) - \alpha_c(t_1 - \delta)) + \|x\|_u(\alpha(t_1 + 0) -$

$\alpha(t_1 - 0)) - \|x\|_u \left(\sum_{\substack{t \in]t_1-\delta, t_1+\delta[\\ t \neq t_1}} (\alpha(t + 0) - \alpha(t - 0)) - \right.$

$\|x\|_u(\beta_c(t_1 + \delta) - \beta_c(t_1 - \delta)) - \|x\|_u(\beta(t_1 + 0) - \beta(t_1 - 0)) -$

$\|x\|_u\left(\sum_{\substack{t \in]t_1-\delta, t_1+\delta[\\ t \neq t_1}} (\beta(t + 0) - \beta(t - 0)) \geq \right.$

$-\frac{A - B}{5} + A - \frac{A - B}{5} - \frac{A - B}{5} - B - \frac{A - B}{5} = \frac{A - B}{5} > 0.$

Thus in this case, we have $I_\alpha \neq I_\beta$ on $\mathfrak{C}([a,b])$.

Suppose finally that $\alpha(t + 0) - \alpha(t - 0) = \beta(t + 0) - \beta(t - 0)$ for all $t \in [a,b]$ but that for some $t_1 \in [a,b]$, $A = \alpha_c(t_1) \neq \beta_c(t_1) = B$. As before we suppose that $A > B$ and that $a < t_1 < b$. Choose $\delta > 0$ so that $\alpha_c(t_1 + \delta) - \alpha_c(t_1) < \frac{A - B}{3}$ and $\beta_c(t_1 + \delta) - \beta_c(t_1) < \frac{A - B}{3}$. Let $x \in \mathfrak{C}([a,b])$ be as sketched:

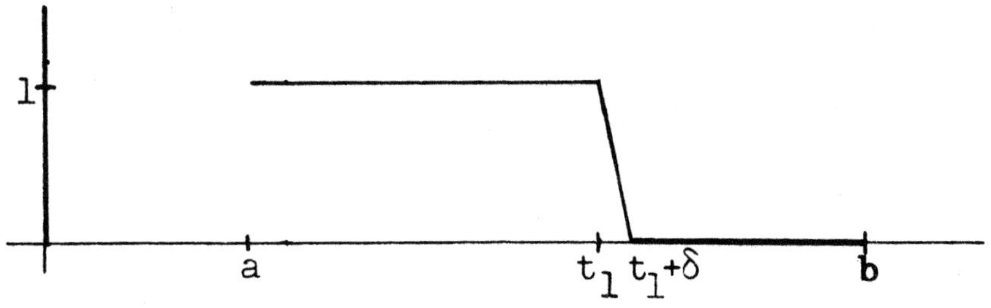

Then $\int_a^b x(t)d\alpha(t) - \int_a^b x(t)d\beta(t) = \int_a^b x(t)d\alpha_c(t) - \int_a^b x(t)d\beta_c(t) \geq$

$\alpha_c(t_1) - \alpha_c(a) - \|x\|_u(\alpha_c(t_1 + \delta) - \alpha_c(t_1)) - \beta_c(t_1) - \beta_c(a) -$

$\|x\|_u(\beta_c(t_1 + \delta) - \beta_c(t_1)) \geq A - B - \frac{A - B}{3} - \frac{A - B}{3} =$

$\frac{A - B}{3} > 0$ (note that $\alpha_c(a) = \beta_c(a) = 0$). Thus, in this case also, we have $I_\alpha \neq I_\beta$ on $\mathfrak{C}([a,b])$.

4.2.5 Remarks. Suppose that a monotone increasing real-valued function α on $[a,b]$ is given. To obtain a useful integral, first consider I_α for $\mathfrak{C}([a,b])$. Then from I_α construct the measure μ corresponding to I_α by Riesz's representation theorem, 4.1.7. Then the integral $\int_{[a,b]} x(t)d\mu(t)$ exists at least for all bounded Borel measurable functions x on $[a,b]$. $\int_{[a,b]} x(t)d\mu(t)$ is called the Lebesgue-Stieltjes integral of x with respect to α. As 4.1.7 shows, this integral is an extension of the Riemann-Stieltjes integral defined for continuous functions. The complexities and special cases involved in dealing with Riemann-Stieltjes integrals for discontinuous functions disappear when we go over to the Lebesgue-Stieltjes integral, and this latter integral is a very natural and useful device for associating a linear functional with monotone functions α.

4.3 The Radon-Nikodym theorem.

Let $x_0 \in \mathfrak{L}_1(R, \mathfrak{M}, \lambda)$, $x_0 \geq 0$, where λ is Lebesgue measure and define $\lambda_{x_0}(A) = \int_A x_0(t)d\lambda(t)$ for $A \subset R$. Then λ_{x_0} is a finite-valued countably additive measure on $\mathfrak{M}$. Moreover, $\lambda(A) = 0$ implies $\lambda_{x_0}(A) = 0$. Thus, by using functions in $\mathfrak{L}_1$ we can generate new measures. The Radon-Nikodym theorem (often called Lebesgue-

Nikodym theorem) gives a very simple characterization, under fairly general hypotheses, of all measures obtainable in this fashion. Namely, if $\lambda(A) = 0$ implies $\mu(A) = 0$ where μ is a countably additive measure and if certain other restrictions hold, then $\mu = \lambda_{x_0}$ for some x_0.

In this section we will often write $\int_A x d\mu$ in place of $\int_A x(t) d\mu(t)$.

4.3.1 Definition. Let T be any set, $\mathfrak{M}$ a σ-algebra of subsets of T, and μ and ν countably additive (possibly infinite) measures on $\mathfrak{M}$ such that subsets of μ-measure zero and ν-measure zero are measurable. The measure ν is said to be absolutely continuous with respect to μ if $\mu(A) = 0$ implies $\nu(A) = 0$ for all $A \epsilon \mathfrak{M}$.

4.3.11 Theorem. Let T be any set, $\mathfrak{M}$ be a σ-algebra of subsets of T, and μ and ν countably additive measures such that $\mu(A) \leq \nu(A)$ for all $A \epsilon \mathfrak{M}$. Then $x \epsilon \mathcal{L}_1(T, \mathfrak{M}, \nu)$ implies $x \epsilon \mathcal{L}_1(T, \mathfrak{M}, \mu)$.

Proof. It suffices by 3.7.72 to prove this result for non-negative real-valued functions. However, for $x \geq 0$, we see from 3.3.2 that for $x \epsilon \mathcal{L}_1(T, \mathfrak{M}, \nu)$ the inequalities $\int_T x(t) d\mu(t) \leq \int_T x(t) d\nu(t) < \infty$ obtain.

4.3.12 Theorem. Let $T, \mathfrak{M}, \mu$, and ν be as in 4.3.1. Suppose that $\mu(T) < \infty$, $\nu(T) < \infty$, and ν is absolutely continuous with respect to μ. Then there is an $\mathfrak{M}$-measurable function y on T such that $0 \leq y(t) < 1$ for all $t \in T$ and

$$\int_T x(t)(1 - y(t))d\nu(t) = \int_T x(t)y(t)d\mu(t) \qquad (*)$$

for all $x \in \mathfrak{L}_2(T, \mathfrak{M}, \mu + \nu)$.

<u>Proof</u>. We write $\lambda = \mu + \nu$ (this λ is not necessarily Lebesgue measure). λ is obviously a countably additive, non-negative, finite measure. By 3.8.6, we see that $\mathfrak{L}_2(T, \mathfrak{M}, \lambda) \subset \mathfrak{L}_1(T, \mathfrak{M}, \lambda)$. Let $I(x) = \int_T x(t)d\nu(t)$ for $x \in \mathfrak{L}_2(T, \mathfrak{M}, \lambda)$. Using 4.3.11 and 3.9.12, we have $|I(x)| \leq \int_T |x|d\nu \leq \int_T |x|d\lambda \leq \|x\|_2\lambda(T)^{1/2} < \infty$. Hence $I(x)$ is a complex number for all $x \in \mathfrak{L}_2(T, \mathfrak{M}, \lambda)$. Since I is obviously linear, I is a bounded linear functional on $\mathfrak{L}_2(T, \mathfrak{M}, \lambda)$. By 3.9.34, there exists a $y^* \in \mathfrak{L}_2(T, \mathfrak{M}, \lambda)$ such that $I(x) = (x,y^*) = \int_T x\overline{y^*}d\lambda$ for all $x \in \mathfrak{L}_2(T, \mathfrak{M}, \lambda$

We now show that $y^* \geq 0$ a.e. (with respect to λ). For $x \in \mathfrak{L}_2(T, \mathfrak{M}, \lambda)$, $x \geq 0$, we have

$$0 \leq I(x) = \int_T xd\nu = \int_T x\overline{y^*}d\lambda = \int_T x\Re y^*d\lambda - i\int_T x\Im y^*d\lambda. \qquad (**)$$

Let $A = \{t: \Im y^*(t) > 0\}$. If $\lambda(A) > 0$, then $\int_T \chi_A \Im y^*d\lambda > 0$, and this violates $(**)$. Thus $\lambda(A) = 0$. Similarly, $\lambda(\{t: \Im y^*(t) < 0\}) = 0$ so that y^* is real-valued a.e. Let $B = \{t: \Re y^*(t) < 0\}$. If $\lambda(B) > 0$, then $\int_T \chi_B \Re y^*d\lambda < 0$ and again this violates $(**)$. Thus

$\lambda(B) = 0$; that is, $y^* \geq 0$ a.e.

Now $\int_T x\,d\nu = \int_T xy^*d\lambda = \int_T xy^*d\mu + \int_T xy^*d\nu$ for all $x \in \mathcal{L}_2(T, \mathcal{m}, \lambda)$. Thus

$$\int_T x(1 - y^*)d\nu = \int_T xy^*d\mu \qquad (***)$$

for all $x \in \mathcal{L}_2(T, \mathcal{m}, \lambda)$.

Let $C = \{t \in T\colon\ y^*(t) \geq 1\}$. Then $\int_T x\chi_C(1 - y^*)d\nu = \int_T x\chi_C y^*d\mu$ for all $x \in \mathcal{L}_2(T, \mathcal{m}, \lambda)$. Evidently, $(1 - y^*)\chi_C \leq 0$ so that for all $x \geq 0$, $x \in \mathcal{L}_2(T, \mathcal{m}, \lambda)$, we have $0 \leq \int_T x\chi_C y^*d\mu = \int_T x\chi_C(1 - y^*)d\nu \leq 0$. Thus $\int_T x\chi_C y^*d\mu = 0$ for all $x \geq 0$, $x \in \mathcal{L}_2(T, \mathcal{m}, \lambda)$. Since any function is a linear combination of non-negative functions, we conclude that $\int_T x\chi_C y^*d\mu = 0$ for all $x \in \mathcal{L}_2(T, \mathcal{m}, \lambda)$.

We now show that $\int_T x\chi_C y^*d\nu = 0$ for all $x \in \mathcal{L}_2(T,\mathcal{m},\lambda)$. As above, we need only show this equality for $x \geq 0$, $x \in \mathcal{L}_2(T, \mathcal{m}, \lambda)$. For $x \geq 0$, we have $\int_T x\chi_C y^*d\mu = 0$, and so $x\chi_C y^* = 0$ a.e. (with respect to μ). Since ν is absolutely continuous with respect to μ, it follows that $x\chi_C y^* = 0$ a.e. (with respect to ν). Thus $\int_T x\chi_C y^*d\nu = 0$.

Finally, let $y = (1 - \chi_C)y^*$. For any $x \in \mathcal{L}_2(X,\mathcal{m},\lambda)$, we apply (***) and obtain $\int_T x(1 - y)d\nu = \int_T x(1-(1-\chi_C)y^*)d\nu$

$= \int_T x(1 - y^*)d\nu + \int_T x\chi_C y^* d\nu = \int_T x(1 - y^*)d\nu = \int_T xy^* d\mu =$ $\int_T xy^* d\mu - \int_T x\chi_C y^* d\mu = \int_T xy^*(1 - \chi_C)d\mu = \int_T xyd\mu$. It is evident that $0 \leq y(t) < 1$ for all $t \in T$, and thus the proof is complete.

4.3.2 Theorem. (Radon-Nikodym) Let $T, \mathfrak{M}, \mu, \nu$, and λ be as in 4.3.12. Then there exists a non-negative, real-valued, measurable function $x_o \in \mathcal{L}_1(T, \mathfrak{M}, \mu)$ such that for all $x \in \mathcal{L}_1(T, \mathfrak{M}, \nu)$ we have $xx_o \in \mathcal{L}_1(T, \mathfrak{M}, \mu)$ and

$$\int_T xd\nu = \int_T xx_o d\mu. \tag{*}$$

Proof. Suppose that $x \in \mathcal{L}_2(T, \mathfrak{M}, \lambda)$. Let y be the function given in 4.3.12. For every positive integer n, $x(1 + y + y^2 + \ldots + y^{n-1}) \in \mathcal{L}_2(T, \mathfrak{M}, \lambda)$ since $1 + y + y^2 + \ldots + y^{n-1}$ is bounded. Thus by 4.3.12, we have

$$\int_T x(1 - y^n)d\nu = \int_T x(1 + y + y^2 + \ldots + y^{n-1})(1-y)d\nu = \int_T x(1 + y + y^2 + \ldots + y^{n-1})yd\mu. \tag{**}$$

Let x be a bounded non-negative real-valued measurable function. Then x is clearly in $\mathcal{L}_2(T, \mathfrak{M}, \lambda)$ and hence it satisfies equation (**). For such x, the sequence of functions $\{x(1 - y^n)\}_{n=1}^{\infty}$ is increasing and converges point-wise to x (recall that $0 \leq y(t) < 1$ for all $t \in T$). The sequence $\{x(y + y^2 + \dots + y^n)\}_{n=1}^{\infty}$ is also increasing and converges to $\frac{xy}{1-y}$. Hence, applying 3.5.11 twice, we obtain $\int_T x d\nu = \lim_{n\to\infty} \int_T x(1-y^n) d\nu = \lim_{n\to\infty} \int_T x(y + y^2 + \dots + y^n) d\mu = \int_T x \frac{y}{1-y} d\mu$. Let $x_0 = \frac{y}{1-y}$. For $x = 1$, the function identically 1, we have $\int_T \frac{y}{1-y} d\mu = \int_T d\nu = \nu(T) < \infty$. Consequently, $x_0 = \frac{y}{1-y} \in \mathcal{L}_1(T, \mathfrak{m}, \mu)$.

Let x be an unbounded non-negative real-valued function in $\mathcal{L}_1(T, \mathfrak{m}, \nu)$. Let $x_n = \min(x,n)$. By the previous paragraph, we have $\int_T x_n d\nu = \int_T x_n x_0 d\mu$. By 3.5.11, we see that $\int_T x d\nu = \lim_{n\to\infty} \int_T x_n d\nu = \lim_{n\to\infty} \int_T x_n x_0 d\mu = \int_T x x_0 d\mu$. Now for any $x \in \mathcal{L}_1(T, \mathfrak{m}, \nu)$, we write x as a linear combination of non-negative real-valued functions in $\mathcal{L}_1(T, \mathfrak{m}, \nu)$ and use the last equality. This proves the equality (*). The assertion that $x x_0 \in \mathcal{L}_1(T, \mathfrak{m}, \mu)$ follows since $|\int_T x x_0 d\mu| = |\int_T x d\nu| < \infty$.

4.3.21 Theorem. Let T be a set, $\mathfrak{m}$ a σ-algebra of subsets of T, and μ and ν non-negative, possibly infinite, countably additive measures on $\mathfrak{m}$ both of which are σ-finite and such that ν is absolutely continuous with respect to μ. Then there is a non-negative, real-valued, measurable function x_o on T such that for all $x \in \mathcal{L}_1(T, \mathfrak{M}, \nu)$ we have $xx_o \in \mathcal{L}_1(T, \mathfrak{M}, \mu)$ and $\int_T x d\nu = \int_T xx_o d\mu$.

Proof. We have $T = \bigcup_{n=1}^{\infty} A_n = \bigcup_{m=1}^{\infty} B_m$ where $\{A_n\}_{n=1}^{\infty}$ and $\{B_m\}_{m=1}^{\infty}$ are pairwise disjoint families of measurable sets such that $\mu(A_n) < \infty$ for $n = 1, 2, \ldots$ and $\nu(B_m) < \infty$ for $m = 1, 2, \ldots$. Let $\{T_n\}_{n=1}^{\infty}$ be a reordering of the family $\{A_n \cap B_m\}_{n=1}^{\infty}{}_{m=1}^{\infty}$. Evidently $\{T_n\}_{n=1}^{\infty}$ is a pairwise disjoint family of measurable sets such that $T = \bigcup_{n=1}^{\infty} T_n$ where $\mu(T_n) < \infty$ and $\nu(T_n) < \infty$ for $n = 1, 2, \ldots$. Let $\mathfrak{M}_n = \{T_n \cap A \colon A \in \mathfrak{M}\}$; μ and ν are countably additive finite measures on $\mathfrak{M}_n$ and, furthermore, $\mu(A) = 0$ implies $\nu(A) = 0$ for all $A \in \mathfrak{M}_n$. Thus by 4.3.2 there exists a non-negative $x_o^{(n)}$ defined on T_n and $\mathfrak{M}_n$-measurable such that $\int_{T_n} x d\nu = \int_{T_n} xx_o^{(n)} d\mu$ for all $x \in \mathcal{L}_1(T, \mathfrak{M}, \nu)$.

Let x_o be defined on T as follows: $x_o(t) = x_o^{(n)}(t)$ for $t \in T_n$ $(n = 1, 2, 3, \ldots)$; x_o is clearly a well-defined, measurable, non-negative, real-valued function. Suppose that $x \in \mathcal{L}_1(T, \mathfrak{M}, \nu)$. Then for all N we have

$$\int_{T_1 \cup \ldots \cup T_N} x d\nu = \sum_{n=1}^{N} \int_{T_n} x d\nu = \sum_{n=1}^{N} \int_{T_n} xx_o d\mu = \int_{T_1 \cup \ldots \cup T_N} xx_o d\mu .$$

We have $|x| \in \mathcal{L}_1(T, \mathfrak{M}, \nu)$ and for each N, $|x\chi_{T_1 \cup \ldots \cup T_N}| \leq |x|$. Thus by 3.5.21, $\int_T x d\nu =$

$$\lim_{N\to\infty} \int_T x\chi_{T_1\cup\ldots\cup T_N} d\nu = \lim_{N\to\infty} \int_{T_1\cup\ldots\cup T_N} x d\nu = \lim_{N\to\infty}$$

$$\int_{T_1\cup\ldots\cup T_N} xx_0 d\mu = \lim_{N\to\infty} \int_T xx_0\chi_{T_1\cup\ldots\cup T_N} d\mu = \int_T xx_0 d\mu.$$

It follows at once that $xx_0 \in \mathcal{L}_1(T, \mathfrak{M}, \mu)$, and the proof is complete.

4.3.22 <u>Definition</u>. Let $-\infty < a < b < \infty$ and let α be a complex-valued function defined on $[a,b]$. α is said to be absolutely continuous on $[a,b]$ if for every $\varepsilon > 0$ there is a $\delta > 0$ such that $\sum_{i=1}^{n} (t_i - u_i) < \delta$ implies $\sum_{i=1}^{n} |\alpha(t_i) - \alpha(u_i)| < \varepsilon$, where $a \leq u_1 < t_1 \leq u_2 < t_2 \ldots \leq u_n < t_n \leq b$.

4.3.23 <u>Theorem</u>. Let $-\infty < a < b < \infty$ and let α be a monotone increasing real-valued function on $[a,b]$ such that $\alpha(a) = 0$. Then α is absolutely continuous in the sense of 4.3.22 if and only if the measure μ_α corresponding by 4.1.7 to the linear functional $I_\alpha(x) = \int_a^b x(t)d\alpha(t)$ is absolutely continuous with respect to Lebesgue measure λ in the sense of 4.3.1.

<u>Proof</u>. Suppose that α is absolutely continuous. Then α is clearly continuous. Hence $\mu_\alpha(\{t\}) = 0$ for all $t \in [a,b]$, and $\mu_\alpha(]t_1,t_2[) = \alpha(t_2) - \alpha(t_1)$. Suppose that $\lambda(A) = 0$. Pick $\varepsilon > 0$. Let δ be as guaranteed by the absolute continuity of α. There exists a set

$G = \bigcup_{n=1}^{\infty}]u_n,t_n[$ such that the $]u_n,t_n[$ are pairwise disjoint, $A \subset G$, and $\lambda(G) < \delta$. (If a or b are in G then intervals of the form $[a,t[$ or $]u,b]$ also occur.) Now for all positive integers N, we have $\sum_{n=1}^{N}(t_n - u_n) \leq \sum_{n=1}^{\infty}(t_n - u_n) = \lambda(G) < \delta$ so that by the absolute continuity of α we have $\sum_{n=1}^{N}(\alpha(u_n) - \alpha(t_n)) < \varepsilon$. Therefore $\mu_\alpha(G) = \sum_{n=1}^{\infty}(\alpha(u_n) - \alpha(t_n)) \leq \varepsilon$. Since ε is arbitrary, we have $\inf\{\mu_\alpha(G): G \supset A,\ G \text{ open}\} = 0$ so that $\mu_\alpha(A) = 0$. Consequently, μ_α is absolutely continuous with respect to λ in the sense of 4.3.1.

Suppose conversely that $\mu_\alpha(A) = 0$ whenever $\lambda(A) = 0$. We first note that α is continuous. Since $\lambda(\{t\}) = 0$ for all $t \in [a,b]$, we have $\mu_\alpha(\{t\}) = 0$ for all $t \in [a,b]$. Thus $\alpha(t + 0) - \alpha(t - 0) = \mu_\alpha(\{t\}) = 0$ for $t \in [a,b]$ and hence α is continuous on $[a,b]$.

By 4.3.2, there is a real-valued, non-negative, $\mathcal{B}$-measurable function x_0 such that for all $x \in \mathcal{L}_1([a,b],\mathcal{B},\mu_\alpha)$ we have $xx_0 \in \mathcal{L}_1([a,b],\mathcal{B},\lambda)$ and

$$\int_{[a,b]} x(t)d\mu_\alpha(t) = \int_{[a,b]} x(t)x_0(t)d\lambda(t). \qquad (*)$$

(Recall that $\mathcal{B}$ represents the Borel sets). Choose $\varepsilon > 0$. By 3.5.4 there is a $\delta > 0$ such that $\int_G x_0(t)d\lambda(t) < \varepsilon$ whenever $\lambda(G) < \delta$. Let $\bigcup_{i=1}^{n}]u_i,t_i[= G$ be such that $\sum_{i=1}^{n}(t_i - u_i) < \delta$. Then $\lambda(G) < \delta$ so that using $(*)$

we have $\sum_{i=1}^{n} (\alpha(t_i) - \alpha(u_i)) = \mu_\alpha(G) = \int_{[a,b]} \chi_G(t)d\mu_\alpha(t) =$ $\int_{[a,b]} \chi_G(t)x_o(t)d\lambda(t) = \int_G x_o(t)d\lambda(t) < \varepsilon$. Thus α is absolutely continuous on $[a,b]$ in the sense of 4.3.22.

4.3.3 Theorem. Let α be a monotone increasing real-valued function on $[a,b]$ such that $\alpha(a) = 0$. Then α is absolutely continuous if and only if $\alpha(t) = \int_{[a,t]} \alpha'(u)d\lambda(u)$ for all $t \in [a,b]$.

Proof. Exercise 3.6.33 implies α' exists a.e. and that $\alpha' \in \mathcal{L}_1([a,b],\mathcal{M},\lambda)$, where $\mathcal{M}$ represents the λ-measurable subsets of $[a,b]$. Thus $\int_{[a,t]} \alpha'(u)d\lambda(u)$ exists and as a function of t it is a monotone increasing, non-negative function which is zero at a. Now suppose that $\alpha(t) = \int_{[a,t]} \alpha'(u)d\lambda(u)$ for all $t \in [a,b]$. Choose $\varepsilon > 0$. By 3.5.4, there is a $\delta > 0$ such that $\lambda(G) < \delta$ implies $\int_G \alpha'(u)d\lambda(u) < \varepsilon$. Suppose that $a \leq t_1 < u_1 \leq t_2 < u_2 \leq \dots \leq t_n < u_n \leq b$ and that $\sum_{i=1}^{n} (u_i - t_i) < \delta$. Let $G = \bigcup_{i=1}^{n}]t_i,u_i[$; then $\lambda(G) < \delta$ so that $\sum_{i=1}^{n} (\alpha(u_i) - \alpha(t_i)) = \int_{\bigcup_{i=1}^{n} [t_i,u_i]} \alpha'(u)d\lambda(u) < \varepsilon$. Consequently, α is absolutely continuous.

Suppose now that α is absolutely continuous. Then by 4.3.23 and 4.3.11, we have $\alpha(t) = \mu_\alpha([a,t]) =$ $\int_{[a,t]} x_o(u)d\lambda(u)$ for some non-negative λ-measurable function

$x_0 \in \mathcal{L}_1([a,b],\mathfrak{M},\lambda)$. Theorem 3.6.34 implies that $\alpha'(t) = x_0(t)$ a.e. in $[a,b]$. Thus $\alpha(t) = \int_{[a,t]} \alpha'(u)d\lambda(u)$ for all $t \in [a,b]$.

4.3.31 Remark. An example of a continuous function that is not absolutely continuous is Lebesgue's singular function s. We give here only a brief description of this function; this is most easily done with the aid of a picture:

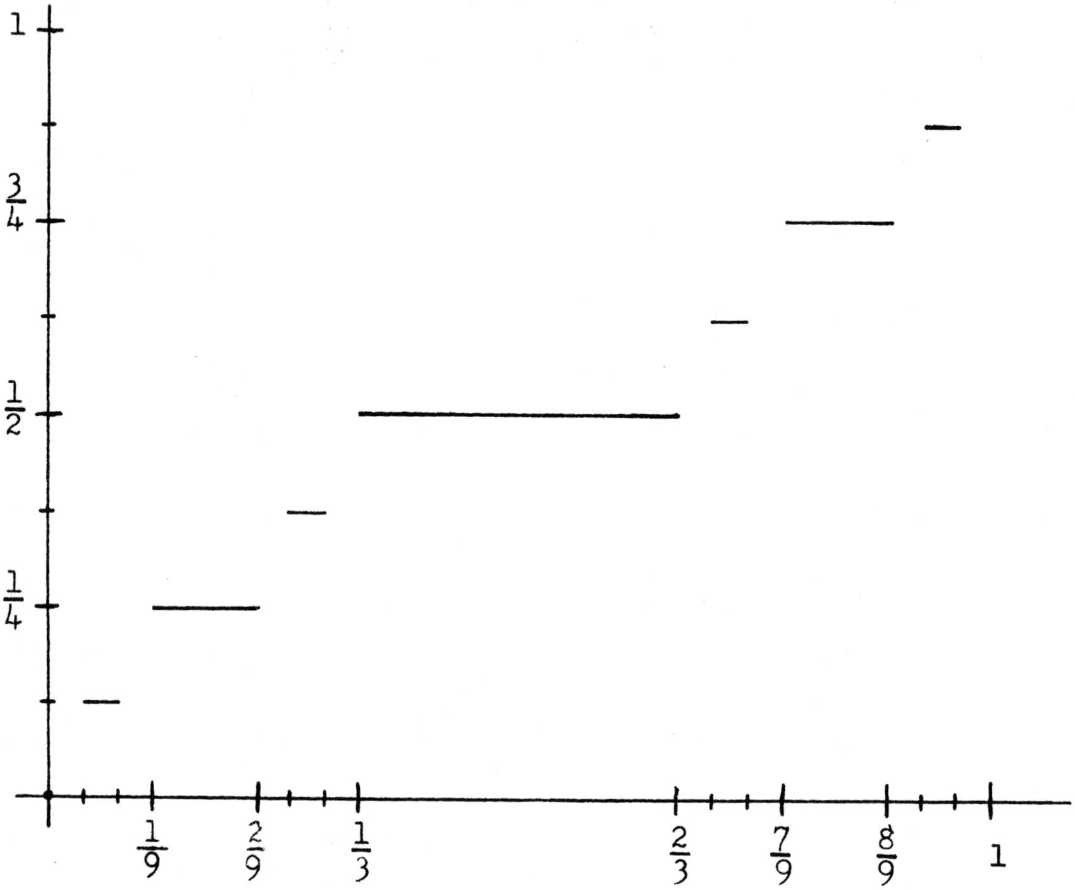

The Lebesgue singular function.

This indicates how s is defined on $[0,1] \cap C'$ (C is the Cantor set). The function s can be extended to a continuous function on all of $[0,1]$. Evidently $s'(t) = 0$ a.e. and $\int_{[0,1]} s'(t)d\lambda(t) = 0$. Since $s(1) = 1$, 4.3.3

tells us that s is not absolutely continuous. (This fact can also be obtained directly from the definition.)

4.3.4 Exercises.

4.3.41 Exercise. Let X be an uncountable set, and $\mathcal{S}$ the family of all subsets of X that are countable or have countable complements, i.e., $A \in \mathcal{S}$ if and only if A is countable or A' is countable. Show that $\mathcal{S}$ is the smallest σ-algebra containing all finite subsets of X. Let $\mu(A) = \begin{cases} \overline{\overline{A}} & \text{if } A \text{ is finite} \\ \infty & \text{if } A \text{ is infinite} \end{cases}$ for all $A \in \mathcal{S}$ and let

$$\nu(A) = \begin{cases} 0 & \text{if } A \text{ is countable} \\ 1 & \text{if } A' \text{ is countable} \end{cases} \text{ for all } A \in \mathcal{S}.$$

Prove that ν is a countably additive measure on $\mathcal{S}$ that is absolutely continuous with respect to μ. Prove that the Radon-Nikodym theorem fails for ν and μ and explain why.

4.3.42 Exercise. Let $X, \mathcal{S}$, and ν be as in 4.3.41, and let

$$\phi(A) = \begin{cases} 0 & \text{if } A \text{ is countable} \\ \infty & \text{if } A' \text{ is countable} \end{cases} \text{ for all } A \in \mathcal{S}.$$

Prove that ϕ is a countably additive measure that is absolutely continuous with respect to ν and find an analogue of the Radon-Nikodym theorem for ϕ and ν.

4.3.43 Final Exercise # 21. Let T be any set and $\mathfrak{M}$ a σ-algebra of subsets of T. Let μ be a finite, countably additive measure on $\mathfrak{M}$ and ν be a countably additive, possibly infinite, measure on $\mathfrak{M}$ such that $\mu(A) = 0$

implies $\nu(A) = 0$ for all $A \varepsilon \mathfrak{M}$. Prove that there exists a set $E \varepsilon \mathfrak{M}$ such that E' is the union of a countable number of sets of finite ν-measure and such that $F \subset E$ and $F \varepsilon \mathfrak{M}$ imply $\nu(F) = 0$ or $\nu(F) = \infty$.

4.3.44 Final Exercise # 22. Prove an analogue of the Radon-Nikodym theorem for the case in which μ is σ-finite, ν is absolutely continuous with respect to μ, but ν need not be σ-finite.

4.3.5 Definition. Let T be any set and $\mathfrak{M}$ any σ-algebra of subsets of T. Let μ and ν be countably additive, possibly infinite, measures on $\mathfrak{M}$. Suppose that there is a set $E \varepsilon \mathfrak{M}$ such that $\mu(E') = \nu(E) = 0$. Then μ and ν are said to be mutually singular.

4.3.51 Theorem. Let T be any set and $\mathfrak{M}$ any σ-algebra of subsets of T. Suppose that μ and ν are σ-finite countably additive measures on $\mathfrak{M}$ such that subsets of sets of μ-measure zero and ν-measure zero belong to $\mathfrak{M}$. Then $\nu = \nu_a + \nu_s$, where ν_a is absolutely continuous with respect to μ, and ν_s and μ are mutually singular. This decomposition is unique and is called the Lebesgue decomposition of ν.

Proof. Case I. Suppose that μ and ν are finite-valued. Note that ν is absolutely continuous with respect to $\mu + \nu$. By the Radon-Nikodym theorem (4.3.2), there is a non-negative measurable function

x_0 defined on T such that $\nu(A) = \int_A x_0 d(\mu + \nu) = \int_A x_0 d\mu + \int_A x_0 d\nu$ for all $A \in \mathcal{M}$.

We now show that $x_0(t) \leq 1$ a.e. For assume that $x_0(t) > 1$ on a set of positive $(\mu+\nu)$-measure. Then there is a $\delta > 0$ such that $x_0(t) \geq 1 + \delta$ on a set of positive $(\mu+\nu)$-measure; we denote this set by B. Now $\nu(B) = \int_B x_0 d(\mu+\nu) \geq (1 + \delta)[\mu(B) + \nu(B)] > \mu(B) + \nu(B) \geq \nu(B)$. This is clearly a contradiction. Consequently, we may suppose that $0 \leq x_0(t) \leq 1$ for all $t \in T$.

Let $E = \{t: x_0(t) = 1\}$; clearly $E \in \mathcal{M}$. Define ν_s by $\nu_s(A) = \nu(E \cap A)$ for $A \in \mathcal{M}$ and ν_a by $\nu_a(A) = \nu(E' \cap A)$ for $A \in \mathcal{M}$. We see at once that ν_s and ν_a are countably additive finite measures on $\mathcal{M}$ and that $\nu = \nu_s + \nu_a$. Clearly $\nu_s(E') = 0$. Moreover, $\mu(E) = 0$ since $\nu(E) = \int_E x_0 d\mu + \int_E x_0 d\nu = \mu(E) + \nu(E)$. Therefore, μ and ν_s are mutually singular.

We now show that ν_a is absolutely continuous with respect to μ; that is, if $A \in \mathcal{M}$ and $\mu(A) = 0$, then $\nu_a(A) = 0$. We have $\int_{A \cap E'} d\nu = \nu(A \cap E') = \int_{A \cap E'} x_0 d\mu + \int_{A \cap E'} x_0 d\nu = \int_{A \cap E'} x_0 d\nu$; note that $\int_{A \cap E'} x_0 d\mu = 0$ since $\mu(A \cap E') = 0$. Hence $\int_{A \cap E'} [1 - x_0(t)] d\nu(t) = 0$. Since $1 - x_0(t) > 0$ for all $t \in A \cap E'$, we infer that $\nu(A \cap E') = 0$ (3.3.6); i.e., $\nu_a(A) = 0$.

Case II. Suppose that μ and ν are σ-finite.

As in 4.3.21, $T = \bigcup_{n=1}^{\infty} T_n$ where the T_n's are pairwise disjoint and μ and ν are finite on T_n. For each n, let $\mu^{(n)}(A) = \mu(A \cap T_n)$ and $\nu^{(n)}(A) = \nu(A \cap T_n)$ for all $A \in \mathfrak{M}$. Evidently, $\mu = \sum_{n=1}^{\infty} \mu^{(n)}$ and $\nu = \sum_{n=1}^{\infty} \nu^{(n)}$. Then by case I, each $\nu^{(h)} = \nu_a^{(n)} + \nu_s^{(n)}$ where $\nu_a^{(n)}$ is absolutely continuous with respect to $\mu^{(n)}$, and $\mu^{(n)}$ and $\nu_s^{(n)}$ are mutually singular. Let $\nu_a = \sum_{n=1}^{\infty} \nu_a^{(n)}$ and $\nu_s = \sum_{n=1}^{\infty} \nu_s^{(n)}$. We leave it to the reader to verify that ν_a is absolutely continuous with respect to μ, and that μ and ν_s are mutually singular.

We postpone the proof of the uniqueness of ν_a and ν_s until Section 4.4.

4.3.6 Theorem. Let E be any compact subset of R containing no isolated points (otherwise known as a bounded perfect set). Then there is a countably additive finite measure μ defined for all Borel sets in R such that $\mu(E) = 1$, $\mu(E') = 0$, and $\mu(\{t\}) = 0$ for all $t \in R$.

Proof. Case I. Suppose that $E'^{-'} \neq 0$. Then E contains an interval and hence $0 < \lambda(E) < \infty$. Let $\mu(A) = \frac{1}{\lambda(E)} \lambda(A \cap E)$ for all Lebesgue measurable sets A; μ evidently satisfies the assertions of the theorem.

Case II. Suppose that $E'^{-'} = 0$. Let $a = \inf E$ and $b = \sup E$. The set $E' \cap \,]a,b[$ is open and hence is the union of a countable family $\{I_n\}_{n=1}^{\infty}$ of pairwise disjoint open intervals. We will write $I_n =]c_n, d_n[$. We say that $I_n \prec I_m$ if $d_n < c_m$.

For every I_n, I_m where $I_n \prec I_m$, there is a k such that $I_n \prec I_k \prec I_m$. Otherwise we would have $E'^{-'} \neq 0$. Similarly, $\{I_n\}_{n=1}^{\infty}$ has no least or greatest member under the ordering $\prec$. Let $\{r_n\}_{n=1}^{\infty}$ be any countable dense subset of $]0,1[$. By Exercise 1.5.37, there is a one-to-one correspondence τ carrying $\{I_n\}_{n=1}^{\infty}$ onto $\{r_n\}_{n=1}^{\infty}$ such that $I_n \prec I_m$ if and only if $\tau(I_n) < \tau(I_m)$. It is a notational matter only to suppose that each $\tau(I_n) = r_n$ $(n = 1, 2, 3, \ldots)$.

Let α be the function on $[a,b]$ defined as follows:

$\alpha(t) = r_n$ if $t \in I_n$ (for $t \in]a,b[\cap E'$);

$\alpha(t) = \inf \{r_n\colon c_n \geq t\}$ for $t \in E$ and $t < b$;

$\alpha(b) = 1$.

We first show that $a \leq t_1 < t_2 \leq b$ implies $\alpha(t_1) \leq \alpha(t_2)$. If $t_2 = b$ this is obvious. We now consider cases. Suppose that $t_1 \in E'$ and $t_2 \in E'$. Then $t_1 \in I_n$ and $t_2 \in I_m$ for some positive integers m and n. Clearly $I_n \preceq I_m$ so that $\alpha(t_1) = r_n \leq r_m = \alpha(t_2)$. Suppose that $t_1 \in E$ and $t_2 \in E'$. Then $t_2 \in I_m$ for some m. Evidently $t_1 \leq c_m$. Hence $\alpha(t_1) = \inf \{r_n\colon c_n \geq t_1\} \leq r_m = \alpha(t_2)$. Suppose that $t_1 \in E'$ and $t_2 \in E$. Then $t_1 \in I_m$ for some m. Since $t_2 \geq d_m$ we have for all $c_n \geq t_2$ that $c_n > d_m$ and hence $r_n > r_m$. Consequently, $\alpha(t_2) = \inf\{r_n: c_n \geq t_2\} \geq r_m = \alpha(t_1)$. Finally, suppose that $t_1 \varepsilon E$ and $t_2 \varepsilon E$. Then $\alpha(t_1) = \inf\{r_n: c_n \geq t_1\} \leq \inf\{r_n: c_n \geq t_2\} = \alpha(t_2)$.

We now show that α is continuous on $[a,b]$. Plainly α is continuous on $[a,b] \cap E'$. Suppose that $t \varepsilon E$ and that $t = c_k$ for some k. Then $\alpha(c_k) = r_k$ and α is trivially right continuous at c_k. Pick $\varepsilon > 0$. Since $\{r_n\}_{n=1}^{\infty}$ is dense in $]0,1[$, there is an $r_n < r_k$ such that $r_n + \varepsilon > r_k$. Clearly, $c_n < c_k$ and $\alpha(c_n) = r_n > r_k - \varepsilon = \alpha(c_k) - \varepsilon$. By the monotonicity of α, α is thus left continuous at c_k. Similarly, α is continuous at each d_k. Suppose now that $t \varepsilon E$ and t is not any c_k or d_k. Pick $\varepsilon > 0$. By the definition of $\alpha(t)$, there is a $c_n > t$ such that $\alpha(t) + \varepsilon > \alpha(c_n)$. Thus α is right continuous at t. Again choose $\varepsilon > 0$. Then there is an $r_n < \alpha(t)$ such that $r_n + \varepsilon > \alpha(t)$, since $\{r_n\}_{n=1}^{\infty}$ is dense in $]0,1[$. We have $c_n < t$ since $\alpha(c_n) = r_n$ and α is monotone. Moreover, $\alpha(c_n) = r_n > \alpha(t) - \varepsilon$. Consequently, α is left continuous at t.

Now let $I_\alpha(x) = \int_a^b x(t)d\alpha(t)$ for all continuous functions on $[a,b]$. Let μ_α be the measure on Borel sets of $[a,b]$ corresponding to I_α by 4.1.7. Since α is continuous, $\mu_\alpha(]u,v[) = \alpha(v) - \alpha(u)$ for $]u,v[\subset [a,b]$ and $\mu_\alpha(\{t\}) = 0$ for all $t \varepsilon [a,b]$. In particular, $\mu_\alpha(I_n) = \alpha(d_n) - \alpha(c_n) = r_n - r_n = 0$ for all n. Hence, by countable additivity, $\mu_\alpha(E' \cap [a,b]) = \mu_\alpha(\bigcup_{n=1}^{\infty} I_n) = 0$. Thus $\mu_\alpha(E) = 1$. Finally, let $\mu(A) = \mu_\alpha(A \cap [a,b])$ for all Borel sets in R. Clearly μ satisfies all the requirements of the theorem.

4.3.61 Remark. The measure μ of 4.3.6 is singular with respect to λ if and only if $\lambda(\bigcup_{n=1}^{\infty} I_n) = b - a$. For example, for the Cantor set $C \subset [0,1]$, we have $\lambda(\bigcup_{n=1}^{\infty} I_n) = \frac{1}{3} + \frac{2}{9} + \ldots + \frac{2^{n-1}}{3^n} + \ldots = 1$, so that any continuous measure concentrated on C is singular with respect to λ.

4.3.62 Theorem. There exists a continuous measure ϕ on $[0,1]$, singular with respect to λ, such that every sub-interval $[t_1,t_2]$ has positive ϕ-measure $(t_1 < t_2)$.

Proof. For each positive integer n, we subdivide $[0,1]$ into 2^n equal parts, each of length 2^{-n}. In each subinterval $[\frac{i}{2^n}, \frac{i+1}{2^n}]$, $i = 0, 1, \ldots, 2^n - 1$, we construct a continuous singular measure $\mu_{i,n}$ with total measure 1. Let $\phi = \sum_{n=1}^{\infty} \frac{1}{2^n} (\sum_{i=0}^{2^n-1} \frac{1}{2^n}\mu_{i,n})$. Since each $\mu_{i,n}$ is singular with respect to λ, there exists an $A_{i,n}$ such that $\lambda(A_{i,n}) = 0$ and $\mu_{i,n}(A'_{i,n}) = 0$. Let $A = \bigcup_{n=1}^{\infty} \bigcup_{i=0}^{2^n-1} A_{i,n}$. Clearly $\lambda(A) = 0$. For all i and n, we have $A' \subset A'_{i,n}$ and hence $\mu_{i,n}(A') = 0$. Thus $\phi(A') = 0$. Clearly ϕ is continuous; that is, $\phi(\{t\}) = 0$ for all $t \in [0,1]$. Suppose $[t_1,t_2] \subset [0,1]$. Then for some i and n, we have $[\frac{i}{2^n}, \frac{i+1}{2^n}] \subset [t_1,t_2]$. Consequently, $\phi([t_1,t_2]) \geq \frac{1}{2^{2n}}\mu_{i,n}([\frac{i}{2^n}, \frac{i+1}{2^n}]) = 2^{-2n} > 0$.

4.3.63 Remark. Computation of integrals $\int_{[a,b]} x(t)d\mu(t)$ is often difficult for singular measures μ. Consider for example the integral $\hat{\mu}(n) = \int_0^1 e^{2\pi inx}d\mu(x)$ where μ is a measure on $[0,1]$ and n is an integer; $\hat{\mu}$ is called the Fourier-Stieltjes transform of μ. Integrals of this type are frequently encountered in harmonic analysis, probability, and mathematical statistics. The evaluation of $\hat{\mu}$ reduces to that of a Lebesgue integral if μ is absolutely continuous with respect to λ; that is, if there is a function $m \in \mathcal{L}_1([0,1])$ such that $\int_{[0,1]} x(t)d\mu(t) = \int_{[0,1]} x(t)m(t)d\lambda(t)$ for continuous functions x on $[0,1]$. If $\mu = \sum_{n=1}^{\infty} a_n\varepsilon_{t_n}$, then we obtain $\hat{\mu}(n) = \sum_{n=1}^{\infty} a_n e^{2\pi int_n}$ $\left(\varepsilon_{t_n}(A) = \begin{cases} 1 & \text{if } t_n \in A \\ 0 & \text{if } t_n \notin A \end{cases}\right.$ for $A \subset [0,1]$, $t_n \in [0,1]$ for $n = 1, 2, \ldots$).

As a quite different example, let ω be the measure concentrated on the Cantor set C corresponding to the Lebesgue singular function. Then $\hat{\omega}(n) = e^{\pi in}\prod_{j=1}^{\infty}\cos(\frac{2\pi n}{3^j})$.

For the details we refer the reader to Hille and Tamarkin, Amer. Math. Monthly 36 (1929), 255. In general, computations involving measures singular with respect to λ are very difficult.

4.3.64 Final Exercise # 23. Let α be a continuous real-valued monotone increasing function on $[a,b]$ such that $\alpha(a) = 0$. Prove that $(\mu_\alpha)_a(A) = \int_A \alpha'(t)d\lambda(t)$ for all Borel sets $A \subset [a,b]$ and that $(\mu_\alpha)_s = \mu_\alpha - (\mu_\alpha)_a$ is singular with respect to λ. Hence infer that μ_α is singular with respect to λ if and only if $\alpha'(t) = 0$ a.e. (with respect to λ).

4.4 The Jordan and Hahn decompositions of a set-function.

4.4.1 Definition. Let T be a set, $\mathfrak{M}$ a σ-algebra of subsets of T, and μ a real-valued countably additive set-function defined on $\mathfrak{M}$. For every $A \in \mathfrak{M}$, let $\mu_+(A) = \sup\{\mu(E): E \in \mathfrak{M}, E \subset A\}$ and $\mu_-(A) = -\inf\{\mu(E): E \in \mathfrak{M}, E \subset A\}$.

4.4.2 Theorem. The set-functions μ_+ and μ_- are finite and non-negative on $\mathfrak{M}$.

Proof. Since $0 \subset A$ for all $A \in \mathfrak{M}$, μ_+ and μ_- are clearly non-negative. Let $\nu = \mu_+ + \mu_-$. Evidently, $\nu(A) \leq \nu(B)$ if $A \subset B$. We will prove that $\nu(T) < \infty$. This will show that ν is finite and hence that μ_+ and μ_- are finite.

Assume that $\nu(T) = \infty$. We will produce by finite induction a decreasing sequence $A_1 \supset A_2 \supset \dots \supset A_n \supset \dots$ of sets in $\mathfrak{M}$ such that $\nu(A_n) = \infty$ and $|\mu(A_n)| \geq n - 1$ $(n = 1, 2, \dots)$. Let $A_1 = T$; obviously $\nu(A_1) = \infty$

and $|\mu(A_1)| \geq 0$. Suppose that $A_1, \ldots, A_k$ have been chosen satisfying the above conditions. Since $\nu(A_k) = \infty$, there is a $B \in \mathcal{M}$, $B \subset A_k$, such that $|\mu(B)| \geq |\mu(A_k)| + k$. If $\nu(B) = \infty$, we let $A_{k+1} = B$; in this case A_{k+1} clearly satisfies the above conditions. If $\nu(B) < \infty$, let $A_{k+1} = A_k \cap B'$. We have $\nu(A_k \cap B') = \infty$, for assume $\nu(A_k \cap B') < \infty$. Then for all $E \in \mathcal{M}$, $E \subset A_k$ we have $|\mu(E)| = |\mu(E \cap B) + \mu(E \cap A_k \cap B')| \leq |\mu(E \cap B)| + |\mu(E \cap A_k \cap B')| \leq \nu(B) + \nu(A_k \cap B') < \infty$. This implies that $\nu(A_k) < \infty$ which is a contradiction. Finally, we have $|\mu(A_k)| = |\mu(A_k \cap B') + \mu(B)| \geq |\mu(B)| - |\mu(A_k \cap B')| \geq |\mu(A_k)| + k - |\mu(A_k \cap B')|$ and hence $|\mu(A_{k+1})| = |\mu(A_k \cap B')| \geq k$. Thus the sequence $\{A_k\}_{k=1}^{\infty}$ has been constructed.

By 2.4.3, we have $\mu(\bigcap_{n=1}^{\infty} A_n) = \lim_{n\to\infty} \mu(A_n)$. As the right side is infinite or does not exist and the left side is a real number, we have arrived at a contradiction, and the theorem is proved.

4.4.3 Theorem. Let T, $\mathcal{M}$, μ, μ_+, and μ_- be as in 4.4.1. Then μ_+ and μ_- are countably additive, finite measures on $\mathcal{M}$, and $\mu = \mu_+ - \mu_-$.

Proof. By 4.4.2, it is sufficient to show that μ_+ and μ_- are countably additive on $\mathcal{M}$, since clearly $\mu_+(0) = \mu_-(0) = 0$. We will show that μ_+ is countably additive; that μ_- is countably additive is shown in a similar manner.

Let $\{A_n\}_{n=1}^{\infty}$ be a family of pairwise disjoint sets of $\mathfrak{M}$. We first show that $\mu_+(\bigcup_{n=1}^{\infty} A_n) \leq \sum_{n=1}^{\infty} \mu_+(A_n)$. Let $E \in \mathfrak{M}$ be such that $E \subset \bigcup_{n=1}^{\infty} A_n$. Then $\mu(E) = \mu(\bigcup_{n=1}^{\infty} (E \cap A_n)) = \sum_{n=1}^{\infty} \mu(E \cap A_n)$, since by hypothesis μ is a countably additive set-function. Since $\mu \leq \mu_+$ and μ_+ is monotone increasing on $\mathfrak{M}$, we have that $\mu(E) \leq \sum_{n=1}^{\infty} \mu_+(E \cap A_n) \leq \sum_{n=1}^{\infty} \mu_+(A_n)$. Since E is an arbitrary set of $\mathfrak{M}$ such that $E \subset \bigcup_{n=1}^{\infty} A_n$, it follows that $\mu_+(\bigcup_{n=1}^{\infty} A_n) \leq \sum_{n=1}^{\infty} \mu_+(A_n)$. We next show that for every real number $\varepsilon > 0$ the inequality $\mu_+(\bigcup_{n=1}^{\infty} A_n) + \varepsilon \geq \sum_{n=1}^{\infty} \mu_+(A_n)$ obtains. For every positive integer n, there exists an $E_n \subset A_n$ such that $\mu(E_n) + \frac{\varepsilon}{2^n} > \mu_+(A_n)$. Adding, we have that $\sum_{n=1}^{\infty} \mu(E_n) + \varepsilon > \sum_{n=1}^{\infty} \mu_+(A_n)$. Consequently, $\mu_+(\bigcup_{n=1}^{\infty} A_n) + \varepsilon \geq \mu(\bigcup_{n=1}^{\infty} E_n) + \epsilon = \sum_{n=1}^{\infty} \mu(E_n) + \epsilon > \sum_{n=1}^{\infty} \mu_+(A_n)$. Since ϵ is arbitrary, $\mu_+(\bigcup_{n=1}^{\infty} A_n) \geq \sum_{n=1}^{\infty} \mu_+(A_n)$. Hence $\mu_+(\bigcup_{n=1}^{\infty} A_n) = \sum_{n=1}^{\infty} \mu_+(A_n)$.

To prove that $\mu = \mu_+ - \mu_-$, let $A \in \mathfrak{M}$ and $B \in \mathfrak{M}$ be such that $B \subset A$. Then $\mu(B) = \mu(A) - \mu(A \cap B')$ (μ is finite-valued). Since $\mu(A \cap B') \geq \inf\{\mu(E): E \in \mathfrak{M},\ E \subset A\} = -\mu_-(A)$ we have that $\mu(B) \leq \mu(A) + \mu_-(A)$. Since B is arbitrary, we have $\mu_+(A) \leq \mu(A) +$

$\mu_-(A)$. Thus $\mu_+ - \mu_- \leq \mu$. To show the reverse inequality, we first note that for $A \varepsilon \mathcal{M}$ and $B \varepsilon \mathcal{M}$ such that $B \subset A$ we have the inequality $\mu(A \cap B') \leq \mu_+(A)$ so that $-\mu(A \cap B') \geq -\mu_+(A)$. Hence $\mu(B) = \mu(A) - \mu(A \cap B') \geq \mu(A) - \mu_+(A)$. Since B is arbitrary, it follows that $-\mu_-(A) \geq \mu(A) - \mu_+(A)$; thus $\mu \leq \mu_+ - \mu_-$. Hence $\mu = \mu_+ - \mu_-$.

4.4.31 Definition. The equality $\mu = \mu_+ - \mu_-$ is called the Jordan decomposition of μ.

4.4.32 Remark. Recall the decomposition in 4.1.8 of the functional I into I_+ and I_-. Let $I_+(x) = \int_T x(t)d\nu_1(t)$ and $I_-(x) = \int_T x(t)d\nu_2(t)$, where ν_1 and ν_2 are non-negative, finite, countably additive Borel measures on $\mathcal{M}$. Define $\nu = \nu_1 - \nu_2$. Then $I(x) = \int_T x(t)d\nu(t)$. Furthermore, $(\nu)_+ = \nu_1$ and $(\nu)_- = \nu_2$. Thus 4.1.8 and the Jordan decomposition of a measure are really two aspects of a single phenomenon.

4.4.4 Theorem. Let T, $\mathcal{M}$, μ, μ_+, and μ_- be as in 4.4.1. Then there exists a $P \varepsilon \mathcal{M}$ such that $\mu_+(P') = 0$ and $\mu_-(P) = 0$; i.e., μ_+ and μ_- are singular with respect to each other.

Proof. For every positive integer n, there is an $E_n \varepsilon \mathcal{M}$ such that $\mu(E_n) \geq \mu_+(T) - \frac{1}{2^n}$. Since μ_+ is monotone increasing on $\mathcal{M}$, we have $\mu(E_n) = \mu_+(E_n) - \mu_-(E_n) \leq \mu_+(T) - \mu_-(E_n) \leq \mu(E_n) - \mu_-(E_n) + \frac{1}{2^n}$ so that

$\mu_-(E_n) \leq \frac{1}{2^n}$. Since $\mu_+(T) = \mu_+(E_n) + \mu_+(E_n')$ we see that

$$\mu_+(E_n) + \frac{1}{2^n} \geq \mu(E_n) + \frac{1}{2^n} \geq \mu_+(T) = \mu_+(E_n) + \mu_+(E_n')$$

and consequently $\mu_+(E_n') \leq \frac{1}{2^n}$.

Let $P = \underline{\lim}_{n\to\infty} E_n = \bigcup_{n=1}^{\infty} (\bigcap_{k=n}^{\infty} E_k)$; then $P \in \mathfrak{M}$. Since $P' = \bigcap_{n=1}^{\infty} (\bigcup_{k=n}^{\infty} E_k')$, it follows that $P' \subset \bigcup_{k=m}^{\infty} E_k'$ for every positive integer m. It follows that $\mu_+(P') \leq \mu_+(\bigcup_{k=m}^{\infty} E_k') \leq \sum_{k=m}^{\infty} \mu_+(E_k') \leq \sum_{k=m}^{\infty} \frac{1}{2^k} = \frac{1}{2^{m-1}}$ for all m. Hence $\mu_+(P') = 0$. We now show that $\mu_-(P) = 0$. Defining $F_n = \bigcap_{k=n}^{\infty} E_k$ we have $F_n \subset F_{n+1}$ so that by 2.4.2 $\mu_-(P) = \mu_-(\bigcup_{n=1}^{\infty} F_n) = \lim_{n\to\infty} \mu_-(F_n)$. Now $\mu_-(F_n) \leq \mu_-(E_{n+\ell}) \leq \frac{1}{2^{n+\ell}}$ for $\ell = 0, 1, 2, \ldots$, so that $\mu_-(F_n) = 0$. Consequently, $\mu_-(P) = \lim_{n\to\infty} \mu_-(F_n) = 0$.

4.4.41 Definition. The decomposition $T = P \cup P'$ is called a Hahn decomposition of T.

4.4.42 Theorem. Let T and $\mathfrak{M}$ be as in 4.4.1. Let μ be a countably additive, extended real-valued set-function defined on $\mathfrak{M}$ such that μ assumes at most one of the values $+\infty$ and $-\infty$. Let μ be a σ-finite measure. Then $\mu = \mu_+ - \mu_-$ where μ_+ and μ_- are countably additive, non-negative (possibly infinite) measures on

$\mathfrak{M}$. Moreover, there exists a $P \in \mathfrak{M}$ such that $\mu_+(P') = 0$ and $\mu_-(P) = 0$.

<u>Proof</u>. By hypothesis, there is a sequence $\{T_n\}_{n=1}^{\infty}$ of sets of $\mathfrak{M}$ such that the T_n are pairwise disjoint and $A \subset T_n$ and $A \in \mathfrak{M}$ implies $-\infty < \mu(A) < +\infty$. Applying 4.4.2, 4.4.3, and 4.4.4 to each T_n in turn, the result follows. We omit the details.

4.4.43 <u>Theorem</u>. The resolution $\nu = \nu_a + \nu_s$ in 4.3.51 is unique if ν is finite.

<u>Proof</u>. Suppose that $\nu = \nu_1 + \nu_2 = \nu_3 + \nu_4$, where ν_1 and ν_3 are absolutely continuous with respect to μ and ν_2 and ν_4 are singular with respect to μ. It follows that $(\nu_1 - \nu_3)_+$ and $(\nu_1 - \nu_3)_-$ are both absolutely continuous with respect to μ. Similarly both $(\nu_4 - \nu_2)_+$ and $(\nu_4 - \nu_2)_-$ are singular with respect to μ. Since $\nu_1 - \nu_3 = \nu_4 - \nu_2$ we have $(\nu_1 - \nu_3)_+ = (\nu_4 - \nu_2)_+$. There exists a $P \in \mathfrak{M}$ such that $(\nu_4 - \nu_2)_+(P) = 0$ and $\mu(P') = 0$. For $A \in \mathfrak{M}$ we have $(\nu_4 - \nu_2)_+(A) = (\nu_4 - \nu_2)_+(A \cap P) + (\nu_4 - \nu_2)_+(A \cap P') = 0 + (\nu_1 - \nu_3)_+(A \cap P') = 0 + 0 = 0$; the next to last equality follows since $\mu(A \cap P') = 0$ and $(\nu_1 - \nu_3)_+$ is absolutely continuous with respect to μ. Hence $(\nu_1 - \nu_3)_+ = 0$. Similarly $(\nu_1 - \nu_3)_- = 0$. Thus $\nu_1 - \nu_3 = (\nu_1 - \nu_3)_+ - (\nu_1 - \nu_3)_- = 0$. Consequently, $\nu_1 = \nu_3$ and hence also $\nu_2 = \nu_4$.

4.4.5 <u>Definition</u>. Let α be a real-valued function on the closed interval $[a,b]$, $a < b$. We define the variation

$\bigvee_{[a,b]} \alpha$ of α on $[a,b]$ to be

$$\bigvee_{[a,b]} \alpha = \sup \left\{ \sum_{j=1}^{n} |\alpha(t_j) - \alpha(t_{j-1})| : a = t_0 < t_1 < \ldots < t_n = b \right\}.$$

If $\bigvee_{[a,b]} \alpha$ is a finite number, the function α is said to have finite variation on $[a,b]$.

4.4.51 Discussion. It may be shown by a category argument that given any closed interval $[a,b]$, there exists a continuous function defined on the interval having infinite variation on any subinterval of $[a,b]$. The continuous function whose graph is illustrated below has infinite variation on $[0,1]$, although its variation is finite on $[\delta,1]$ for every $\delta, 0 < \delta < 1$.

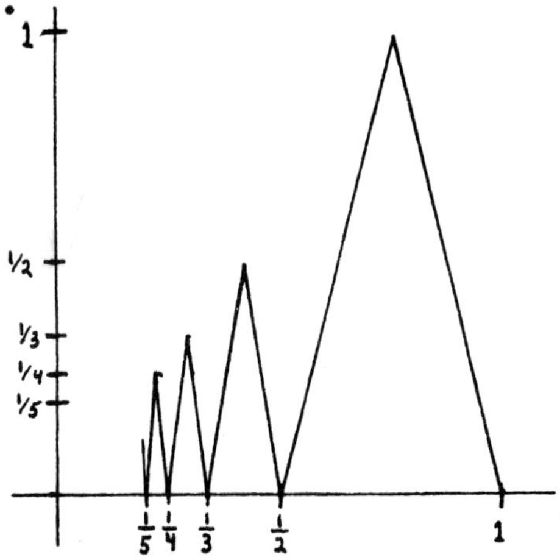

Dirichlet's function D (see 3.6.25) is an example of a discontinuous function having infinite variation on every subinterval of $[0,1]$ not a point.

Let a and b be real numbers such that $a < b$. Let α be a real-valued function on $[a,b]$ such that

$\bigvee_{[a,b]} \alpha < \infty$. Define $\alpha_+(x)$ for $a < x \le b$ by $\alpha_+(x) = \bigvee_{[a,x]} \alpha$; set $\alpha_+(a) = 0$. Then α_+ is a bounded increasing function on $[a,b]$; $\alpha_- = \alpha_+ - \alpha$ can also be shown to be an increasing function on $[a,b]$. That is, every function of finite variation is the difference of two monotone increasing functions.

Let $x \in \mathfrak{C}([a,b])$. The functional $I_\alpha(x) = \int_a^b x(t)d\alpha(t)$ is a linear functional on $\mathfrak{C}([a,b])$. (This is the usual Riemann-Stieltjes integral; it exists for x continuous and α of finite variation.) Since $|I_\alpha(x)| \le \|x\|_u \cdot \bigvee_{[a,b]} \alpha$, this linear functional is bounded and consequently continuous. By 4.1.8, we may write $I_\alpha = (I_\alpha)_+ - (I_\alpha)_-$. It turns out that $(I_\alpha)_+ = I_{\alpha_+}$ and $(I_\alpha)_- = I_{\alpha_-}$. By 4.1.7 we may write $I_{\alpha_+}(x) = \int_{[a,b]} x(t)d\mu_1(t)$ and $I_{\alpha_-}(x) = \int_{[a,b]} x(t)d\mu_2(t)$, where μ_1 and μ_2 are non-negative, extended real-valued, countably additive Borel measures. It can be shown that $(\mu_1 - \mu_2)_+ = \mu_1$ and $(\mu_1 - \mu_2)_- = \mu_2$. Thus there is a strong analogy among the indicated decomposition of $I_\alpha(x) = \int_{[a,b]} x(t)d(\mu_1 - \mu_2)(t)$, the decomposition of the corresponding measure $(\mu_1 - \mu_2)$, and the decomposition of α into $\alpha_+ - \alpha_-$.

Definition 4.4.5 can be extended to complex-valued functions with no change. The preceding two paragraphs remain valid with, of course, suitable modifications. However, we will not go into this here.

4.4.52 Résumé. We collect together here some of the principal results of sections 4.2, 4.3, and 4.4. These results relate chiefly to decompositions of functions and measures.

Let a and b be real numbers such that $a < b$. Let α be a complex-valued function defined on $[a,b]$ such that α has finite variation on $[a,b]$. We may set $\alpha = \beta_1 + i\beta_2$ where β_1 and β_2 are real-valued functions on $[a,b]$. We have $\underset{[a,b]}{V}\beta_j < \infty$ and hence by 4.4.51, $\beta_j = \beta_{j_+} - \beta_{j_-}$ where β_{j_+} and β_{j_-} are increasing on $[a,b](j = 1, 2)$. By 4.2.2, $\beta_{j_+} = (\beta_{j_+})_c + (\beta_{j_+})_d$ and $\beta_{j_-} = (\beta_{j_-})_c + (\beta_{j_-})_d$. A final decomposition is obtained by writing $(\beta_{j_+})_c = (\beta_{j_+})_a + (\beta_{j_+})_s$ and $(\beta_{j_-})_c = (\beta_{j_-})_a + (\beta_{j_-})_s$ where γ_a represents an absolutely continuous function and γ_s represents a singular (with respect to λ) function. A function γ_s is said to be singular (with respect to λ) if $\gamma'_s(t) = 0$ a.e. (with respect to λ). (Refer to 4.3.64).

An analogous decomposition is obtained for an arbitrary countably additive, complex-valued Borel measure μ defined on $[a,b]$. As noted before, decompositions of functions of finite variation, of measures, and of linear functionals are basically equivalent.

4.5 Fubini's theorem. In contemporary analysis, there are two theorems which may be said to form the cornerstones of the subject. One of these theorems is Lebesgue's theorem on dominated convergence (3.5.21). The other result is called Fubini's theorem. To it we now turn our attention.

Let T and U be sets. Let $\mathfrak{M}$ and $\mathfrak{N}$ be rings of subsets of T and U, respectively, with corresponding measures μ and ν. Consider the Cartesian product (see 1.2) $T \times U$ of T with U. We wish to define on some σ-algebra of subsets of $T \times U$ a set-function that extends the notion of measure as introduced separately in $\mathfrak{M}$ and $\mathfrak{N}$. In particular, our product measure ϕ is to have the property that $\phi(A \times B) = \mu(A) \cdot \nu(B)$ for all $A \in \mathfrak{M}$ and $B \in \mathfrak{N}$.

4.5.1 Definition. Let T and U be sets, and let $\mathfrak{M}$ and $\mathfrak{N}$ be σ-algebras of subsets of T and U, respectively. Consider the family of all subsets of the product space of the form $A \times B$ where $A \in \mathfrak{M}$ and $B \in \mathfrak{N}$. Sets of the form $A \times B$ are said to be measurable rectangles. Let $\mathfrak{M} \times \mathfrak{N}$ denote the smallest σ-algebra of subsets of $T \times U$ that contains all measurable rectangles.

As an example, let $T = U = [0,1]$ and $\mathfrak{M} = \mathfrak{N}$ be the family of all Borel subsets of $[0,1]$. Then $\mathfrak{M} \times \mathfrak{N}$ is the family of all Borel subsets of $[0,1] \times [0,1]$.

4.5.11 Lemma. Let T and U be sets and suppose that $A_1 \subset T$, $A_2 \subset T$, $B_1 \subset U$, and $B_2 \subset U$. Then

i) $(A_1 \times B_1) \cap (A_2 \times B_2) = (A_1 \cap A_2) \times (B_1 \cap B_2)$;

ii) $(A_1 \times B_1) \cap (A_2 \times B_2)' = [(A_1 \cap A_2') \times B_1] \cup [(A_1 \cap A_2) \times (B_1 \cap B_2')]$.

We omit the proofs.

4.5.12 Theorem. Suppose that $Q \varepsilon \mathfrak{M} \times \mathfrak{N}$. Then

i) $\{t: t \varepsilon T, (t,u) \varepsilon Q\} \varepsilon \mathfrak{M}$ for all $u \varepsilon U$ and

ii) $\{u: u \varepsilon U, (t,u) \varepsilon Q\} \varepsilon \mathfrak{N}$ for all $t \varepsilon T$.

Proof. Let $\mathcal{S}$ be the family of all sets in $\mathfrak{M} \times \mathfrak{N}$ for which assertions i) and ii) hold. We may obviously consider only i); ii) is proved similarly in all cases. We first show that $A \times B \varepsilon \mathcal{S}$ for all measurable rectangles $A \times B$. For each $u \varepsilon U$, we have

$$\{t: t \varepsilon T, (t,u) \varepsilon A \times B\} = \begin{Bmatrix} A & \text{if} & u \varepsilon B \\ 0 & \text{if} & u \notin B \end{Bmatrix} \varepsilon \mathfrak{M}.$$

We now prove that $\mathcal{S}$ is a σ-algebra. Suppose that $S_1, S_2, \ldots, S_n, \ldots \varepsilon \mathcal{S}$. Then for each $u \varepsilon U$,

$$\{t: t \varepsilon T, (t,u) \varepsilon \bigcup_{n=1}^{\infty} S_n\} = \bigcup_{n=1}^{\infty} \{t: t \varepsilon T, (t,u) \varepsilon S_n\} \varepsilon \mathfrak{M}.$$

Suppose that $S \varepsilon \mathcal{S}$. For each $u \varepsilon U$, $\{t: t \varepsilon T, (t,u) \varepsilon S'\} = \{t: t \varepsilon T, (t,u) \varepsilon S\}' \varepsilon \mathfrak{M}$. Hence $S' \varepsilon \mathcal{S}$. Consequently, $\mathcal{S}$ is a σ-algebra.

Since $\mathfrak{M} \times \mathfrak{N}$ is the smallest σ-algebra containing all measurable rectangles, we have $\mathfrak{M} \times \mathfrak{N} \subset \mathcal{S}$. But by definition, $\mathcal{S} \subset \mathfrak{M} \times \mathfrak{N}$, and hence $\mathfrak{M} \times \mathfrak{N} = \mathcal{S}$.

4.5.13 Theorem. Let f be an extended real-valued function on $T \times U$ that is $\mathfrak{M} \times \mathfrak{N}$-measurable. Then for every fixed $u \varepsilon U$, the function $f(t,u)$ of t is $\mathfrak{M}$-measurable on T and for every fixed $t \varepsilon T$, the function $f(t,u)$ of u is $\mathfrak{N}$-measurable on U.

The proof is very like that of 4.5.12 and is omitted.

For our study of product measures, we need a purely set-theoretic fact, which we next state and prove.

4.5.2 Theorem. Let X be any set and $\mathcal{A}$ an algebra of subsets of X. Then the σ-algebra generated by $\mathcal{A}$ is the smallest family $\mathcal{N}_0$ of subsets of X that contains $\mathcal{A}$ and satisfies

i) if $\{A_n\}_{n=1}^{\infty} \subset \mathcal{N}_0$ and the A_n are pairwise disjoint, then $\bigcup_{n=1}^{\infty} A_n \in \mathcal{N}_0$;

ii) if $\{B_n\}_{n=1}^{\infty} \subset \mathcal{N}_0$ and $B_n \supset B_{n+1}$ for $n = 1, 2, 3, \ldots$, then $\bigcap_{n=1}^{\infty} B_n \in \mathcal{N}_0$.

In particular, if $\mathcal{A}$ is an algebra satisfying i) and ii), then $\mathcal{A}$ is a σ-algebra.

Proof. Step 1. We show that $\mathcal{N}_0$ is closed under the formation of finite intersections. Let $\mathcal{N}_1 = \{B \in \mathcal{N}_0\colon\ B \cap A \in \mathcal{N}_0$ for all $A \in \mathcal{A}\}$. Clearly $\mathcal{N}_0 \supset \mathcal{N}_1 \supset \mathcal{A}$. We will show that $\mathcal{N}_1$ also satisfies i) and ii). Suppose that $\{B_n\}_{n=1}^{\infty}$ is a pairwise disjoint family of sets in $\mathcal{N}_1$. Let $A \in \mathcal{A}$. Then $B_n \cap A \in \mathcal{N}_0$ for $n = 1, 2, \ldots$ and the $B_n \cap A$ are pairwise disjoint. By i), $\left(\bigcup_{n=1}^{\infty} B_n\right) \cap A = \bigcup_{n=1}^{\infty} (B_n \cap A) \in \mathcal{N}_0$. Thus $\bigcup_{n=1}^{\infty} B_n \in \mathcal{N}_1$ and $\mathcal{N}_1$ satisfies i). Suppose that $C_1 \supset C_2 \supset \ldots \supset C_n \supset \ldots$, $C_n \in \mathcal{N}_1$. Then for $A \in \mathcal{A}$, we have $\left(\bigcap_{n=1}^{\infty} C_n\right) \cap A = \bigcap_{n=1}^{\infty} (C_n \cap A) \in \mathcal{N}_0$ and hence $\bigcap_{n=1}^{\infty} C_n \in \mathcal{N}_1$. Thus $\mathcal{N}_1$ satisfies ii). Since $\mathcal{N}_0$ is the smallest family containing $\mathcal{A}$ and satisfying i) and ii), we have $\mathcal{N}_0 = \mathcal{N}_1$.

This means that $A \in \mathcal{A}$ and $B \in \mathcal{N}_o$ imply $A \cap B \in \mathcal{N}_o$.

Let $\mathcal{N}_2 = \{B \in \mathcal{N}_o\colon\ B \cap C \in \mathcal{N}_o \text{ for all } C \in \mathcal{N}_o\}$. Clearly $\mathcal{N}_o \supset \mathcal{N}_2 \supset \mathcal{A}$. With arguments similar to those above, we see that $\mathcal{N}_2$ satisfies i) and ii). Hence $\mathcal{N}_o = \mathcal{N}_2$. This shows that $A \in \mathcal{N}_o$ and $B \in \mathcal{N}_o$ imply $A \cap B \in \mathcal{N}_o$.

Step 2. We prove now that the family $\mathcal{N}_o$ is closed under the formation of countable intersections. Let $\{B_n\}_{n=1}^{\infty} \subset \mathcal{N}_o$. For each positive integer n, let $C_n = B_1 \cap \dots \cap B_n$. Then by step 1, each $C_n \in \mathcal{N}_o$. Clearly $C_n \supset C_{n+1}$ for $n = 1, 2, \dots$. By applying ii) to the C_n's, we have $\bigcap_{n=1}^{\infty} B_n = \bigcap_{n=1}^{\infty} C_n \in \mathcal{N}_o$.

Step 3. We show next that $\mathcal{N}_o$ is a σ-algebra. Let $\mathcal{N}_3 = \{C \in \mathcal{N}_o\colon\ C' \in \mathcal{N}_o\}$. Clearly $\mathcal{A} \subset \mathcal{N}_3 \subset \mathcal{N}_o$. Suppose that $\{C_n\}_{n=1}^{\infty} \subset \mathcal{N}_3$. Then using step 2, $(\bigcup_{n=1}^{\infty} C_n)' = \bigcap_{n=1}^{\infty} C_n' \in \mathcal{N}_o$. Thus $\bigcup_{n=1}^{\infty} C_n \in \mathcal{N}_3$. The family $\mathcal{N}_3$ is closed under countable unions, and in particular satisfies i). Suppose that $\{B_n\}_{n=1}^{\infty} \subset \mathcal{N}_3$. Then $(\bigcap_{n=1}^{\infty} B_n)' = \bigcup_{n=1}^{\infty} B_n' \in \mathcal{N}_3 \subset \mathcal{N}_o$. Hence $\bigcap_{n=1}^{\infty} B_n \in \mathcal{N}_3$ and in particular $\mathcal{N}_3$ satisfies ii). Consequently, $\mathcal{N}_o = \mathcal{N}_3$. Since $\mathcal{N}_3$ is closed under complementation and the formation of countable unions, $\mathcal{N}_o$ is a σ- algebra.

Step 4. The family $\mathcal{N}_o$ is the smallest σ-algebra containing $\mathcal{A}$ because any σ-algebra containing $\mathcal{A}$ must satisfy properties i) and ii) and hence contain $\mathcal{N}_0$.

4.5.21 Theorem. The σ-algebra $\mathcal{M} \times \mathcal{N}$ is the smallest family $\mathcal{P}$ of sets containing all measurable rectangles $A \times B$ and such that

i) if $\{A_n\}_{n=1}^{\infty} \subset \mathcal{P}$ and the A_n are pairwise disjoint then $\bigcup_{n=1}^{\infty} A_n \in \mathcal{P}$;

ii) if $\{B_n\}_{n=1}^{\infty} \subset \mathcal{P}$ and $B_n \supset B_{n+1}$ for $n = 1, 2, \ldots,$ then $\bigcap_{n=1}^{\infty} B_n \in \mathcal{P}$.

Proof. Let $\mathcal{A} = \left\{ \bigcup_{j=1}^{m} (A_j \times B_j) : A_j \times B_j \text{ is a measurable rectangle} \right\}$; that is, $\mathcal{A}$ consists of all finite unions of measurable rectangles. We will show that $\mathcal{A}$ is an algebra of sets. The family $\mathcal{A}$ is obviously closed under finite unions. For any $\bigcup_{j=1}^{m} (A_j \times B_j) \in \mathcal{A}$, we have $\left(\bigcup_{j=1}^{m} (A_j \times B_j)\right)' = \bigcap_{j=1}^{m} (A_j \times B_j)' = \bigcap_{j=1}^{m} [(A_j' \times U) \cup (A_j \times B_j')]$. This is a union of finite intersections of measurable rectangles and hence is a member of $\mathcal{A}$. Consequently, $\mathcal{A}$ is an algebra of sets.

We show now that $\mathcal{A} \subset \mathcal{P}$. We have the identity $(A_1 \times B_1) \cup (A_2 \times B_2) = (A_1 \times B_1) \cup [(A_2 \times B_2) \cap (A_1 \times B_1)'] = (A_1 \times B_1) \cup [(A_2 \times B_2) \cap ((A_1' \times U) \cup (A_1 \times B_1'))] = (A_1 \times B_1) \cup [((A_2 \cap A_1') \times B_2) \cup ((A_1 \cap A_2) \times (B_2 \cap B_1'))]$. The expression in brackets is the disjoint union of members of $\mathcal{P}$ and hence is also in $\mathcal{P}$. Hence the entire expression is the disjoint union of two sets in $\mathcal{P}$ and is in $\mathcal{P}$. Thus $(A_1 \times B_1) \cup (A_2 \times B_2) \in \mathcal{P}$. By induction it is now easy to see that $\mathcal{A} \subset \mathcal{P}$.

Theorem 4.5.2 now implies that $\mathcal{M} \times \mathcal{N} = \mathcal{P}$.

4.5.3 __Theorem.__ Let T, U, $\mathcal{M}$, and $\mathcal{N}$ be as in 4.5.1. Let μ and ν be σ-finite countably additive measures on $\mathcal{M}$ and $\mathcal{N}$, respectively. Let $Q \in \mathcal{M} \times \mathcal{N}$. Then

ia) $\mu\{t \in T: (t,u) \in Q\}$ is an $\mathcal{N}$-measurable function of u;

ib) $\nu\{u \in U: (t,u) \in Q\}$ is an $\mathcal{M}$-measurable function of t;

ii) $\int_U \mu\{t \in T: (t,u) \in Q\}\, d\nu(u) = \int_T \nu\{u \in U: (t,u) \in Q\} d\mu(t)$.

__Proof.__ Step 1. Let $T = \bigcup_{m=1}^{\infty} T_m$ where the T_m are pairwise disjoint sets in $\mathcal{M}$ and $\mu(T_m) < \infty$. Let $U = \bigcup_{n=1}^{\infty} U_n$ be a similar dissection of U. We will now show that if $P \in \mathcal{M} \times \mathcal{N}$ and $P \cap (T_m \times U_n)$ has properties ia), ib), and ii) for all m and n, then P also has properties ia), ib), and ii). We note that it suffices to verify ia) and ii) in all cases since ib) is very like ia).

Now $\{t \in T: (t,u) \in P\} = \bigcup_{m,n=1}^{\infty} \{t \in T: (t,u) \in P \cap (T_m \times U_n)\}$ and hence $\mu\{t \in T: (t,u) \in P\} = \sum_{m,n=1}^{\infty} \mu\{t \in T: (t,u) \in P \cap (T_m \times U_n)\}$. Therefore, P has property ia).

Using the hypotheses on $P \cap (T_m \times U_n)$ and 3.5.1, we have $\int_U \mu\{t \varepsilon T: (t,u) \varepsilon P\} d\nu(u) =$

$\int_U \sum_{m,n=1}^{\infty} [\mu\{t \varepsilon T: (t,u) \varepsilon P \cap (T_m \times U_n)\}]d\nu(u) =$

$\sum_{m,n=1}^{\infty} \int_U \mu\{t \varepsilon T: (t,u) \varepsilon P \cap (T_m \times U_n)\} d\nu(u) =$

$\sum_{m,n=1}^{\infty} \int_T \nu\{u \varepsilon U: (t,u) \varepsilon P \cap (T_m \times U_n)\}d\mu(t) =$

$\int_T \sum_{m,n=1}^{\infty} [\nu\{u \varepsilon U: (t,u) \varepsilon P \cap (T_m \times U_n)\}]d\mu(t) =$

$\int_T \nu\{u \varepsilon U: (t,u) \varepsilon P\}d\mu(t)$. This shows that P also has property ii).

Step 2. Let $\mathcal{P}$ be the family of all $P \varepsilon \mathfrak{m} \times \mathfrak{n}$ for which $P \cap (T_m \times U_n)$ satisfies ia), ib), and ii) for all m and n. Let $A \times B$ be a measurable rectangle. Then $\{t \varepsilon T: (t,u) \varepsilon A \times B\} = \begin{cases} A & \text{if } u \varepsilon B \\ 0 & \text{if } u \notin B \end{cases}$ so that

$\mu\{t \varepsilon T: (t,u) \varepsilon A \times B\} = \begin{cases} \mu(A) & \text{if } u \varepsilon B \\ 0 & \text{if } u \notin B \end{cases} = \mu(A)\chi_B(u)$.

Consequently, $\int_U \mu\{t \varepsilon T: (t,u) \varepsilon A \times B\}d\nu(u) = \mu(A)\nu(B)$.

Likewise, $\int_T \nu\{u \varepsilon U: (t,u) \varepsilon A \times B\}d\mu(t) = \mu(A)\nu(B)$.

Hence $A \times B$ has properties ia), ib), and ii), and <u>a fortiori</u>, $(A \times B) \cap (T_m \cap U_n)$ has the same properties. Hence $\mathcal{P}$ contains all measurable rectangles.

Suppose that $\{P_r\}_{r=1}^{\infty}$ is a pairwise disjoint countable subfamily of $\mathcal{P}$. Since

$\mu\{t \in T: (t,u) \in (\bigcup_{r=1}^{\infty} P_r) \cap (T_m \times U_n)\} =$

$\sum_{r=1}^{\infty} \mu\{t \in T: (t,u) \in P_r \cap (T_m \times U_n)\}$ we see that ia) follows for $(\bigcup_{r=1}^{\infty} P_r) \cap (T_m \times U_n)$ for all m and n.

Moreover, $\int_U \mu\{t \in T: (t,u) \in (\bigcup_{r=1}^{\infty} P_r) \cap (T_m \times U_n)\}\, d\nu(u) =$

$\sum_{r=1}^{\infty} \int_U \mu\{t \in T: (t,u) \in P_r \cap (T_m \times U_n)\} d\nu(u) =$

$\sum_{r=1}^{\infty} \int_T \nu\{u \in U: (t,u) \in P_r \cap (T_m \times U_n)\} d\mu(t) =$

$\int_T \nu\{u \in U: (t,u) \in (\bigcup_{r=1}^{\infty} P_r) \cap (T_m \times U_n)\} d\mu(t)$ and consequently $(\bigcup_{r=1}^{\infty} P_r) \cap (T_m \times U_n)$ has property ii) for all m and n. Hence $\bigcup_{r=1}^{\infty} P_r \in \mathcal{P}$.

Suppose finally that $C_1 \supset C_2 \supset \ldots \supset C_r \supset \ldots$ where each $C_r \in \mathcal{P}$. We will show that $\bigcap_{r=1}^{\infty} C_r \in \mathcal{P}$. Properties ia) and ib) hold for $(\bigcap_{r=1}^{\infty} C_r) \cap (T_m \times U_n)$ for all m and n by 3.1.31. We now verify ii). Using 2.4.3 and 3.5.21, we obtain

$\int_U \mu\{t \in T: (t,u) \in (\bigcap_{r=1}^{\infty} C_r) \cap (T_m \times U_n)\} d\nu(u) =$

$\int_U \mu(\bigcap_{r=1}^{\infty} \{t \in T: (t,u) \in C_r \cap (T_m \times U_n)\}) d\nu(u) =$

$\int_U \lim_{r\to\infty} \mu\{t \in T: (t,u) \in C_r \cap (T_m \times U_n)\} d\nu(u) =$

$\lim_{r\to\infty} \int_U \mu\{t \in T: (t,u) \in C_r \cap (T_m \times U_n)\} d\nu(u)$. The dominating function of 3.5.21 is $\mu\{t \in T: (t,u) \in C_1 \cap (T_m \times U_n)\}$. Similarly $\int_T \nu\{u \in U: (t,u) \in (\bigcap_{r=1}^{\infty} C_r) \cap (T_m \times U_n)\} d\mu(t) = \lim_{r\to\infty} \int_T \nu\{u \in U: (t,u) \in C_r \cap (T_m \times U_n)\} d\mu(t) = \lim_{r\to\infty} \int_U \mu\{t \in T: (t,u) \in C_r \cap (T_m \times U_n)\} d\nu(u)$. Thus ii) holds for $\mathcal{P}$. (The hypothesis that μ and ν be σ-finite is required only in showing that $\mathcal{P}$ has property ii).)

The above three paragraphs show that $\mathcal{P}$ satisfies the conditions of 4.5.21. Consequently $\mathcal{P} = \mathcal{M} \times \mathcal{N}$ and, by step 1, $\mathcal{P}$ consists of those sets $P \in \mathcal{M} \times \mathcal{N}$ such that P has properties ia), ib), and ii).

4.5.31 Exercise. Let $T = U = [0,1]$, and let $\mathcal{M} = \mathcal{N}$ be the Borel sets of $[0,1]$. Let μ be Lebesgue measure and ν be defined by $\nu(E) = \begin{cases} \overline{\overline{E}} & \text{if } E \text{ is finite} \\ \infty & \text{if } E \text{ is infinite} \end{cases}$.

Finally let $D = \{(t,t) \in T \times U: 0 \leq t \leq 1\}$. Show that $\int_T \nu\{u \in U: (t,u) \in D\} d\mu(t) = 1$ and $\int_U \mu\{t \in T: (t,u) \in D\} d\nu(u) = 0$, and explain why 4.5.3 fails.

4.5.32 Exercise. Let $T = U = R$ where R denotes the real numbers and let $\mathcal{M}$ and $\mathcal{N}$ be the Borel sets in R. Show that $\mathcal{M} \times \mathcal{N}$ is precisely all the Borel sets in the plane.

4.5.33 Final Exercise # 24. Let T be any set, $\mathcal{M}$ a σ-algebra of subsets, and μ a σ-finite countably additive measure on $\mathcal{M}$. Let U be R, $\mathcal{N}$ be the Borel sets of R, and

ν be Lebesgue measure. Let f be a non-negative, extended real-valued, $\mathfrak{M}$-measurable function on T. Define
$V^*f = \{(t,u) \in T \times R: \ 0 \leq u \leq f(t)\}$ and
$V_*f = \{(t,u) \in T \times R: \ 0 \leq u < f(t)\}$.
Prove that V^*f and V_*f are $\mathfrak{M} \times \mathfrak{N}$ -measurable and that $\mu \times \nu(V_*f) = \mu \times \nu(V^*f) = \int_T f(t)d\mu(t)$. [$\mu \times \nu$ is defined in 4.5.34].

4.5.34 Definition. Let T, U, $\mathfrak{M}$, $\mathfrak{N}$, μ, and ν be as in 4.5.3. For $P \in \mathfrak{M} \times \mathfrak{N}$, let $\mu \times \nu(P) = \int_U \mu\{t \in T: (t,u) \in P\}d\nu(u)$.

4.5.35 Theorem. Under the hypotheses of 4.5.34, the set-function $\mu \times \nu$ is a countably additive (possibly infinite) σ-finite measure on $\mathfrak{M} \times \mathfrak{N}$.

Proof. Suppose that $\{P_r\}_{r=1}^{\infty}$ is a pairwise disjoint family of sets in $\mathfrak{M} \times \mathfrak{N}$. Then $\mu \times \nu(\bigcup_{r=1}^{\infty} P_r) =$

$\int_U \mu\{t \in T: \ (t,u) \in \bigcup_{r=1}^{\infty} P_r\}d\nu(u) =$

$\int_U \mu(\bigcup_{r=1}^{\infty} \{t \in T: \ (t,u) \in P_r\})d\nu(u) =$

$\int_U (\sum_{r=1}^{\infty} \mu\{t \in T: \ (t,u) \in P_r\})d\nu(u) =$

$\sum_{r=1}^{\infty} \int_U \mu\{t \in T: \ (t,u) \in P_r\}d\nu(u) = \sum_{r=1}^{\infty} (\mu \times \nu)(P_r)$.

Since the other postulates for a measure are clearly satisfied, $\mu \times \nu$ is a measure.

Let $T = \bigcup_{m=1}^{\infty} T_m$ and $U = \bigcup_{n=1}^{\infty} U_n$ be pairwise disjoint

unions of sets of finite μ-measure and ν-measure, re-
spectively. Then $T \times U = \bigcup\limits_{m=1}^{\infty} \bigcup\limits_{n=1}^{\infty} (T_m \times U_n)$ and, moreover,
$(\mu \times \nu)(T_m \times U_n) = \mu(T_m) \cdot \nu(U_n) < \infty$ for all m and
n (see step 2 of 4.5.3). Consequently $\mu \times \nu$ is a
σ-finite measure.

4.5.36 <u>Theorem</u>. Let X be any set, $\mathscr{S}$ a σ-algebra of subsets
of X, and ϕ a countably additive measure on $\mathscr{S}$.
Let $\overline{\mathscr{S}}$ be the smallest σ-algebra of subsets of X containing $\mathscr{S}$ and all subsets of sets of ϕ-measure zero.
Then $\overline{\mathscr{S}}$ consists of all sets of the form $(S \cap N_1') \cup N_2$
where $S \varepsilon \mathscr{S}$ and N_1 and N_2 are subsets of sets of
ϕ-measure zero. Define $\overline{\phi}$ on $\overline{\mathscr{S}}$ by the relation
$\overline{\phi}((S \cap N_1') \cup N_2) = \phi(S)$. Then $\overline{\phi}$ is a well-defined
countably additive measure on $\overline{\mathscr{S}}$ and, moreover, $\overline{\phi}(M) = 0$
and $N \subset M$ imply $\overline{\phi}(N) = 0$.

The proof is omitted.

4.5.37 <u>Definition</u>. A measure space $(X, \mathscr{S}, \phi)$ such that all
subsets of sets of measure zero are measurable is called
complete. The measure $\overline{\phi}$ as defined in 4.5.36 is
called the completion of ϕ.

4.5.38 <u>Theorem</u>. Let $T, U, \mathscr{M}, \mathscr{N}, \mu,$ and ν be as in 4.5.3 and
suppose that $(T, \mathscr{M}, \mu)$ and $(U, \mathscr{N}, \nu)$ are complete.
Suppose also that $M \varepsilon \mathscr{M} \times \mathscr{N}$ where $\mu \times \nu(M) = 0$ and
that $N \subset M$. Then $\mu\{t \varepsilon T: (t,u) \varepsilon N\} = 0$ for all
$u \varepsilon U$ except for a set of ν-measure zero. A similar
result obtains for $\nu\{u \varepsilon U: (t,u) \varepsilon N\}$.

Proof. Clearly $0 = \mu \times \nu(M) = \int_U \mu\{t \in T: (t,u) \in M\} d\nu(u)$. Therefore $\mu\{t \in T: (t,u) \in M\} = 0$ except for a set of ν-measure zero. Since $\{t \in T: (t,u) \in N\} \subset \{t \in T: (t,u) \in M\}$ for all $u \in U$, we see that $\mu\{t \in T: (t,u) \in N\} = 0$ except for a set of ν-measure zero.

4.5.4 Theorem. (Fubini's Theorem) Let T and U be sets, and let $\mathfrak{M}$ and $\mathfrak{N}$ be σ-algebras of subsets of T and U, respectively. Let $\mathfrak{M} \times \mathfrak{N}$ be as defined in 4.5.1. Let μ and ν be σ-finite countably additive complete measures on $\mathfrak{M}$ and $\mathfrak{N}$, respectively. Let $\overline{\mathfrak{M} \times \mathfrak{N}}$ and $\overline{\mu \times \nu}$ be as defined in 4.5.36. Finally let f be a non-negative, real-valued, $\overline{\mathfrak{M} \times \mathfrak{N}}$-measurable function on $T \times U$. Then

ia) the function on T defined by $f(t,u)$ is $\mathfrak{M}$-measurable for all u except for a set of ν-measure zero, and

ib) the function on U defined by $f(t,u)$ is $\mathfrak{N}$-measurable for all t except for a set of μ-measure zero.

Also the function $\int_U f(t,u) d\nu(u)$ on T is $\mathfrak{M}$-measurable and the function $\int_T f(t,u) d\mu(t)$ on U is $\mathfrak{N}$-measurable.

Finally,

ii) $\int_{T \times U} f(t,u) d\overline{\mu \times \nu}(t,u) = \int_T \int_U f(t,u) d\nu(u) d\mu(t) = \int_U \int_T f(t,u) d\mu(t) d\nu(u)$.

Proof. In each step we will prove ia) and the equality $\int_{T \times U} f(t,u) d\overline{\mu \times \nu}(t,u) = \int_U \int_T f(t,u) d\mu(t) d\nu(u)$ since the remaining assertions are similar.

Step 1. Let $f = \chi_Q$ where $Q \in \mathcal{M} \times \mathcal{N}$. For a fixed $u \in U$, we have $\chi_Q(t,u) =$
$\begin{cases} 1 & \text{if } (t,u) \in Q \\ 0 & \text{if } (t,u) \notin Q \end{cases} = \chi_{\{t \in T:\ (t,u) \in Q\}}$ and this is $\mathcal{M}$-measurable by 4.5.12. Hence ia) holds for $f = \chi_Q$. Now, using 4.5.3 and 4.5.34, we have $\int_{T \times U} \chi_Q(t,u)\, d\overline{\mu \times \nu}(t,u) =$
$\overline{\mu \times \nu}(Q) = \mu \times \nu(Q) = \int_U \mu\{t \in T:\ (t,u) \in Q\} d\nu(u) =$
$\int_U \int_T \chi_Q(t,u)\, d\mu(t)\, d\nu(u)$ and hence the second equality in ii) holds.

Step 2. Let $f = \chi_P$ where $P \in \overline{\mathcal{M} \times \mathcal{N}}$. Then $P = (Q \cap M') \cup N$ where $Q \in \mathcal{M} \times \mathcal{N}$ and M and N are subsets of sets of $\mu \times \nu$-measure zero (4.5.36). By 4.5.38, $\mu\{t \in T:\ (t,u) \in M\} = 0$ and $\mu\{t \in T:\ (t,u) \in N\} = 0$ except for a set of ν-measure zero. Consequently, $\mu\{t \in T:\ (t,u) \in (Q \cap M') \cup N\} = \mu\{t \in T:\ (t,u) \in Q\}$ except for a set of ν-measure zero. Thus ia) is true for χ_P. From the above and 4.5.3 we have $\int_T \chi_P(t,u)\, d\mu(t) =$
$\mu\{t \in T:\ (t,u) \in P\} = \mu\{t \in T:\ (t,u) \in Q\} = \int_T \chi_Q(t,u)\, d\mu(t)$
for almost all u. Consequently, applying step 1 to χ_Q, we obtain $\int_U \int_T \chi_P(t,u)\, d\mu(t)\, d\nu(u) = \int_U \int_T \chi_Q(t,u)\, du(t)\, d\nu(u) =$
$\int_{T \times U} \chi_Q(t,u)\, d\overline{\mu \times \nu}(t,u) = \overline{\mu \times \nu}(Q) = \overline{\mu \times \nu}(P) =$
$\int_{T \times U} \chi_P(t,u)\, d\overline{\mu \times \nu}(t,u)$.

The theorem is now obvious for non-negative simple $\overline{\mathcal{M} \times \mathcal{N}}$-measurable functions.

Step 3. Let f be any non-negative $\overline{\mathcal{M} \times \mathcal{N}}$-measurable function. There exists an increasing sequence $\{s_n\}_{n=1}^{\infty}$ of simple $\overline{\mathcal{M} \times \mathcal{N}}$-measurable functions such that $\lim_{n\to\infty} s_n = f$ on $T \times U$. Since for each n, $s_n(t,u)$ is $\mathcal{M}$-measurable as a function of t for almost all u, we see that $\lim_{n\to\infty} s_n(t,u) = f(t,u)$ is $\mathcal{M}$-measurable as a function of t for almost all u. Thus f satisfies ia). Since ii) holds for each s_n, we may apply 3.5.11 to obtain

$$\int_{T\times U} f(t,u)\,d\overline{\mu\times\nu}(t,u) = \lim_{n\to\infty} \int_{T\times U} s_n(t,u)\,d\overline{\mu\times\nu}(t,u) =$$

$$\lim_{n\to\infty} \int_U \int_T s_n(t,u)\,d\mu(t)\,d\nu(u) = \int_U \lim_{n\to\infty} \int_T s_n(t,u)\,d\mu(t)\,d\nu(u) =$$

$$\int_U \int_T f(t,u)\,d\mu(t)\,d\nu(u).$$

This completes the proof.

4.5.41 Theorem. Let T, U, $\mathcal{M}$, $\mathcal{N}$, μ, and ν be as in 4.5.4. Let f be $\overline{\mathcal{M} \times \mathcal{N}}$-measurable. If any of the integrals

$$\int_{T\times U} |f(t,u)|\,d\overline{\mu\times\nu}(t,u),\quad \int_T \int_U |f(t,u)|\,d\nu(u)\,d\mu(t),$$

$$\int_U \int_T |f(t,u)|\,d\mu(t)\,d\nu(u)$$ is finite, then all three are finite and equal and, moreover, the integrals

$$\int_{T\times U} f(t,u)\,d\overline{\mu\times\nu}(t,u),\quad \int_T \int_U f(t,u)\,d\nu(u)\,d\mu(t),$$

$$\int_U \int_T f(t,u)\,d\mu(t)\,d\nu(u)$$ are finite and equal.

Proof. Write $f = f^+ - f^-$ where $f^+ = \max(f,0)$ and $f^- = -\min(f,0)$ and apply 4.5.4 to these functions.

4.5.42 Remark. It would be convenient if in 4.5.4 we could consider all functions f on $T \times U$ for which ia) and ib) hold, instead of being compelled to verify that f is measurable $\overline{\mathfrak{M} \times \mathfrak{N}}$. This is not the case, however: ia) and ib) do not imply that f is $\overline{\mathfrak{M} \times \mathfrak{N}}$ measurable. To see this, let $T = U$, where T is uncountable, let $\mathfrak{M} = \mathfrak{N}$ be the smallest σ-algebra containing all points, and let $\mu = \nu$ be the measure assigning the value 1 to sets with countable complements and the value 0 to countable sets. Let $D = \{(t,t): t \in T\}$. Then if $f = \chi_D$, f satisfies ia) and ib), but is not $\overline{\mathfrak{M} \times \mathfrak{N}}$-measurable.

4.5.5 Theorem. Let a and b be real numbers such that $a < b$. Let μ and ν be any countably additive non-negative finite Borel measures on $[a,b]$. Let M and N be defined on $[a,b]$ by

$$M(t) = \tfrac{1}{2}[\mu([a,t]) + \mu([a,t[)]$$
$$N(t) = \tfrac{1}{2}[\nu([a,t]) + \nu([a,t[)].$$

Then M and N are bounded Borel measurable functions and $\int_{[a,b]} M(t)d\nu(t) + \int_{[a,b]} N(t)d\mu(t) = \mu([a,b])\nu([a,b])$.

Proof. Since M and N are monotone increasing functions on $[a,b]$, they are obviously Borel measurable. Let $Q = \{(t,u) \in [a,b] \times [a,b]: u \leq t\}$. Since Q is compact, Q is a Borel set and hence $Q \in \mathfrak{M} \times \mathfrak{N}$ (4.5.32). By 4.5.3 ii), we have

$$\int_{[a,b]} \mu\{t \in [a,b]: (t,u) \in Q\}d\nu(u) = \int_{[a,b]} \nu\{u \in [a,b]:$$

$(t,u) \in Q\}\, d\mu(t)$ or

$$\int_{[a,b]} \mu([u,b])d\nu(u) = \int_{[a,b]} \nu([a,t])d\mu(t).$$ Hence

$$\int_{[a,b]} \mu([a,b])d\nu(u) - \int_{[a,b]} \mu([a,u[)d\nu(u) = \int_{[a,b]} \nu([a,t])d\mu(t)$$

or $$\mu([a,b])\nu([a,b]) = \int_{[a,b]} \mu([a,u[)d\nu(u) + \int_{[a,b]} \nu([a,t])d\mu(t).$$

Interchanging μ and ν, we see that

$$\mu([a,b])\nu([a,b]) = \int_{[a,b]} \nu([a,t[)d\mu(t) + \int_{[a,b]} \mu([a,u])d\nu(u).$$

Adding the last two equations, we obtain

$$2\mu([a,b])\nu([a,b]) = \int_{[a,b]} [\nu([a,t]) + \nu([a,t[)]d\mu(t) +$$

$$\int_{[a,b]} [\mu([a,u[) + \mu([a,u])]d\nu(u) = 2\int_{[a,b]} N(t)d\mu(t) +$$

$$2\int_{[a,b]} M(u)d\nu(u).$$

Note. In what follows the symbol $\int_a^b f(t)dt$ will always represent the Lebesgue integral $\int_{[a,b]} f(t)d\lambda(t)$.

4.5.51 Theorem. Let f and g be absolutely continuous functions on $[a,b]$. Then

$$f(b)g(b) - f(a)g(a) = \int_a^b [f(t)g'(t) + f'(t)g(t)]dt.$$

Proof. Case 1. Suppose that f and g are absolutely continuous monotone increasing functions. Define $\mu(E) = \int_E f'(t)dt$ and $\nu(E) = \int_E g'(t)dt$ for all Borel sets $E \subset [a,b]$. By 4.3.3, we have $\mu([a,t]) = \int_a^t f'(u)du = f(t) - f(a)$ and $\nu([a,t]) = g(t) - g(a)$ for all $t \in [a,b]$.

It is also easy to see that $\int_{[a,b]} \phi(t)d\mu(t) = \int_a^b \phi(t)f'(t)dt$ and $\int_{[a,b]} \phi(t)d\nu(t) = \int_a^b \phi(t)g'(t)dt$ for all measurable functions ϕ. (For characteristic functions of measurable sets, this is the definition of μ and ν. For simple functions, the relation is obvious by linearity, and for arbitrary ϕ it then follows by 3.2.12 and 3.5.11.) The functions M and N as defined in 4.5.5 are thus given by $M(t) = f(t) - f(a)$ and $N(t) = g(t) - g(a)$. By 4.5.5, we now have $[f(b) - f(a)][g(b) - g(a)] = \int_{[a,b]} [f(t) - f(a)]d\nu(t) + \int_{[a,b]} [g(t) - g(a)]d\mu(t) = \int_a^b [f(t) - f(a)]g'(t)dt + \int_a^b [g(t) - g(a)]f'(t)dt = \int_a^b f(t)g'(t)dt - f(a)\int_a^b g'(t)dt + \int_a^b g(t)f'(t)dt - g(a)\int_a^b f'(t)dt = \int_a^b [f(t)g'(t) + g(t)f'(t)]dt - f(a)[g(b) - g(a)] - g(a)[f(b) - f(a)]$ and hence $f(b)g(b) - f(a)g(a) = \int_a^b [f(t)g'(t) + f'(t)g(t)]dt$.

Case 2. Suppose that f and g are absolutely continuous functions. Then $f = f_1 - f_2$ and $g = g_1 - g_2$ where f_1, f_2, g_1, and g_2 are absolutely continuous monotone increasing functions. Applying case 1, we obtain $f_i(b)g_j(b) - f_i(a)g_j(a) = \int_a^b f_i(t)g_j'(t)dt + \int_a^b g_j(t)f_i'(t)dt$ $(i = 1, 2, j = 1, 2)$. Subtracting these equalities for $i = 1, 2$ with j fixed, we get $f(b)g_j(b) - f(a)g_j(a) = \int_a^b f(t)g_j'(t)dt + \int_a^b g_j(t)f'(t)dt$.

Subtracting these equalities for $j = 1, 2$, we have

$$f(b)g(b) - f(a)g(a) = \int_a^b f(t)g'(t)dt + \int_a^b g(t)f'(t)dt.$$

4.5.52 Exercise. Extend the results of 4.5.5 and 4.5.51 to intervals of the form $]-\infty,a]$, $[a,\infty[$, and $]-\infty,\infty[$.

4.5.6 Theorem. (The second mean value theorem for integrals) Let α and β be monotone increasing functions on $[a,b]$, and let β be continuous. Let μ be the Borel measure corresponding by 4.2.5 to $\beta - \beta(a)$. Define $\alpha(a - 0) = \alpha(a)$ and $\alpha(b + 0) = \alpha(b)$. Then there exists a $\xi \in [a,b]$ such that

$$\frac{1}{2}\int_{[a,b]} [\alpha(t + 0) + \alpha(t - 0)]d\mu(t) = \alpha(a)[\beta(\xi) - \beta(a)] + \alpha(b)[\beta(b) - \beta(\xi)].$$

Proof. Let ν be the measure corresponding by 4.2.5 to $\alpha - \alpha(a)$. Since β is continuous, we have $M(t) = \frac{1}{2}[\mu([a,t]) + \mu([a,t[)] = \beta(t) - \beta(a)$. We also have $N(t) = \frac{1}{2}[\nu([a,t]) + \nu([a,t[)] - \alpha(a) = \frac{1}{2}[\alpha(t + 0) + \alpha(t - 0)] - \alpha(a)$. By 4.5.5, we have $[\beta(b) - \beta(a)]\cdot[\alpha(b) - \alpha(a)] = \int_{[a,b]} [\beta(t) - \beta(a)]d\nu(t) + \int_{[a,b]} \left\{\frac{1}{2}[\alpha(t + 0) + \alpha(t - 0)] - \alpha(a)\right\}d\mu(t)$ or

$$\beta(b)\alpha(b) - \beta(a)\alpha(b) - \beta(b)\alpha(a) + \beta(a)\alpha(a) = \int_{[a,b]} \beta(t)d\nu(t) - \beta(a)\alpha(b) + \beta(a)\alpha(a) + \frac{1}{2}\int_{[a,b]} [\alpha(t + 0) + \alpha(t - 0)]d\mu(t) - \alpha(a)\beta(b) + \alpha(a)\beta(a).$$

Hence $\beta(b)\alpha(b) - \beta(a)\alpha(a) - \int_{[a,b]} \beta(t)d\nu(t) = \frac{1}{2}\int_{[a,b]} [\alpha(t + 0) + \alpha(t - 0)]d\mu(t)$. Now since β is continuous, $[a,b]$ is connected, and

$\min\{\beta(t): a \leq t \leq b\}\nu([a,b]) \leq \int_{[a,b]} \beta(t)d\nu(t) \leq \max\{\beta(t): a \leq t \leq b\}\nu([a,b])$, there exists a $\xi \in [a,b]$ such that $[\alpha(b) - \alpha(a)]\beta(\xi) = \int_{[a,b]} \beta(t)d\nu(t)$. Consequently $\beta(b)\alpha(b) - \alpha(a)\beta(a) - [\alpha(b) - \alpha(a)]\beta(\xi) = \frac{1}{2}\int_{[a,b]} [\alpha(t + 0) + \alpha(t - 0)]d\mu(t)$. This is equivalent to $\frac{1}{2}\int_{[a,b]} [\alpha(t + 0) + \alpha(t - 0)]d\mu(t) = \alpha(a)[\beta(\xi) - \beta(a)] + \alpha(b)[\beta(b) - \beta(\xi)]$.

4.5.61 Exercise. Suppose that $\phi \in \mathcal{L}_1([a,b])$ and that p is a function on $[a,b]$ such that one of the following holds:

i) p is a non-negative decreasing function;

ii) p is a non-negative increasing function;

iii) p is a monotone function.

Prove that, when i), ii), or iii), respectively, holds there exists a $\xi \in [a,b]$ such that

i) $\int_a^b p(t)\phi(t)dt = p(a)\int_a^\xi \phi(t)dt$;

ii) $\int_a^b p(t)\phi(t)dt = p(b)\int_\xi^b \phi(t)dt$; or

iii) $\int_a^b p(t)\phi(t)dt = p(a)\int_a^\xi \phi(t)dt + p(b)\int_\xi^b \phi(t)dt$,

respectively.

We next give an application of Fubini's theorem showing that proving joint measurability of $f(t,u)$ is an essential and often non-trivial part of the argument.

4.5.7 Theorem. Let f and g be in $\mathcal{L}_1(R)$, λ be Lebesgue measure, and $\mathcal{M}$ be the family of Lebesgue measurable sets in R. Let $f*g(t) = \int_{-\infty}^{\infty} f(t - u)g(u)du$. Then $f*g(t)$ is a real number for almost all t, $f*g \in \mathcal{L}_1(R)$, and $\|f*g\|_1 \leq \|f\|_1 \|g\|_1$. (The function $f*g$ is called the convolution of f and g.)

Proof. Suppose it already known that $f(t - u)g(u)$ is $\overline{\mathcal{M} \times \mathcal{M}}$-measurable in $R \times R$. Then by Fubini's theorem,

$$\int_{-\infty}^{\infty} \int_{-\infty}^{\infty} |f(t - u)g(u)|dtdu = \int_{-\infty}^{\infty} |g(u)|(\int_{-\infty}^{\infty} |f(t)|dt)du =$$

$$\int_{-\infty}^{\infty} |g(u)|du \cdot \int_{-\infty}^{\infty} |f(t)|dt = \|f\|_1 \cdot \|g\|_1.$$ Consequently,

$$\|f*g\|_1 = \int_{-\infty}^{\infty} |\int_{-\infty}^{\infty} f(t - u)g(u)du|dt \leq \int_{-\infty}^{\infty} \int_{-\infty}^{\infty} |f(t - u)||g(u)|dudt =$$

$\|f\|_1 \cdot \|g\|_1$. This also shows that $f*g(t)$ is finite for almost all t.

We now proceed to show that $f(t - u)g(u)$ is $\overline{\mathcal{M} \times \mathcal{M}}$-measurable in $R \times R$. The function $g(u)$ is $\overline{\mathcal{M} \times \mathcal{M}}$-measurable since for each $a \in R$, $\{(t,u) \in R \times R: g(u) > a\} = R \times \{u: g(u) > a\} \in \mathcal{M} \times \mathcal{M}$. Thus we have only to show that $f(t - u)$ is $\overline{\mathcal{M} \times \mathcal{M}}$-measurable for all $f \in \mathcal{L}_1(R)$.

Suppose that $f = \chi_{]a,b[}$. Then $f(t - u) = \chi_{]a,b[}(t-u) = \begin{cases} 1 & \text{if } t - u \in]a,b[\\ 0 & \text{otherwise} \end{cases}$. Now the set of points $(t,u) \in R \times R$ for which $f(t - u) = 1$, or, equivalently, for which $a + u < t < b + u$ is open in $R \times R$ and hence is in $\mathfrak{M} \times \mathfrak{M}$.

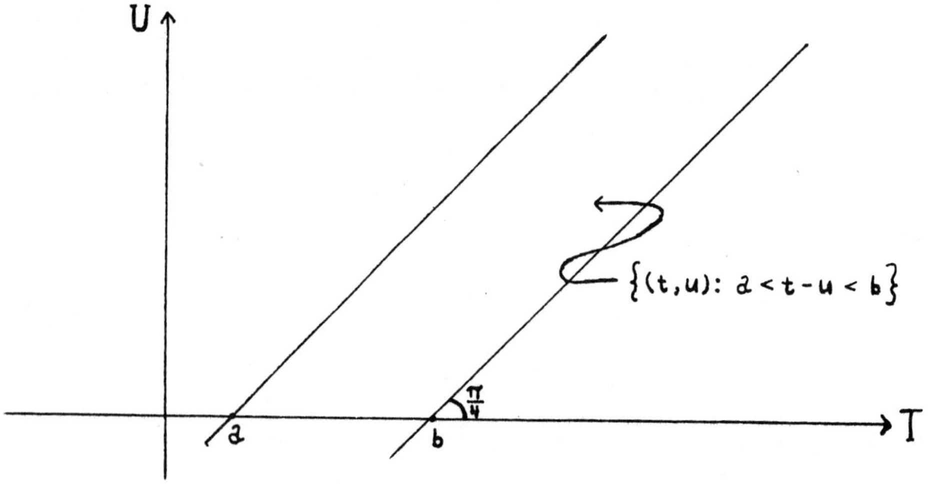

(See diagram.) Consequently $f(t - u) = \chi_{]a,b[}(t - u)$ is $\mathfrak{M} \times \mathfrak{M}$-measurable.

Suppose that $f = \chi_G$ where G is open. Since G is a countable union of pairwise disjoint open intervals $]a_n, b_n[$, we have $\chi_G(t - u) = \sum_{n=1}^{\infty} \chi_{]a_n,b_n[}(t - u)$. Thus $\chi_G(t - u)$ is a countable sum of $\mathfrak{M} \times \mathfrak{M}$-measurable functions (it is in fact the characteristic function of an open set) and is therefore $\mathfrak{M} \times \mathfrak{M}$-measurable.

Let $\mathcal{S}$ be the family of all subsets A of R such that $\chi_A(t - u)$ is $\mathfrak{M} \times \mathfrak{M}$-measurable. The previous paragraph shows that $\mathcal{S}$ contains all open sets in R. Suppose that $A \in \mathcal{S}$. Then $\chi_{A'}(t - u) = 1 - \chi_A(t - u)$, which is $\mathfrak{M} \times \mathfrak{M}$-measurable and hence $A' \in \mathcal{S}$. Thus $\mathcal{S}$ is closed under complementation. Suppose that $A, B \in \mathcal{S}$. Then $\chi_{A \cap B}(t - u) = \chi_A(t - u) \cdot \chi_B(t - u)$ is measurable so that $A \cap B \in \mathcal{L}$. Hence $\mathcal{L}$ is an algebra. Let $\{A_n\}_{n=1}^{\infty}$ be a pairwise disjoint subfamily of $\mathcal{L}$. Then $\chi_{\bigcup_{n=1}^{\infty} A_n}(t - u) = \sum_{n=1}^{\infty} \chi_{A_n}(t - u)$ is $\mathfrak{M} \times \mathfrak{M}$-measurable. Hence $\bigcup_{n=1}^{\infty} A_n \in \mathcal{L}$. Now let $B_1 \supset B_2 \supset \ldots$ be a decreasing sequence of sets in $\mathcal{L}$. Then $\chi_{\bigcap_{n=1}^{\infty} B_n}(t - u) = \lim_{n\to\infty} \chi_{B_n}(t - u)$ is $\mathfrak{M} \times \mathfrak{M}$-measurable so that $\bigcap_{n=1}^{\infty} B_n \in \mathcal{L}$. Consequently, by 4.5.2, $\mathcal{L}$ contains the smallest σ-algebra containing all open sets; that is, $\mathcal{L}$ contains all Borel sets. Therefore, if A is a Borel set, then $\chi_A(t - u)$ is $\mathfrak{M} \times \mathfrak{M}$-measurable.

Suppose that $B \in \mathfrak{M}$. The set B is of the form $A \cup N$ where A is a Borel set, $\lambda(N) = 0$, and $A \cap N = 0$. To see this, we use 2.3.492 to obtain for each $k = 1, 2, \ldots$ an increasing sequence $\{F_{n,k}\}_{n=1}^{\infty}$ of closed sets such that $F_{n,k} \subset B \cap [-k,k]$ and $\lim_{n\to\infty} \lambda(F_{n,k}) = \lambda(B \cap [-k,k])$. Now $B = (\bigcup_{k=1}^{\infty} \bigcup_{n=1}^{\infty} F_{n,k}) \cup N$ where $N = B \cap (\bigcup_{k=1}^{\infty} \bigcup_{n=1}^{\infty} F_{n,k})'$. Clearly $A = \bigcup_{k=1}^{\infty} \bigcup_{n=1}^{\infty} F_{n,k}$ is a Borel set and is disjoint from N. Also we have for each positive integer ℓ, $\lambda(N \cap [-\ell,\ell]) = \lambda(B \cap (\bigcup_{k=1}^{\infty} \bigcup_{n=1}^{\infty} F_{n,k})' \cap [-\ell,\ell]) \leq \lambda(B \cap [-\ell,\ell] \cap (\bigcup_{n=1}^{\infty} F_{n,\ell})') = \lambda(B \cap [-\ell,\ell]) - \lambda(\bigcup_{n=1}^{\infty} F_{n,\ell}) = \lambda(B \cap [-\ell,\ell]) - \lim_{n\to\infty} \lambda(F_{n,\ell}) = 0$. Consequently, $\lambda(N) = 0$. We now see that $\chi_B(t - u) = \chi_A(t - u) + \chi_N(t-u)$.

Thus in order to prove that $\chi_B(t-u)$ is $\overline{\mathcal{M} \times \mathcal{M}}$-measurable, it suffices to prove that $\chi_N(t-u)$ is $\overline{\mathcal{M} \times \mathcal{M}}$-measurable. Now $\{(t,u) \in R \times R: \chi_N(t-u) = 1\} = \{(t,u) \in R \times R: t-u \in N\} = \bigcup_{n=1}^{\infty} P_n$ where $P_n = \{(t,u) \in R \times R: t-u \in N \text{ and } |u| \leq n\}$. We now show that $\overline{\lambda \times \lambda}(P_n) = 0$. Let G be an open set such that $G \supset N$ and $\lambda(G) < \frac{\varepsilon}{2n}$. Let $H_n = \{(t,u) \in R \times R: t-u \in G \text{ and } |u| \leq n\}$. Then H_n is a Borel set and $\lambda \times \lambda(H_n) < \frac{\varepsilon}{2n} \cdot 2n = \varepsilon$. Then $\overline{\lambda \times \lambda}(P_n) \leq \lambda \times \lambda(H_n) < \varepsilon$ and hence $\overline{\lambda \times \lambda}(P_n) = 0$. We conclude that $\lambda(\bigcup_{n=1}^{\infty} P_n) = 0$ and hence that $\chi_N(t-u)$ is zero a.e. (with respect to $\overline{\lambda \times \lambda}$). Thus $\chi_N(t-u)$ is $\overline{\mathcal{M} \times \mathcal{M}}$-measurable.

It is now clear that functions of the form $\sum_{j=1}^{n} \alpha_j \chi_{A_j}(t-u)$ where $A_j \in \mathcal{M}$ are $\overline{\mathcal{M} \times \mathcal{M}}$-measurable in $R \times R$. For any non-negative measurable function f, we have $f(t-u) = \lim_{n\to\infty} S_n(t-u)$ where each S_n is simple. Consequently for non-negative measurable functions f, $f(t-u)$ is $\overline{\mathcal{M} \times \mathcal{M}}$-measurable. Finally the result follows for all $f \in \mathcal{L}_1(R)$ since f is a linear combination of non-negative measurable functions.

<u>Remark</u>. From here until 4.5.8 (not including 4.5.8), $\mathcal{L}_p$ $(p \geq 1)$ will always denote $\mathcal{L}_p(R)$ and $\int f(t)dt$ and $\int f$ will denote $\int_R f(t)d\lambda(t)$. Let $\mathcal{L}_p * \mathcal{L}_q$ denote the set of all functions $f*g$ where $f \in \mathcal{L}_p$ and $g \in \mathcal{L}_q$.

In 4.5.7, we have proved that $\mathcal{L}_1 * \mathcal{L}_1 \subset \mathcal{L}_1$. The reverse inclusion has been shown recently by Walter Rudin. In the following theorem we will generalize the result $\mathcal{L}_1 * \mathcal{L}_1 \subset \mathcal{L}_1$ proved in 4.5.7.

4.5.71 Theorem. Let $p > 1$, $q > 1$, and suppose that $\frac{1}{p} + \frac{1}{q} - 1 > 0$. Let r be defined by the relation $\frac{1}{r} = \frac{1}{p} + \frac{1}{q} - 1$. Then $\mathcal{L}_p(R) * \mathcal{L}_q(R) \subset \mathcal{L}_r(R)$ and, moreover, for $f \in \mathcal{L}_p$ and $g \in \mathcal{L}_q$ we have $\|f * g\|_r \leq \|f\|_p \|g\|_q$.

4.5.711 Lemma. (Young's inequality) Let λ and μ be positive numbers such that $\lambda + \mu < 1$. Let $f \in \mathcal{L}_{\frac{1}{1-\lambda}}$ and $g \in \mathcal{L}_{\frac{1}{1-\mu}}$. Then

$$|\int fg| \leq \left[\int |f|^{\frac{1}{1-\lambda}} |g|^{\frac{1}{1-\mu}}\right]^{1-\lambda-\mu} \left[\int |f|^{\frac{1}{1-\lambda}}\right]^{\mu} \left[\int |g|^{\frac{1}{1-\mu}}\right]^{\lambda} .$$

Proof. Let F, G, and H be non-negative measurable functions on R. Obviously $\mu + \lambda + (1 - \mu - \lambda) = 1$. Thus by 3.8.3,

$$\int FGH \leq (\int F^{\frac{1}{1-\mu-\lambda}})^{1-\mu-\lambda} (\int G^{\frac{1}{\mu}})^{\mu} (\int H^{\frac{1}{\lambda}})^{\lambda} . \qquad (*)$$

Let $G = |f|^{\frac{\mu}{1-\lambda}}$, $H = |g|^{\frac{\lambda}{1-\mu}}$, and $F = (G^{\frac{1}{\mu}} H^{\frac{1}{\lambda}})^{1-\mu-\lambda}$.

Now we have $\int FGH = \int G^{\frac{1-\mu-\lambda}{\mu}} H^{\frac{1-\mu-\lambda}{\lambda}} GH = \int G^{\frac{1-\lambda}{\mu}} H^{\frac{1-\mu}{\lambda}} = \int |f| \cdot |g|$. Hence, using (*), we obtain $|\int fg| \leq \int |fg| =$

$$\int FGH \leq (\int G^{\frac{1}{\mu}} H^{\frac{1}{\lambda}})^{1-\mu-\lambda} (\int |f|^{\frac{1}{1-\lambda}})^{\mu} (\int |g|^{\frac{1}{1-\mu}})^{\lambda} =$$

$$(\int |f|^{\frac{1}{1-\lambda}} |g|^{\frac{1}{1-\mu}})^{1-\mu-\lambda} (\int |f|^{\frac{1}{1-\lambda}})^{\mu} (\int |g|^{\frac{1}{1-\mu}})^{\lambda} .$$

This is the desired inequality.

Proof of 4.5.71. Let $f \in \mathcal{L}_p$ and $g \in \mathcal{L}_q$. Let λ and μ be such that $\frac{1}{1-\lambda} = p$ and $\frac{1}{1-\mu} = q$. Evidently $\lambda = 1 - \frac{1}{p}$, $\mu = 1 - \frac{1}{q}$, and $1 - \lambda - \mu = \frac{1}{p} + \frac{1}{q} - 1 = \frac{1}{r}$. Hence, applying 4.5.711, we have for $t \in R$, $|f*g(t)| \leq \int|f(t-u)| \cdot |g(u)|du \leq (\int|f(t-u)|^p|g(u)|^q du)^{1/r} (\int|f(t-u)|^p du)^{1-1/q}(\int|g(u)|^q du)^{1-1/p} = (\int|f(t-u)|^p \cdot |g(u)|^q du)^{1/r} (\int|f|^p)^{1-1/q}(\int|g|^q)^{1-1/p}$. Thus

$|f*g(t)|^r \leq (\int|f(t-u)|^p|g(u)|^q du)(\int|f|^p)^{r-r/q}(\int|g|^q)^{r-r/p}$

and so $\int|f*g(t)|^r dt \leq (\int|f|^p)^{r-r/q}(\int|g|^q)^{r-r/p} \cdot$

$(\int\int|f(t-u)|^p|g(u)|^q du dt)$. Since $\int\int|f(t-u)|^p \cdot$

$|g(u)|^q dt du = \int(|g(u)|^q \int|f(t)|^p dt)du = (\int|g|^q)(\int|f|^p) < \infty$, Fubini's theorem (4.5.41) applies and we have $\int|f*g(t)|^r dt \leq (\int|f|^p)^{1+r-r/q}(\int|g|^q)^{1+r-r/p} < \infty$. Taking r-th roots, we obtain $\|f*g\|_r \leq (\int|f|^p)^{\frac{1}{r}+1-\frac{1}{q}} (\int|g|^q)^{\frac{1}{r}+1-\frac{1}{p}} =$

$(\int|f|^p)^{1/p}(\int|g|^q)^{1/q} = \|f\|_p\|g\|_q$. Consequently, $f * g \in \mathcal{L}_r$, and $\|f*g\|_r \leq \|f\|_p \cdot \|g\|_q$.

4.5.72 Theorem. Let $f \in \mathcal{L}_1$ and $g \in \mathcal{L}_q$ where $1 < q < \infty$. Then $f * g \in \mathcal{L}_q$ and $\|f*g\|_q \leq \|f\|_1 \cdot \|g\|_q$.

Proof. Let $q' = \frac{q}{q-1}$; then $\frac{1}{q} + \frac{1}{q'} = 1$. Recall that by 3.8.31, $\int|\phi\psi| \leq (\int|\phi|^q)^{1/q} (\int|\psi|^{q'})^{1/q'}$. Hence by 3.8.31, we have $|f*g(t)| = |\int f(t-u)g(u)du| \leq \int|f(t-u)| \cdot$

$|g(u)|du = \int|f(t-u)|^{1/q'}|f(t-u)|^{1/q} |g(u)|du \leq$

$(\int|f(t-u)| \cdot |g(u)|^q du)^{1/q} (\int|f(t-u)|du)^{1/q'} =$

$(\int|f(u)|du)^{1/q'}\ (\int|f(t-u)|\cdot|g(u)|^q du)^{1/q}$ for $t \in R$. Then $\int|f*g(t)|^q dt \leq (\int|f|)^{q/q'}(\int\int|f(t-u)|\cdot|g(u)|^q du dt) = (\int|f|)^{q/q'}(\int|f|)(\int|g|^q) = (\int|f|)^{q/q'+1}\cdot(\int|g|^q)$ so that $\|f*g\|_q \leq (\int|f|)^{1/q'+1/q}(\int|g|^q)^{1/q} = \|f\|_1 \cdot \|g\|_q$. Thus $f * g \in \mathcal{L}_q$, and $\|f*g\|_q \leq \|f\|_1 \cdot \|g\|_q$.

4.5.73 Exercise. Let $1 < p < \infty$ and $p' = \frac{p}{p-1}$. If $f \in \mathcal{L}_p$ and $g \in \mathcal{L}_{p'}$, then $f * g(t)$ exists for all t and is bounded.

4.5.74 Final Exercise # 25. Let μ be any complex-valued countably additive Borel measure on R such that $|\mu|(R) < \infty$ (refer to 4.1.82). Let $1 \leq p < \infty$, and let $f \in \mathcal{L}_p$. For $t \in R$ define $f * \mu(t) = \int f(t-u)d\mu(u)$. Prove that $f * \mu \in \mathcal{L}_p$ and that $\|f*\mu\|_p \leq \|f\|_p \cdot |\mu|(R)$.

4.5.75 Remark. For $\phi \in \mathcal{L}_2$ and $f \in \mathcal{L}_1$, define $T_f(\phi) = f * \phi$. Plainly $T_f(\alpha\phi + \beta\psi) = \alpha T_f(\phi) + \beta T_f(\psi)$ and $\|T_f(\phi)\|_2 \leq \|f\|_1 \cdot \|\phi\|_2$. That is, T_f is a bounded linear operator carrying $\mathcal{L}_2$ into $\mathcal{L}_2$. The theory of linear operators on Hilbert spaces has been extensively developed. The mapping $f \rightarrow T_f$ is an isomorphism of $\mathcal{L}_1$, and so certain questions about $\mathcal{L}_1$ can be answered by reference to the operators T_f.

4.5.8 Fubini's theorem in certain non-σ- finite situations. For a locally compact Hausdorff space X, we will denote $\mathfrak{C}_{\infty\infty}(X)$ for the set of all complex-valued continuous functions that vanish outside of compact subsets of X. Let T and U be arbitrary locally compact Hausdorff spaces. Let I, respectively J, be a complex-valued linear functional defined on $\mathfrak{C}_{\infty\infty}(T)$, respectively $\mathfrak{C}_{\infty\infty}(U)$, that is real-valued and non-negative for real-valued non-negative functions. The space $T \times U$ is also a locally compact Hausdorff space. Let K be the linear functional on $\mathfrak{C}_{\infty\infty}(T \times U)$ defined by $K(x) = I_t(J_u x(t,u))$ for $x \in \mathfrak{C}_{\infty\infty}(T \times U)$. This definition is meaningful since $J_u(x(t,u)) \in \mathfrak{C}_{\infty\infty}(T)$. It is also true that $K(x) = J_u(I_t\, x(t,u))$. Let μ, ν, and λ be countably additive Borel measures corresponding to I, J, and K, respectively, by the Riesz representation theorem for locally compact Hausdorff spaces (refer to 4.1.7).

Suppose that $x \in \mathcal{L}_1(T \times U, \lambda)$. Then for almost all t, $x(t,u)$ is a ν-measurable function on U, and for almost all $u, x(t,u)$ is a μ-measurable function on T. Moreover, $\int_{T\times U} x(t,u)d\lambda(t,u) = \int_T \int_U x(t,u)d\nu(u)d\mu(t) = \int_U \int_T x(t,u)d\mu(t)d\nu(u)$. We also observe that for a non-negative function $x \in \mathcal{L}_1(T,\mu)$ and a non-negative function $y \in \mathcal{L}_1(U,\nu)$, we have $x(t)y(u) \in \mathcal{L}_1(T\times U,\lambda)$ and $\int_{T\times U} x(t)y(u)d\lambda(t,u) = \int_T x(t)d\mu(t) \cdot \int_U y(u)d\nu(u)$. We omit all proofs here, and refer the interested reader to Naĭmark's Normirovannye Kol'ca, (Gostehizdat, Moscow, 1956), pp. 137-140.

4.5.81 __Note__. Fubini's theorem may fail if the measures are required to be only finitely additive. Let $\mathfrak{F}$ be the space of all real-valued continuous functions on R such that $L_+(f) = \lim_{t\to\infty} f(t)$ and $L_-(f) = \lim_{t\to-\infty} f(t)$ exist and are finite. For functions in $\mathfrak{F}$, we define addition and scalar multiplication point-wise; under these operations $\mathfrak{F}$ is a linear space. We define $\|f\| = \sup\{|f(t)|: t \in R\}$ for $f \in \mathfrak{F}$.

For L_+ we define a set-function μ_+ as follows. For every open set $G \subset R$, let $\mu_+(G) = \sup\{L_+(f): 0 \le f \le \chi_G$ and $f \in \mathfrak{F}\}$. We note that

$$\mu_+(G) = \begin{cases} 1 & \text{if } G \text{ contains an interval of the form }]a,\infty[\\ 0 & \text{otherwise} \end{cases}.$$

For any set $A \subset R$, we define $\mu_+(A) = \inf\{\mu_+(G): G$ open and $G \supset A\}$. The set-function μ_+ can be shown to be finitely additive on the smallest algebra of sets containing all open sets. We have $\int_R f(x)d\mu_+(x) = L_+(f)$ for $f \in \mathfrak{F}$.Finally, we note that $\mu_+(R) = 1$ and that for bounded sets $B \subset R$ we have $\mu_+(B) = 0$. Consequently $\lim_{n\to\infty} \mu_+([-n,n]) = 0 < 1 = \mu_+(\bigcup_{n=1}^{\infty}[-n,n])$ so that μ_+ is not countably additive. The set-function μ_- is defined in like manner.

Let $f \in \mathfrak{F}$ be a function such that $L_+(f) = 1$ and $L_-(f) = 0$. Then

$$\int_R \int_R f(t-u)d\mu_+(t)d\mu_-(u) = \int_R L_+(f)d\mu_-(u) = L_+(f) = 1$$

whereas

$$\int_R \int_R f(t - u)d\mu_-(u)d\mu_+(t) = \int_R L_-(f)d\mu_+(t) = L_-(f) = 0.$$

Hence Fubini's theorem fails for these set-functions.

4.6 Computation of conjugate spaces.

4.6.1 Definition. Let E be a normed linear space over K (or R). A linear functional on E is a function f defined on E with values in K (or R) such that $f(\alpha x + \beta y) = \alpha f(x) + \beta f(y)$ for $x, y \in E$ and $\alpha, \beta \in K$ (or R). The linear functional f is said to be bounded if $\frac{|f(x)|}{\|x\|} \leq A$ for some A and all $x \in E$, $x \neq 0$. The number $\|f\| = \sup \left\{ \frac{|f(x)|}{\|x\|} : x \in E, x \neq 0 \right\}$ is called the norm of f. Let E^* denote the set of all bounded linear functionals on E. Addition and scalar multiplication are defined point-wise for members of E^*. With these operations, E^* forms a normed linear space; E^* is called the conjugate space of E (sometimes the adjoint space of E).

4.6.11 Theorem. Let E be a normed (not necessarily complete) linear space over K (or R). Then E^* is a complete normed linear space over K (or R). That is, E^* is a Banach space.

Proof. Plainly E^* is a linear space. We first verify that the norm defined on E^* is indeed a norm. Evidently $f(0) + f(0) = f(0 + 0) = f(0)$ or $f(0) = 0$ so that

$\|0\| = 0$. If $f \neq 0$, then $f(x) \neq 0$ for some $x \neq 0$. Consequently $\frac{|f(x)|}{\|x\|} > 0$ and, therefore, $\|f\| > 0$. For $f \in E^*$ and $\alpha \in K$ (or R), we have $\|\alpha f\| = \sup\left\{\frac{|\alpha f(x)|}{\|x\|} : x \in E, x \neq 0\right\} = |\alpha| \cdot \sup\left\{\frac{|f(x)|}{\|x\|} : x \in E, x \neq 0\right\} = |\alpha| \cdot \|f\|$.

Let $\varepsilon > 0$. Choose x_0 such that $\frac{|f(x_0) + g(x_0)|}{\|x_0\|} + \varepsilon > \|f + g\|$. Then $\|f + g\| < \frac{|f(x_0) + g(x_0)|}{\|x_0\|} + \varepsilon \leq \frac{|f(x_0)|}{\|x_0\|} + \frac{|g(x_0)|}{\|x_0\|} + \varepsilon \leq \|f\| + \|g\| + \varepsilon$. Since ε is arbitrary, it follows that $\|f + g\| \leq \|f\| + \|g\|$.

We now show that E^* is complete. Suppose that $\{f_n\}_{n=1}^{\infty}$ is a sequence of functions in E^* such that $\lim_{m,n\to\infty} \|f_n - f_m\| = 0$. This means that

$$\lim_{m,n\to\infty} \left[\sup\left\{\frac{|f_n(x) - f_m(x)|}{\|x\|} : x \in E, x \neq 0\right\}\right] = 0.$$

Thus for $x \in E$, $x \neq 0$, $\{f_n(x)\}_{n=1}^{\infty}$ is a Cauchy sequence in K (or R); for $x = 0$ this is trivially true. Since K (or R) is complete, the sequence $\{f_n(x)\}_{n=1}^{\infty}$ has a limit for all $x \in E$. Let $f(x) = \lim_{n\to\infty} f_n(x)$ for $x \in E$.

Let $x, y \in E$ and $\alpha, \beta \in K$ (or R). Since $\lim_{n\to\infty} f_n(x) = f(x)$, $\lim_{n\to\infty} f_n(y) = f(y)$, and $\lim_{n\to\infty} \alpha f_n(x) + \beta f_n(y) = \lim_{n\to\infty} f_n(\alpha x + \beta y) = f(\alpha x + \beta y)$, we see that $f(\alpha x + \beta y) = \alpha f(x) + \beta f(y)$. Hence f is a linear functional. We will now show that $\sup\left\{\frac{|f(x)|}{\|x\|} : x \in E,\right.$

$x \neq 0 \} < \infty$ or, equivalently, that $\sup\{|f(x)|: x \in E, \|x\| = 1\} < \infty$. Since $\lim_{m,n\to\infty} \|f_n - f_m\| = 0$, there exists an N such that $|f_N(x) - f_m(x)| < 1$ for $m \geq N$ and all x such that $\|x\| = 1$. Thus $|f_m(x)| < |f_N(x)| + 1 \leq \|f_N\| + 1$ for $m \geq N$ and all x such that $\|x\| = 1$. Consequently, $|f(x)| = \lim_{m\to\infty} |f_m(x)| \leq \|f_N\| + 1$ for all x such that $\|x\| = 1$. It follows that $\sup\{|f(x)|: x \in E, \|x\| = 1\} \leq \|f_N\| + 1 < \infty$ and hence f is a bounded linear functional.

It remains to show that $\lim_{n\to\infty} \|f_n - f\| = 0$. Choose $\varepsilon > 0$. Let N (depending on ε) be so that $|f_N(x) - f_m(x)| \leq \frac{\varepsilon}{2}$ for $m \geq N$ and all x such that $\|x\| = 1$. Then $|f_N(x) - f(x)| = \lim_{m\to\infty} |f_N(x) - f_m(x)| \leq \frac{\varepsilon}{2}$ for all x such that $\|x\| = 1$. Thus $\|f_N - f\| \leq \frac{\varepsilon}{2}$. Now for $m \geq N$ we have $\|f_m - f\| \leq \|f_m - f_N\| + \|f_N - f\| < \frac{\varepsilon}{2} + \frac{\varepsilon}{2} = \varepsilon$. Hence $\lim_{m\to\infty} \|f_m - f\| \leq \varepsilon$. Since ε is arbitrary, this implies that $\lim_{m\to\infty} \|f_m - f\| = 0$.

4.6.2 Theorem. Let E be a normed linear space (over R or K), M any linear subspace of E. Let f be a bounded (real-valued or complex-valued) linear functional defined on M. Then there exists a linear functional F on E such that $F(x) = f(x)$ for all $x \in M$ and $\|F\|_{(E)} = \|f\|_{(M)}$.

Proof. Case I. Suppose that E is a real linear space and hence that f is real-valued. For all $x \in E$, define

$p(x) = \|f\|_{(M)} \cdot \|x\|$. Evidently, p is positively homogeneous and subadditive. Moreover, $f(x) \leq p(x)$ for all $x \varepsilon M$. By 2.6.2, there exists a real-valued linear functional F on E such that $F(x) = f(x)$ for all $x \varepsilon M$ and $F(x) \leq p(x)$ for all $x \varepsilon E$. Since $-F(x) = F(-x) \leq p(-x) = p(x)$, we have $F(x) \geq -p(x)$ for all $x \varepsilon E$. Consequently, $|F(x)| \leq p(x)$ for all $x \varepsilon E$. Thus $\|F\|_{(E)} = \sup\left\{\frac{|F(x)|}{\|x\|} : x \varepsilon E, \ x \neq 0\right\} \leq \|f\|_{(M)}$. Since the reverse inequality is clear, we see that $\|F\|_{(E)} = \|f\|_{(M)}$.

Case II. Suppose that E is a complex linear space and hence that f is complex-valued. Let $f(x) = f_1(x) + if_2(x)$ for $x \varepsilon M$ where f_1 and f_2 are real-valued functions. Plainly f_1 and f_2 are additive and real-homogeneous. From the equality $f_1(ix) + if_2(ix) = f(ix) = if(x) = i[f_1(x) + if_2(x)] = -f_2(x) + if_1(x)$ we see that $f_2(x) = -f_1(ix)$. Hence $f(x) = f_1(x) - if_1(ix)$ for $x \varepsilon M$. Clearly $|f_1(x)| \leq |f(x)| \leq \|f\|_{(M)}$ for $x \varepsilon M$. By case I, f_1 can be extended to a real-valued, real-homogeneous, linear functional F_1 on E such that $\|F_1\|_{(E)} = \|f_1\|_{(M)}$. Let $F(x) = F_1(x) - iF_1(ix)$ for all $x \varepsilon E$. Obviously F is additive and real-homogeneous, and is an extension of f. We have $F(ix) = F_1(ix) - iF_1(-x) = iF_1(x) + F_1(ix) = i[F_1(x) - iF_1(ix)] = iF(x)$ and hence for any complex number $a + bi$, the identity $F((a + bi)x) = F(ax) + F(ibx) = aF(x) + ibF(x) = (a + bi)F(x)$ obtains. That is, F is complex homogeneous and thus linear.

Let $x \in E$ be fixed; then $F(x) = |F(x)|e^{i\theta}$ for some real number θ. Now $|F(x)| = e^{-i\theta}F(x) = F(e^{-i\theta}x) = F_1(e^{-i\theta}x) - iF_1(ie^{-i\theta}x)$ so that, equating real parts, we obtain $|F(x)| = F_1(e^{-i\theta}x)$. Thus $|F(x)| = F_1(e^{-i\theta}x) \leq \|f_1\|_{(M)} \|e^{-i\theta}x\| = \|f_1\|_{(M)} \cdot \|x\| \leq \|f\|_{(M)} \cdot \|x\|$. Hence $\|F\|_{(E)} \leq \|f\|_{(M)}$. The reverse inequality is clear.

4.6.201 Note. Theorem 4.6.2 is often called the Hahn-Banach theorem. The complex case is due to Bohnenblust and Sobczyk (1938) and Suhomlinov (1938).

4.6.21 Theorem. Let E be a normed linear space and let $x_o \in E$. Then there exists an $f \in E^*$ such that $f(x_o) = \|x_o\|$ and $\|f\| = 1$.

4.6.22 Theorem. Let E be a normed linear space, and M a linear subspace of E. Let $x_o \in E$ and let $d = \inf \{\|x - x_o\|: x \in M\}$. Suppose further that $d > 0$. Then there is an $f \in E^*$ such that $f(x) = 0$ for all $x \in M$, $f(x_o) = d$, and $\|f\| = 1$.

Theorems 4.6.21 and 4.6.22 are obvious special cases of 4.6.2. We omit the proofs.

4.6.3 Theorem. (Riesz's theorem) Let T be a compact subset of R. Let $\mathfrak{C}(T)$ be all complex-valued continuous functions on T. $\mathfrak{C}(T)$ is a linear space with the operations addition and scalar multiplication defined point-wise. For $x \in \mathfrak{C}(T)$, define $\|x\| = \max \{|x(t)|: t \in T\}$. Under this norm, $\mathfrak{C}(T)$ is a complex Banach space. $\mathfrak{C}(T)^*$ can be identified with $\mathfrak{M}(T)$, the space of all complex, countably additive, Borel measures on T such that $|\mu|(T) < \infty$. The correspondence between $\mathfrak{C}(T)^*$ and $\mathfrak{M}(T)$ is made as follows. To $\mu \in \mathfrak{M}(T)$ we associate $f_\mu \in \mathfrak{C}(T)^*$ which is defined by $f_\mu(x) = \int_T x(t)d\mu(t)$ for $x \in \mathfrak{C}(T)$. This correspondence is one-to-one, onto and linear. Moreover, it is norm-preserving; i.e., $\|\mu\| = |\mu|(T) = \|f_\mu\|$.

4.6.31 Example. Let M be a linear subspace of $\mathfrak{C}(T)$. Let $x_0 \in \mathfrak{C}(T)$ be such that $d = \inf\{\|x - x_0\|: x \in M\} > 0$. Then there exists a complex countably additive Borel measure μ on T such that $\int_T x_0(t)d\mu(t) = d$, $\int_T xd\mu = 0$ for all $x \in M$, and $|\mu|(T) = 1$.

4.6.32 Theorem. Let T be a locally compact subspace of R. Let $\mathfrak{C}_{\infty\infty}(T)$ be as in 4.5.8. Let $\mathfrak{C}_\infty(T)$ denote the set of all complex-valued continuous functions x on T such that for every $\varepsilon > 0$, the set $\{t \in T: |x(t)| \geq \varepsilon\}$ is compact. Addition, scalar multiplication, and the norm are defined for $\mathfrak{C}_\infty(T)$ and $\mathfrak{C}_{\infty\infty}(T)$ as they are for $\mathfrak{C}(T)$. Let $\mathfrak{M}(T)$ be as in 4.6.3. Then $\mathfrak{C}_\infty(T)^*$ and $\mathfrak{C}_{\infty\infty}(T)^*$ are identifiable with $\mathfrak{M}(T)$ just as in 4.6.3.

Both 4.6.3 and 4.6.32 are merely refined statements of 4.1.7 and 4.1.8. The details are easily checked, and are omitted.

4.6.33 Example. Let $T = \{1, 2, \ldots, n, \ldots\}$. Then $\mathfrak{C}_\infty(T)$ just consists of all sequences $x = \{x(n)\}_{n=1}^{\infty}$ for which

$\lim_{n\to\infty} x(n) = 0$. It is clear that as soon as a countably additive measure on T is determined for one-membered subsets $\{n\}$, it is determined for all subsets A of T. Indeed, $\mu(A) = \sum_{n\in A} \mu(\{n\})$ for $A \subset T$. Moreover, $|\mu|(T) = \sum_{n=1}^{\infty} |\mu(\{n\})|$. Thus $\mu \in \mathfrak{M}(T)$ if and only if $\sum_{n=1}^{\infty} |\mu(\{n\})| < \infty$. Hence $\mathfrak{M}(T)$ can be identified with $\ell_1(T)$, and we can identify the conjugate space of $\mathfrak{C}_{\infty}(T)$ with $\ell_1(T)$. Every bounded linear functional on $\mathfrak{C}_{\infty}(T)$ has the form $x \to \sum_{n=1}^{\infty} x(n)\mu(n)$, where $\sum_{n=1}^{\infty} |\mu(n)| < \infty$. The number $\sum_{n=1}^{\infty} |\mu(n)|$ is the norm of the functional.

This example is generalizable to <u>any</u> infinite set D. Let $\mathfrak{C}_{\infty}(D)$ be all complex functions on D that are arbitrarily small in absolute value outside of finite sets. Then $\mathfrak{C}_{\infty}(D)^*$ is $\ell_1(D)$, the space of all complex functions μ on D such that $\|\mu\|_1 = \sum_{t\in D} |\mu(t)| < \infty$. The functional corresponding to μ is, of course, the mapping $x \to \sum_{t\in D} x(t)\mu(t)$, for all $x \in \mathfrak{C}_{\infty}(D)$.

4.6.4 <u>Theorem</u>. Let $(T, \mathfrak{M}, \mu)$ be a measure space with $\mu(T) < \infty$. Let f be a bounded linear functional on $\mathfrak{L}_p(T, \mathfrak{M}, \mu)$ $(1 \leq p < \infty)$. Let $p' = \frac{p}{p-1}$ for $p > 1$ and $p' = \infty$ for $p = 1$. Then there is a $y \in \mathfrak{L}_{p'}(T, \mathfrak{M}, \mu)$ such that

$$f(x) = \int_T x(t)y(t)d\mu(t) \qquad (*)$$

for all $x \in \mathfrak{L}_p$, and $\|f\| = \|y\|_{p'}$. The correspondence of f to y is a linear isomorphism of $\mathcal{L}_p^*$ onto $\mathcal{L}_{p'}$ that preserves norm.

Proof. Case I. Suppose that $f(\chi_B) \geq 0$ for all $B \varepsilon \mathfrak{M}$. For $B \varepsilon \mathfrak{M}$, let $\Phi(B) = f(\chi_B)$. The set-function Φ is a countably additive non-negative measure. If $\mu(B) = 0$, then $\Phi(B) = f(\chi_B) = f(0) = 0$. Thus Φ is absolutely continuous with respect to μ. By the Radon-Nikodym theorem (4.3.2), there exists a $y \varepsilon \mathcal{L}_1$, $y \geq 0$, such that $\Phi(B) = \int_B y(t)d\mu(t)$ for $B \varepsilon \mathfrak{M}$. The equality (*) is now evident for characteristic functions of measurable sets; indeed, $f(\chi_B) = \Phi(B) = \int_B y(t)d\mu(t) = \int \chi_B(t)y(t)d\mu(t)$. The equality (*) is now obvious for simple functions S. Now let x be any non-negative function in $\mathcal{L}_p$, and let $\{S_n\}_{n=1}^{\infty}$ be an increasing sequence of simple functions such that $\lim_{n\to\infty} S_n = x$ everywhere on T (3.2.12). Then $\|S_n\|_p \leq \|x\|_p$ for all n, and hence $f(S_n) = \int_T S_n(t)y(t)d\mu(t) \leq \|x\|_p\|f\|$ for all n. By 3.5.11, we have $\lim_{n\to\infty} \int_T S_n(t)y(t)d\mu(t) = \int_T x(t)y(t)d\mu(t) < \infty$ and $xy \varepsilon \mathcal{L}_1$. By 3.5.21, we have $\lim_{n\to\infty} \int |S_n(t) - x(t)|^p d\mu(t) = 0$, since $|S_n - x|^p \leq x^p$. Hence $\|S_n - x\|_p \to 0$ as $n \to \infty$, and $\lim_{n\to\infty} f(x_n) = f(x)$. It follows that $f(x) = \int_T x(t)y(t)d\mu(t)$.

Suppose now that $p > 1$. To show $y \varepsilon \mathcal{L}_{p'}$, let z be any measurable bounded function on T such that

$0 \le z \le y$. Then we have $\int z^{p'} \le \int z^{p'-1} y \le$ $\|z^{p'-1}\|_p \|f\|$, by 3.8.31. But $\|z^{p'-1}\|_p = (\int (z^{p'-1})^p)^{1/p} =$ $(\int z^{\frac{p}{p-1}})^{1/p} = (\int z^{p'})^{1/p}$. Hence we have $\|z\|_{p'} =$ $(\int z^{p'})^{1-\frac{1}{p}} \le \|f\|$. It follows that $\|z\|_{p'}$ is bounded, and hence y itself is in $\mathcal{L}_{p'}$. Thus (*) is proved. Hölder's inequality 3.8.21 shows that $\|f\| \le \|y\|_{p'}$, while the function $\|y\|_{p'}^{-\frac{1}{p-1}} y^{p'-1} \in \mathcal{L}_p$ shows that $\|f\| \ge \|y\|_{p'}$.

The case $p = 1$ is handled similarly. If $\mu\{t: t \in T, y(t) > \alpha\}$ is positive for all $\alpha > 0$, then there is a function $x \in \mathcal{L}_1$ such that $\int_T x(t)y(t)d\mu(t) = \infty$; and the norm of f is the number $\inf\{\alpha: \alpha > 0, \mu\{t: t \in T, y(t) > \alpha\} = 0\}$. This number, the "ess sup" of y, is often written as $\|y\|_\infty$. (For $T = [0,1]$, $\mu = \lambda$, and y continuous, $\|y\|_\infty$ is the maximum of $y(t)$.)

Case II. Let f be any bounded linear functional on $\mathcal{L}_p(T, \mathcal{M}, \mu)$. For $B \in \mathcal{M}$, let $\Phi(B) = f(\chi_B)$. We have $\Phi = \Phi_1 - \Phi_2 + i(\Phi_3 - \Phi_4)$ where Φ_i is a non-negative real-valued measure $(i = 1, 2, 3, 4)$. Applying case I to each Φ_i, the result follows.

4.6.41 <u>Note</u>. Theorem 4.6.4 for $p > 1$ is true for arbitrary measure spaces, even if not σ-finite. For $p = 1$, it is not in general true, but is true for σ-finite measure spaces.

INDEX

SYMBOLS INDEX

Latin:

Greek:

Other:

RR